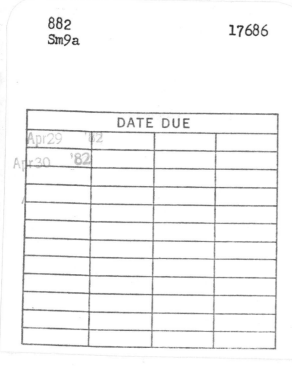

AESCHYLEAN TRAGEDY

AESCHYLEAN TRAGEDY

BY

HERBERT WEIR SMYTH

BIBLO and TANNEN
NEW YORK
1969

Originally published 1924

Reprinted 1969

by

Biblo and Tannen Publishers, Inc.
63 Fourth Avenue   New York, N.Y. 10003

Library of Congress Catalog Card No. 67-19531

882
Sm 9a
17686
June 1978

Printed in U.S.A. by
NOBLE OFFSET PRINTERS, INC.
NEW YORK 3, N. Y.

PREFATORY NOTE

These Lectures, here printed as written for delivery, were prepared during my residence in Europe in 1922, and at places without libraries containing books on Greek literature. Since my return I have had the advantage of consulting Heinemann's *Die tragischen Gestalten der Griechen in der Weltliteratur*, published in 1922. To this work I am indebted for information concerning certain German tragedies that deal with the chief personages of the *Prometheus* and the *Orestea*.

By agreement with the authorities of the University of California, these Lectures are designed to serve as an introduction to a further study of the Mind and Art of Aeschylus, to be published by Harvard University at some future date.

CONTENTS

CHAPTER I

INTRODUCTION

In rapid succession the Greeks created many forms of poetry, until in the tragic drama they united the dialogue and narrative speech of epic with the choral ode. The rise of tragedy was as rapid as its decline. Thespis, its nominal founder, was still living ten years before the traditional year of the birth of Aeschylus, who shaped the nascent art into the mould it retained throughout antiquity. The narrow bounds of a single century contain all of Greek tragic art in its highest perfection. Exhausted by the teeming fertility of their genius, the Greeks surrendered to the moderns the opportunity to attempt to surpass what they had begun. With Euripides, Greek tragedy virtually came to an end. No one of his successors could dispute his preëminence as the voice of a common humanity. The stars of the Alexandrian Pleiad cast no radiance beyond the court of the Ptolemies. Of the predecessors of Aeschylus scarcely a fragment remains. Before and behind, darkness—only the figures of the Tragic Three emerge like a triple peak amid the surrounding gloom.

Nearest of the Three to the beginnings of that sovereign art which, by its triune harmony of music, the dance, the spoken and the sung word, seemed to the Greeks themselves the most perfect of all forms of poetry, stands the poet whom a famous modern critic has ventured to rank along with Shakespeare as the greatest dramatic genius of all time. Aeschylus'

[1]

genius is to be first measured only by comparison
with that of his fellow craftsmen who went before
and who came after him in his own ancient world.
For, as the Life of the poet, compiled in antiquity,
truly says, "the opinion which regards Sophocles as a
more finished tragic poet is indeed correct; but let
it be borne in mind that after Thespis, Phrynichus,
and Choerilus, to raise tragedy to such a pitch of
greatness was more difficult for Aeschylus than it
was for Sophocles, the successor of Aeschylus, to
bring it to its perfection." Sophocles is indeed the
greater artist, but Aeschylus is the greater genius; yet
not solely by reason of his priority in time. "Be born
a genius" was Ruskin's first rule.

It has required no little exercise of will to limit
my theme to the absolute art of Aeschylus. For I
purpose to deal with the first great dramatist of the
world without regard to the lesser stars whose earlier
light he overpowered, and, unless the pressure on
my self-restraint proves too insistent, without much
reference to his successors, who shine partly in their
own radiance, partly by reflection of his earlier
rising. Were I to adventure my fortunes even on
the subject, no less compelling than alluring, of the
origin of tragedy and the evolution of the art to the
year 499 B.C. when Aeschylus first appeared as a
contestant for the prize which had been established
only a generation earlier, these Lectures had ended
before they had fairly begun; and I should unconsciously have followed the illustrious example of the
story of the life and opinions of Tristam Shandy,
most of which was covered by the large discourse
of his Uncle Toby during the prenatal existence of the
hero proper.

In truth not only the genesis of tragedy but the early history of the tragic art is a land where the light is as darkness; nor would I here contribute any counsel of my own in the effort to clear away the immemorial obscurity. Much reading may indeed make a man at least negatively wise. It is not without profit that I have followed after Dieterich and Ridgeway and Gilbert Murray and many others in their quest to discover the great secret of the origin of that "goat song," from which, in the fulness of time, arose the majestic choral chants, the magniloquent description, and the incisive dialogue of the *Agamemnon*. From that quest some emerge with the assurance that from the ritual of the spirits of vegetation came the contest of will that pervades tragedy, the resultant disaster, the messenger's speech, and the epiphany of a god. It was the worship of Dionysus, which, by the alchemy of Hellenic genius, was shaped into the art that symbolized the processes of nature, forever dying, forever reborn. Others would dethrone Dionysus as the god of tragedy at its inception, and banish him to his original province, the satyric drama, itself named from the wild Satrae dwelling about Mt. Pangaeus in Thrace. It was the worship of the spirits of ancestors in tomb-ritual that gave the primal impetus to the creation of tragedy. The "master of those who know" knew little or nothing, it would seem, about the rude beginnings of the art.

I confess to a certain insecurity in the possession of this late and hard-won knowledge. Advancing years teach caution, and I am still content to be impounded among the reactionaries who will not abandon the authority of Aristotle. Now the author of the *Poetics*, when he does not know a thing, is wont to say that he does not know it, and he is apparently well aware that there were disputable questions about the early history of the drama. Yet he entertains no doubt that tragedy took its rise from the leaders of the dithyramb, the song sacred to Dionysus; a statement expressly supported by that fiery spirit Archilochus in the seventh century: "Well do I know," he says, "how to lead the dithyramb when my senses are thundered away by wine." Revolt from the authority of Aristotle opens the perilous path to the trackless wastes of anthropology; and with the result that a current tendency in the study of Greek drama no longer seeks to interpret that drama primarily out of itself or its immediate antecedents. It seeks to discover at every hand survivals of the most primitive rituals or beliefs, and to let those survivals, charged with all their primitive significance, determine the character and the structure of the play. With the attempt to discover beneath the surface in any monument of literature indications of an earlier stage of thought, I have of course only the heartiest sympathy. But, as in days long past it was said by some one more caustic than truthful, that Greek literature seemed to exist for no other reason than to afford illustrations of the rules of Greek grammar, so now it looks as if Aeschylus, Sophocles, and Euripides owe their capital importance to the happy fact that their plays are material for the anthropologist, who alone holds the master key to open the treasure house of poesy.

I will not surrender the *Agamemnon*, nor even the *Eumenides*, to the anthropologist, much as I respect that worthy when he does not glean amid an alien corn. My obligations to Miss Jane Harrison are profound; yet when I read Aeschylus in the light of her researches I seem to be suffering from an attack of intellectual delirium tremens. My eyes are dimmed to the splendor of his majesty by insistent images not only of snakes, proper to the pathology of that disease, but also of sprites, goblins, and demons that seem to peer out between the sonorous verses seeking to regain their ancient potency; even as the vaporous spirits fluttered about Odysseus on his descent to the dolorous regions of the lower world and with shrilling cries sought a taste of the blood that would restore to them their former consciousness. Long association with Westermarck's great work on the origin of human marriage has had an untoward effect on an otherwise estimable academic person of my acquaintance. He maintains to the wife of his bosom that their marriage owes its happiness to the sole fact that it is a survival of the primitive capture of woman—a custom fortunately (for the anthropologist) still existing among the savage tribes of Australia.

In a word I cannot view without apprehension the growing tendency to let the unsubstantial ghosts of the illimitable past of man's infancy direct the interpretation of the Greek drama in the period of its full splendor. Solomon's temple, for all that it was builded of the cedars of Lebanon, was greater than the sum of its structural parts—it was the temple of the Living God. Nor is the majesty of the shrine of art to suffer diminution of its glory by decomposition into terms of stated dimension.

Another aspect of pre-Aeschylean tragedy I here leave likewise in the obscurity of silence. The few and bare facts concerning the forerunners of our poet, are they not set down in the books of the chronicles of Greek literature? But obstinate questionings assail us the moment we would go deeper and seek to define the nature of primitive tragedy and the satyric drama, once they had been evolved out of the dithyramb. What, for example, were the so-called "spoken lines" by which Arion interrupted the progress of the choral song of fifty voices in honor of Dionysus? Were they uttered by the chorus-leader in answer to the questions of the chorus and did they thus prompt Thespis to his significant innovation— the introduction of a single actor who impersonated now the god of wine and now some other character? As for the satyric drama, the invention of which is ascribed to Pratinas, an elder contemporary of Aeschylus, not even the Croisets have clarified it to a perfect understanding; but that noble pair of brothers wrote too early to have burned much incense on the altar of anthropology. Pratinas is indeed known in another field as a tolerable lyric poet whose soul rebelled against the encroachment of flute instrumentation on the song. Choerilus, "King among the Satyrs," is reported to have improved masks. Greater than either was Phrynichus, of whom we shall hear later. His figure is not altogether unsubstantial. He is said to have introduced female parts, which were of course taken by men, as they were in Shakespeare's time. Aeschylus, his debtor in the *Persians* and elsewhere, may owe to him, his older contemporary, the impetus to give to women the prominent part that constitutes a marked feature of his dramatic economy. Nevertheless, all in all, of the immediate spiritual kindred of the poet who gave direction to the later history of tragedy, nothing remains whereby his genius may be measured with theirs. Eclipsed by his greater radiance, and by the injuries of time, their works have perished in oblivion. From the bare titles of Thespis' plays, if genuine, and from those of his pre-Aeschylean successors, it may be inferred that other choruses than those attendant on the god of wine might sing the lyric odes, the essential portion of the play; and that heroes were impersonated who had no concern with the life of the son of hapless Semele blasted by the lightning splendor of her omnipotent lover, the high god Zeus. Yet for Aeschylus, as for his successors, the theater in which the legends of the heroic past were envisaged, remained the sanctuary of the god, compacted of divinity and humanity; whose mortal part entailed on him suffering and struggle with a rejecting world, and whose immortal part so triumphed that, latest of the gods, he was received into the celestial society of Olympus.

If thus far by cautious steering I have escaped the whirlpool of Charybdis that sucks in and casts forth the too adventurous mariner, I am too wary likewise to be dashed against the rock of Scylla—the theory of the absolute nature of tragic art.

From his very primacy in time, Aeschylus has long been a magnet that has attracted philosophic aesthetics to the determination of the essence of the tragic—to the veritable *Ding an sich*. In the *Agamemnon*, which he reverenced as if divine, Goethe found the keystone of all aesthetic inquiry; and lesser critics than Goethe, though of the same race (for which the problem of the relation of moral to tragic guilt has a particular fascination), hold that

Aeschylus discovered the absolute conception of tragic art and that he fixed that conception for all time. On this limitless theme I will say here only this much.

The purely aesthetic, as distinguished from the intellectual, effect of the tragic drama of the Greeks was attained by elevated action and melodious verse, by satisfaction of the just demands of emotion in its deeper forms, and, as regards sensible embodiment, only herein differing from the loftiest modern tragedies, by harmonious musical and orchestric accompaniment. What we call "the tragedies of life" are our defeats, due for the most part to lapses of reason, to inability to scan the horizon of our acts, to flaws of character, which hurt most ourselves and others less or even not at all. Tragedy, as art, is the mirror of these defeats. Greek tragedy, as tragedy, because it is "heroic," deals with the sufferings of immortal beings or of mortal men and women normally of loftier station than ourselves, or, if of like common clay with ourselves, who appear to enjoy a loftier estate through the ennobling dignity of time. Greek tragedy does not inevitably end with death or a similar catastrophe. Its theme, however, is generally, in the last issue, such defects of character as occasion exceptional calamities, calamities that bring ruin to men set between a cruel choice, and not only to themselves but to the lives of others. In Aeschylean tragedy, in particular, that ruin involves not only the individual but also his descendants, whole families, and even entire nations. In Agamemnon ambition overmastered his nobler self: he sacrificed his daughter to retain his authority as commander of the expedition against Troy. That crime destroyed himself, his wife's honor, and her life at the hands of her own son. Eteocles lacked self-restraint: of his own headstrong will he slew his brother. Xerxes' desire to take vengeance on a land beyond the sea brought defeat to himself and disaster to his people.

In the last analysis, Aeschylean tragic drama presents the features common to the tragic drama of later times. As drama, it is the spectacle of a conflict of will, human or divine, or of man's will encountering obstacles internal or external, such as the sense of moral rectitude, the reasonable or unreasonable judgments of others, the sheer force of circumstance, the very contradictions of life itself. It sets forth, in condensed form, a story normally of antique times, acted by people who impersonate the characters of the story. It presents a series of crises culminating in a supreme crisis. It depicts action or the growth of action (all in fact that Aristotle's πρᾶχις connotes) as determined by character and circumstance; and conversely, the influence of action on character and circumstance. Aeschylean tragedy seeks to find peace for the soul troubled by the spectacle of limitless capacity for good involved in limitless ruin; peace for the soul, because it discerns that human life is somehow correlated to the demands of a moral world by the mystical union of Fate with the will of God.

On some aspects and illustrations of these statements I propose to dwell in the further course of these Lectures. My present concern is not with the question of tragic guilt and the relation of punishment to the offense, nor indeed with any part of the terminology of aesthetics. I am dealing with the ever-living drama, the drama of a great artistic craftsman.

As drama, his plays must be visualized by the imagination. No grace of style, no cunning art of description, can in the faintest degree supply the place of that contribution which we must bring to the understanding of a play twenty-five centuries old: the spoken word, the choral song alternating with the dialogue, the statuesque grouping of the main actors, the freer movements of the secondary personages, and the nature of the chorus on whom the words and deeds of the actors react as they react on ourselves—all must be reborn by the coöperation of our individual creative faculty.

Aeschylean tragedy is full of startling and thrilling scenes, scenes that at times outdo the sensationalism of Euripides; yet they were not designed to produce a mere emotional effect. Aeschylus would not let emotion be secured at the sacrifice of tragic pity and tragic fear: pity for undeserved misfortune, fear lest a like misfortune befall ourselves. By the intensified life of his characters he raises us to a heightened consciousness of living. The legends which form the substratum of his plays, legends that are more often a national possession than severely local, he has so shaped that at the outset we discover ourselves confronted by moral and religious problems of profound significance. Io, wandering transformed through the world, arrives at the rocky height in uttermost Scythia where Prometheus is riveted by command of Zeus: is the supreme god a just god? The daughters of Danaüs, fleeing from the persecution of their detested suitors, seek the protection of the land of their primal ancestress: is mercy due the suppliant when hospitality spells peril? Is neutrality possible when the choice lies between war and the

recognition of the rights of the oppressed? A free
people is justly triumphant at its victory that rendered a barbarous enemy impotent for the conquest
of the world: is the thrill of triumph to be tempered
by no warning to the victor to beware the divine justice that brings low all arrogance? The mysterious
beckonings of Fate, the awfulness of the battle waged
by ambition against duty to man and God, the ways
of God to man—these are the conceptions that inter-
penetrate the tragic dramas of the soldier-poet
Aeschylus. Not the exquisite refinement of the
art of Sophocles, not Euripides' varied portrayal of
man as he is, can vie with the massive imagination
linked with moral grandeur that distinguishes their
predecessor.

Thus it is, in the presence of such an art, ancient
no less than modern, by grace of the contributive
sympathy of reason and emotion, we make a startling discovery. We had thought to have been merely
witnesses of the actions or feelings of others in the
mimic world of art. We have, however, for the
moment, been actual participants in the shock of
will against will at its utmost tension, have been
participants in the struggle of passion with duty as
it has been visualized on the stage. From the representation of that shock of conflict, condensed into
the crisis of a lifetime, we depart tranquilized, re-
joiced to realize that it is not ourselves who have
suffered, but constrained to pity by the sufferings of
others. The burden of our mistakes and misdoings
has been lightened by the high consolation of art.
In such moments, when we are transported above the
level of our petty selves, whether by a Greek or a
modern dramatist (for it is equally possible with

both), we are tempted to the belief that art, the symbol of beauty, wedded to reason, is, save for the Divine, the true, the permanent reality, the rest but shadow; tempted to accept in full the equation of that Hellene cast upon the shores of a northern world, surrendered in his youth to death because he was loved of the gods, the poet who discerned the equivalence of beauty and truth, now in a Grecian urn, now in the splendor of nature shaped by no mortal hand.

Genius is wont to display its most authentic quality when it works in a restricted field or with a stubborn material. The Greek choral ode is obligated to preserve all but mathematical balance of rigid quantitative responsion. Greek tragedy marks the supremacy of the artist working in a field and with a material imposed on him from without and therefore an invigorating challenge to his imagination and his fancy. Aeschylus might not survey at will the varied incidents of life showing forth a spectacle charged with tragic value. He rested under the compulsion to use an ancient story as the medium for his picture of mankind, the drama of human personality and its environment, and the crisis of a human life. To this rule there are only three certain exceptions in the period of the bloom of classical tragedy:[1] the *Capture of Miletus* and the *Women of Phoenicia* by Aeschylus' contemporary Phrynichus, and the *Persians* by Aeschylus himself. All three were *pièces d'occasion*, their themes actual events of recent date. Only the magnitude of the struggle between Orient and Occident could cause tragedy to desert its proper

---

[1] The restriction to the great age of tragedy has in mind such plays as Moschion's *Themistocles* and Theodectes' *Mausolus*.

domain, the heroic past. With themes derived from
the ancient myths Greek tragedy could make a more
universal appeal because it was not under the compulsion of the realities of present circumstance.

The Athenian tragic poets were rarely self-
conscious as regards their art. Sophocles knew that
his proper style had passed through two preparative
periods. Aeschylus, for his part, voiced his indebtedness to Homer. His famous saying that his tragedies
were only morsels from the great banquet of the
sovereign epic poet has no deeper significance than
that he derived the wellspring of his fables from the
ample ocean of the heroic epics, which, apart from
Hesiod, were in his day still undissociated from the
name of Homer; from the Cyclic poems, whose
themes were the events of the Trojan war at large,
the fate of the house of Oedipus, the fortunes of the
suppliant daughters of Danaüs. All were legends
that to the Greeks formed the repository of the history of their race and all were exclusively Greek in
origin. The vast periphery of Hellenic myth and
legend included nothing derived from a purely
external source.

So far as the fable alone is concerned, Aeschylus
set the type. To the end Greek tragedy remained
'epic' recast. But with this distinction: either an
epic directly furnished the material for the story; or
the poet had recourse to a legend already recast from
the epic and charged with moral emotion by one of
his lyric predecessors. Stesichorus "bore on his lyre
the burden of epic song," as Quintilian put it;
and his handling of the tale of Clytaemestra and
Orestes, influenced by Delphic tradition, had a profound influence on the Orestean trilogy of Aeschylus.

In some cases, too, the dramatist may have drawn both on the epic and on the lyric setting of an heroic tale; and at times he could avail himself of the mythological researches and speculations of such special students as Pherecydes. Not a single play of any Greek poet is absolutely original in the sense that both the fable and the characters were purely creations of his own imagination.

Yet the myth, fixed in its essential outline, was also plastic. The myths of the ancient heroes were in a measure to Aeschylus what the stories in Plutarch, Holinshed, and the Italian romances were to Shakespeare—sources to be remodeled for the stage and its idealized transcript of life. Unlike the Elizabethans, however, Aeschylus was matched in a public contest in a religious festival, matched with his rivals, Choerilus, Pratinas, Phrynichus, Sophocles, all working on lines similar to his own, and each competing for the prize.

The material of myth, the instrument which set his mind in motion, was often crude, dimly outlined, rebellious to his purpose, because it was incoherent, inconsistent, or improbable. But whatever the improbability of the original story, its effect was nullified because, as Coleridge remarks about the first scene in *King Lear*, the improbability was already rooted in popular belief—"*Märchen noch so wunderbar, Dichterkünste machen's wahr.*" In the selection of his basal mythical material, Aeschylus' first care was to discover whether it might yield a theme capable of providing an action which, in its visible imitation, should induce the proper tragic effect—the ruin of a heroic personage through the antagonism of conflicting wills or obligations, and also a reconciliation that would eliminate blind forces and discover in their stead the compulsion of a moral law inherent in the very nature of man or of the universe itself. The myth must incarnate alike a moral problem and a moral solution. Professing no systematic theory of philosophy or theology, the poet must yet let the final issue restore our confidence in the security of a rational and equitable apportionment of things, a security that had been shattered by the spectacle of the discord between what is and what should be. The fable, too, must be such as to justify the presence of a choral group, the very center of the play; and it must yield a crisis or a series of crises. The story, so handled as to produce a dramatic action, came first. Second in rank to plot, came the drawing of character, involved in, or identified with, the action; ordinarily, at least, not independent of the action.

The social conditions and civilization of the heroic age must be fairly, if not accurately, reproduced. The heroes and heroines whose deeds and words were born of an age long overpast must be interfused with the spirit of the present, without disloyalty either to past or to present. The myth, reflecting the manners, the customs, and the religious sanctities of a ruder time, must subsist, its significance surrendered to the spirit of the poet's own age because interpenetrated by conceptions alien in part to the heroic personages envisaged by a mimetic art.

But, apart from this field where the originality of the poet might find occasion for its display, the old story was stable on its base. It is the old stories, the old ballads, the old pictures, once heard or seen, that never stale in childhood; and age discovers in them a profounder significance than the knowledge bought by the growing years.

A deeper import
Lurks in the legend told my infant years
Than lies upon that truth we live to learn.

Foreknowledge of the plot is not a narcotic to curiosity. Foreknowledge is a challenge to the intelligence. Yet the ancients did not enjoy an equal opportunity with the moderns to put their intelligence to the test by a repeated hearing of a favorite play; and thus bring to its appreciation a keener power to judge the delineation of character, the reaction of altered circumstance on character, and to recognize those warnings of impending disaster which are uttered unconsciously or pass unheeded by the persons of the play whose fortunes are at stake. The delight of foreknowledge must, it would seem, have a limit; yet I have heard of a lady who is said to have listened with increased satisfaction to the hundredth performance of the *Magic Flute*. (Of course, the rehearing of a play is not identical with seeing reproduced on the stage a familiar story previously undramatized.) In the fifth century before Christ at least only new tragedies were given at the annual dramatic festival. To this rule a unique exception is authenticated. It was established by state decree that any person desiring to reproduce a play of Aeschylus should be "granted a chorus," that is, have the right to revive the work of the master.

An ancient philosopher remarks that children love to simulate fear. For adults, older children that they are, the terrible has a fascination when its horrors can be assuaged through the mediation of art.

The legends of early Greece formed an inexhaustible repository of tales of revolting crime and its retribution. Remote in time, their very antiquity cast a glamor over the annals of bloodshed, adultery, revenge, the ingratitude of sons, a father's curse, and every defiance of the laws of God and man.

Roman history under the earlier Caesars, the chronicles of the Sforzas, the Borgias, and the Romanoffs, alone can rival the far-off tales of crime which tradition reported of the famous and infamous personages who figured as heroes on the Athenian stage. The house of Atreus has here preëminence. From Pelops to Orestes were accumulated horrors from which our poet might draw the material for his fables. The earliest atrocities he omits as impertinent to the ancestral guilt of Agamemnon. The wife of Atreus, Agamemnon's father, was corrupted by his brother Thyestes; Atreus' revenge was the banquet, served to Thyestes, of his own sons' flesh; Agamemnon slaughtered his daughter for ambition's sake; his wife was unfaithful to her absent husband with Thyestes' son; she slew her husband on his return home and, together with her paramour, was killed by her own son. Of the earlier evils in the house of Oedipus, the lost plays *Laïus* and *Oedipus* told the tale; the extant play of the trilogy is mindful of the curse pronounced against his two sons, who divide their father's inheritance by the sword. The daughters of Danaüs, all save one, killed their husbands on their wedding night. In the *Athamas*, the title-hero, in his madness, hunted his son Learchus as a deer; his wife Ino threw his other son Melicertes into a boiling cauldron and leaped with the body into the sea. In the *Ixion*, the hero of that name, angry at

his father-in-law for demanding a promised bridal
gift, caused him to fall into a burning pit; and was
purified of his crime by Zeus, yet he made an attempt
on the Queen of Heaven, and thenceforth was
chained hand and foot to a wheel on which he
revolved perpetually in the lower world.

The perpetrators of such revolting deeds won
for themselves 'heroic' proportions because they
were seen through the magnifying mist of antiquity.
Even the dastard Aegisthus is thus installed under
the heroic canopy. It was not the subject matter but
the manner cf their artistic adaptation that charged
the sanguinary myths of Ancient Greece with a spirit
suitable for the tragic stage. And it is precisely so
with the Elizabethan drama filled with horrors by
Seneca from abroad and by native taste. One
difference should, however, not be left unnoticed.
Blood, which flows in plenteous streams in Shakespeare, was never spilled before the audience in any
play of Aeschylus. The Greek dramatist utilized the
physical limitations of his art to the end that the
moral significance of a sanguinary deed should not
be endangered by the actual sight of blood.

The lyric predecessors of Aeschylus no doubt
had already begun to discern a spiritual content in
the ancient stories of brutal crime. It is, however,
in the dramatist that we discover the process in full
play. The sinister myths of far-off times were to be
enlightened by emotion and thought. Abhorring her
deed, the sympathy of the spectator for the doer was
to be won by understanding all the multiple motives
that drove Clytaemestra to the accomplishment of
her dreadful purpose. The appalling end of Eteocles
and his brother was to be sought in the character

they had inherited from Oedipus. The myth, reflecting the passions of a barbarous age, was thus made the medium to convey in beautiful form the significance of life that transcends alike the boundaries of the original tale and of the poet's own sphere of time. Epic, nay even lyric, pathos was thus intensified. The inner forces that dominate man's spiritual life took visible and concrete shape. Though no preacher, Aeschylus appealed to the undertone of religious consciousness of an audience assembled in the sanctuary of a god. He moralized, he idealized. With a few actors at his disposition he created a microcosm of life. He related the significant action to the moral order of the world.

In his all too rapid summary of the history of tragedy, Aristotle says this of Aeschylus: "he first introduced a second actor, diminished the importance of the chorus, and assigned the leading part to the dialogue." Now I am not unmindful of that fine epigram in the *Anthology* which puts into the mouth of Thespis the words "A younger race shall reshape all this, and infinite time will make more inventions yet; but mine are mine." I would not diminish the true fame of Thespis by an undue appreciation of his greater successor. Yet it might fairly be argued that Aeschylus is a claimant for the title of 'founder' of the tragic drama. Thespis' single actor served only to create an intermezzo between choral chants. But only with the second actor did there become possible that conflict of will, which to us, if not consciously to Aristotle, is the very essence of the drama. Only with the second actor, can plot, character-drawing, the reaction of an event upon the soul, the reaction of man on man, be knit into the

very fabric of dramatic art. All the rest of Aeschylus'
significant innovations are as nothing in comparison,
though they never lost their authority—the regulation of the forms of the dance, the fashioning of
costume, the installation of the iambic trimeter as
the appropriate verse of dialogue. As two Homeric
champions contend in arms in the presence of a
nameless crowd, so now, with the second actor, two
forces, incorporated in living though mimic personages, are arrayed in antagonism in the presence
of the choral mass. The enrichment of plot and the
delineation of character through the addition of a
third actor, adopted by Aeschylus in his old age from
his youthful rival Sophocles, made possible the
Orestea; yet that addition was not needed to produce
the majesty of the *Prometheus Bound.*

Aeschylean art ranges over the whole Greek
world, though he favored Argos of all the cities of the
motherland. Like Marlowe and Milton he knows
the art to poetize geography. The adventurous
Ionian wanderers on the sea, the explorers of the
regions beyond the farthest Greek settlements, gave
wing to his imagination and transported him to the
uttermost parts of the earth, to the trackless wastes
of Scythia, to Colchis, to the Caucasus. We behold
Danaüs just arrived from the land of the Nile; the
ghost of Darius rising from his tomb in Susa. The
most approved method to win the applause of the
audience, declares the Theatrical Director in Goethe's
Faust, is to range from heaven through earth to hell.
It was in the first region that Aeschylus laid one
scene of his *Weighing of Souls;* his *Sisyphus* will have
been familiar with the last-named place.

Far wider also is the range in time in Aeschylus as compared with either Sophocles or Euripides. Not content with stories of the heroic age, he carries us back to the earliest mythical period and indeed to the infancy of the world, to the very beginning of the rule of Zeus and to the dawn of human civilization. In the *Prometheus Bound* looms the shadowy figure of Cronus, the rebel against his father Uranus, only himself to be overthrown in turn by his own son. The hero, himself a Titan, wars on the side of Zeus against his fellow Titans, champions of the older order of things, establishes Zeus on his throne, and distributes to the gods their several prerogatives. In the *Suppliant Maidens* we are removed to an age far earlier than the Trojan war or the defense of Thebes by the son of Oedipus. Even recent history found a voice in a play at once political and religious. Only eight years had passed since the Athenians had raised the song of victory over the destruction of the Persian armada at Salamis, and now they sat in the theater enthralled by the story of that destruction, dramatized by the poet who had himself been a participant in the event. Everywhere Aeschylus found God in history.

In the extant works of Sophocles only once is a god moved within the range of human eyes. Aeschylus was extraordinarily fond of themes which rendered it possible to disclose beings of the divine world in actual presence. In the *Prometheus Bound* apart from Io (and she is the daughter of a river-god, a fact on which the poet lays no stress) it is only divine beings that function. The Titan protagonist is a god, though we are apt to regard him solely in the light of a human tragic hero by reason of his opposition to Zeus. Even the Chorus, womanly in their tenderness, compassion, and daring, are the offspring of the god whose waters encircle the world. The daughters of Oceanus represent a personification in which the ethical surpasses the physical element, of which Power and Force, the servitors of Zeus, are the rude incarnations. The *Prometheus Unbound* displays Earth, the Titan's mother, Heracles, the descendant of Io, and, as Chorus, the Titans released from Tartarus by the clemency of Zeus. In the *Weighing of Souls* Zeus will have been represented as holding aloft the balance in the scales of which are the lives of Achilles and Memnon. The last part of the *Orestea* is virtually only a battle between older and younger divinities, and Zeus, though not present in person, is the ultimate dominant force. Apollo speaks in the name of his father and it is the daughter of Zeus who assuages the wrath of the daemonic chorus. Hera appeared in the *Xantriae*, and in the *Priestesses* the Queen of Heaven was seen in the disguise of a beggar woman. Hermes, who, in the *Oedipus at Colonus*, is unseen, took visible form as the divine herald in the *Prometheus Bound*, the *Memnon*, and the *Ransom of Hector*. At the bidding of his brother Apollo, in the *Eumenides*, he is the guide of Orestes from Delphi to Athens, the city of refuge. In the *Archer-Maidens* Actaeon is turned by Artemis into a stag, either because he had seen her bathing or because he had boasted of his superiority in hunting; and as punishment for his temerity he was torn to pieces by his own hounds. In the *Danaïds* Aphrodite in person pleads before a human court the force of love as a universal power in order to secure the acquittal of the daughter of Danaüs who had refused to slay her husband. The Daughters of the Sun bewail the fate of their brother, Phaëthon, who for one day drove the chariot of his sire and in requital for his audacity was blasted by the thunderbolt. Dionysus, the god of the drama, in the existing remains of Greek tragedy is celebrated only in Euripides' *Bacchae* and in the hymn in his honor in Sophocles' *Antigone*. No less than eight or nine plays of Aeschylus center on the god, whose history presents some of the profoundest problems in ancient religion. His birth was probably the theme of the *Semele*, though it may be doubted whether here the poet represented the mother as destroyed by the appearance of Zeus in person. The *Nurses of Dionysus* faintly indicates by its title the subject of another play. An entire trilogy, the *Lycurgea*, was devoted to the opposition encountered by the religion of Dionysus in the north. In the *Edoni* Lycurgus, king of the people of that name, derides the god on his appearance. "Who is this womanish youth," he asks, "whose followers wear tunics and Lydian fox-skins reaching to their feet?" Flageolet, cymbal, and timbrel mark "the barbarous dissonance of Bacchus and his revellers," so alien to the temperate spirit of normal Greek music. The very house of Lycurgus is filled with the god, it totters in Bacchic revelry. The *Bassarae* recounted the rejection of Dionysus by Orpheus, the rending of the recusant by Thracian maenads, and his burial by the Muses. In the *Xantriae*, a word ordinarily interpreted as 'wool-carders,' the female ministers of Dionysus "tear asunder" the limbs of their victims. The *Pentheus* will have anticipated in large part the *Bacchae*, one of the most famous plays of Euripides.

Apart from the Olympian hierarchy, the gods of the sea figured largely on the divine stage of Aeschylus: Oceanus and his daughters, the Nereïds, attendants of silver-footed Thetis, herself a goddess of the sea, though wedded to Peleus; changeful Proteus, too, and Glaucus of Anthedon, the fisherman who ate of a magic herb and thereby became a prophet and a sea-god. The Lord of the Sea himself may have been first captured for the scenic stage by the beauty of Amymone, a daughter of Danaüs. In extant tragedy Poseidon appears only in the *Trojan Women* of Euripides.

The race of the celestial gods, superhumanized through their majesty and power, was never in Hellenic belief far removed from the race of living men. Even among the spectators of the plays of Aeschylus were men who might claim an Olympian pedigree as far-off descendants of the Immortals. As our poet, in the *Niobe*, says of the kinsmen of the heroine:

The seed of gods,
Men near to Zeus; for whom on Ida burns,
High in clear air, the altar of their Sire;
Nor hath their race yet lost the blood divine.[2]

Niobe herself, the daughter of Zeus-born Tantalus; Heracles, the son of Zeus and Alcmene; Perseus, the child of Zeus and Danaë, ancestor of the royal line of Argos, and many others, bring Olympus down to earth.

But the genius of the poet was not content to body forth in visible presence the gods, the demigods, and their offspring. His somber imagination evoked from the nether world daemonic beings and spectral

---

[2] *Frag.* 162, translated by Jebb.

apparitions—the Erinyes, divine, yet not of the race
of the Olympians; the ghosts of Darius and Clytaemestra return to earth to warn and threaten.
The *Spirit-Raisers* or *Soul-Conductors* is the tantalizing title of a satyric play. Madness (Lyssa) took
visible form in the *Xantriae*, as later in Euripides'
Heracles. In fact, marvelous and monstrous beings
have a large place in the dramaturgy of Aeschylus,
though not all are impersonated as participants in the
physical action: Ocean on his bird-horse, horned Io,
Harpies that snatch his food from Phineus, snake-
haired Gorgons, man-hating Amazons, the Phorcides,
swanlike in form, one-eyed and of a single tooth,
griffins, the sharp-beaked hounds of Zeus, the Keres,
bodiless souls; awful, mysterious in its dread potency
is the power that has no other name than "daimon."

Aeschylus was not partial to purely local legends
or local cults: the *Eumenides* attaches the foundation
of the High Court of the Areopagus to the appeal of
the matricide Orestes for justice at the hands of the
patron deity of Athens. The fable of Prometheus
may have ended with the establishment of the torch
race in honor of the Titan, now become the god of the
Attic potters. In the *Oreithyia* Boreas carried off the
Athenian maiden of that name as she was drawing
water from a spring too far from the city for her
security. The *Women of Aetna* celebrated the worship of the Palici, ancient Sicel divinities whose protecting power was invoked to guide to happy fortune
the city newly founded by King Hiero, the patron
of poets.

In the wider world of the national heroic legend,
most of the great personages of the remoter and
nearer past make their appearance on the Aeschylean

stage. Ixion of the rolling wheel is there, as is
Sisyphus of the rolling stone. Heracles, starting for
his labors in the western world, shoots the eagle that
has been rending the vitals of Prometheus, now to be
reconciled to Zeus after aeons of torment. In the
Daughters of Phorcus his ancestor Perseus encounters
those monstrous maidens; and Perseus' mother,
Danaë of the brazen tower and golden shower,
appears in the other members of the trilogy, the *Net-
Draggers* and *Polydectes*. The Danaïds are there, all
except one, slayers of their husbands; but not in
Aeschylus condemned to carry water in their leaking
vessels, their unending task in the lower world.
Niobe, daughter of Tantalus, suffers the penalty for
her boast that she was a more prolific mother than
Latona. In the play that bears her name Aeschylus
had opportunity to employ his favorite device of
long silences. The grief-stricken mother restrained
her grief on hearing that Latona's twin children,
Apollo and Artemis, had slain her seven sons and
seven daughters. When she found voice, it is she
who may have thus expressed her agony:

> Alone of gods, Death loves not gifts; with him
> Nor sacrifice nor incense aught avails;
> He hath no altar and no hymns of gladness;
> Prayer stands aloof from him, Persuasion fails.[3]

Aeschylus has not forgotten the mountain maid,
Atalante, bidden by her father to be the bride of the
swiftest footed, and outstripped by crafty Meilanion
and his golden apples—"*declinat cursus aurumque
volubile tollit.*" Phrixus and Helle escape the machi-
nations of their stepmother Ino and are rescued on

---

[3] *Frag.* 161, translated by Symonds.

the ram with the golden fleece. The story of the
Argo, says the *Odyssey*, was new and the delight of
all. Aeschylus dramatized it in a trilogy consisting
of the *Cabiri*, *Hypsipyle*, and *Argo*. The mystic
character of the Cabiri, divinities of Lemnos, did not
prevent our grave poet from the audacity of introducing drunken persons into the scene. Hypsipyle
is a figure in the "Lemnian horror," that deed,
famous in story, of the woman of Lemnos who slew
her husbands. The city of Cadmus, Thebes of the
seven gates, was full of ancient memories, fit themes
for the scenic art. It was the birthplace of the god
men worshipped by their presence in the theater.
It was the home of Oedipus, whose ill-starred fortunes were enstaged by Aeschylus before his great
successor created the most thrilling and perfectly
planned drama of the ancient world. Aeschylus'
Laïus and *Oedipus* are lost, but in the final play of
the trilogy we are carried back to the fatal passion
that brought into the world the unhappiest of men,
whose curse doomed his two sons to perish by mutual
slaughter. The *Seven against Thebes* recounts the
first siege of the city by the Argives led by Polynices
exiled by his brother. The story of its capture by the
descendants of the first assailants seems to have been
made the theme of another group of plays, in one of
which Theseus, the type of Hellenic chivalry, granted
permission to Adrastus to bury at Eleusis the bodies
of the Argives who had fallen before the walls of
Thebes. Myths are often indeterminate as regards
their date; and Athens was ever ready to find a place
for its one great legendary hero in the national myths
concerning events in which it had played no part.
Theseus is as timeless as the legend he annexed.

Myths tend also to overlap their original boundaries. So the foundation of the Nemean games was
associated with the march of the Argives to attack
Thebes. On their way northward a spring was shown
to the Argives at Nemea by the nurse of the son of
Queen Eurydice. During her absence the child
Opheltes was killed by a serpent; and to commemorate that event, as the beginning of the doom of their
expedition, the Argives instituted funeral games in
honor of the princely babe. Aeschylus, we know,
wrote a tragedy called *Nemea*. He also wrote a
satyric play that had to do with another national
festival, the Isthmian games; a fact that recalls his
famous *mot* on witnessing a contest at boxing there.
Turning to his friend Ion, the poet (for in classical
Greece poets frequented the stadium), Aeschylus remarked "You see the effect of training. The spectators cry aloud, the man who has been struck is silent."

Wide as is the range of Aeschylus among the
ancient stories of his race, most of the legends he
enstaged are witnesses to the preëminence and popularity of the "tale of Troy divine" as told by Homer
and the Cyclic bards. In his consideration of the
nature of the fables of tragedy, Aristotle remarks
that neither *Iliad* nor *Odyssey* would yield more than
one, or at most two subjects for the tragic stage;
whereas the *Cyprian Lays* yielded many, the *Little
Iliad* no less than eight. One tragedy, the *Rhesus*,
probably a work of the fourth century, is the only
extant play whose theme is taken directly from the
Iliad. From the *Odyssey* Aeschylus derived his
Penelope, the *Circe*, certainly a satyric play, and the
Bone-Collectors. The *Iliad* furnished the poet with
the idea that he employed in the *Weighing of Souls*.

In the twenty-second book of the epic poem, Zeus places in his balance two lots of death—one of Achilles, one of Hector. In the drama, when Achilles and Memnon are contending in arms, Zeus weighs in his balance their souls, while their mothers, Thetis and Eos, the Dawn, stand below, on the side of each the scale that holds the life of her child. The allegory in Homer is transformed by Aeschylus into a tragic theme. The fate of Memnon formed the subject of a special drama. In the dewdrops of the early morning, Greek fancy found the "the tears of Eos," shed by the mother every morning for the death of her son.

Famous in antiquity was the poet's dramatic handling of the story that runs from the sixteenth to the twenty-second book of the *Iliad*. The dramatic version needed for its exposition an entire trilogy, the *Myrmidons*, the *Nereïds*, and the *Ransom of Hector* or the *Phrygians*. Scant as are the fragments, we may venture to recover the outlines of the action. The Achaeans, hard beset and despairing of relief without Achilles, implore their leader to lay aside his wrath against Agamemnon. Achilles relents so far as to permit his friend Patroclus to take his armor and attack the Trojans. After slaying Sarpedon, the son of Zeus, Patroclus falls by the hand of Hector. Apprized by Antilochus of the loss of his companion, Achilles replies "Antilochus, bewail me the living more than him that's dead." His lamentation and his cry "My arms! My arms!" bring his divine mother from the sea.

In the *Nereïds* we may suppose that Thetis has new armor forged by Hephaestus, and, accompanied by her sisters, who form the Chorus, she brings it to her son. The last member of the trilogy could not well rival in pathos the Homeric foretype—Achilles in his tent, aged Priam, unattended, on his knees before the youthful Greek warrior, doing that which no man had ever done before: kissing the hands of the man who had killed his son. The obligatory presence of a chorus, the Phrygians who accompanied Priam on his mission, created a moving, but a different, situation. Achilles, we know, heard the many prayers and plaints, sat long in stony silence, only at last to consent to receive ransom for the body of the man who had killed his dearest friend.

The story of Salaminian Ajax, defeated in his contest with Odysseus for the arms of the dead Achilles, condensed by Sophocles into a single play, occupied an entire trilogy of Aeschylus (the *Contest for the Arms*, the *Thracian Women*, and the *Women of Salamis*). Sophocles made the hero fall upon his sword; Aeschylus, in accordance with the normal type, had a messenger announce his death.

Each of the three great tragedians wrote a *Philoctetes*. In the first century after Christ all three plays were extant, and were compared by Dio Chrysostom, from whom we learn something of the lost work of Aeschylus and of Euripides. Aeschylus gave no place to Heracles or even to Neoptolemus, on whom the reaction of Odysseus' craft constitutes, in Sophocles, the finest feature of the drama; and his version made Philoctetes lend himself to the Greek cause by the feigned story of Odysseus that Agamemnon and Odysseus were dead and Hector triumphant. In the judgment of Dio, Aeschylus was distinguished by the primitive grandeur and austerity of his style; by his power to embody the spirit of tragedy and to depict the manners of the heroic age.

It would take too long to tell of Europe, fearful for the fate of Sarpedon, Zeus' son and hers, who had left her to battle against the Greeks at Troy; of Telephus, who appeared in the play bearing his name and perhaps also in the *Mysians;* of Palamedes, who rivaled Prometheus as a benefactor of mankind, and of the many other heroes and heroines, whose deeds recorded in the epic chronicles were rescued from oblivion by the dramatist. Most conspicuous for his station of all the Homeric heroes whose unhappy fate on their return from Troyland won them a place on the tragic stage was Agamemnon, King of Men.

His bloody end was already known to the poet of the *Odyssey.* In Aeschylus' shaping of the story, Agamemnon's sacrifice of his daughter is recovered from the past to justify the sudden and awful taking-off of the king whose continued leadership of the Trojan expedition had been purchased by his daughter's blood. That fateful deed may have formed the subject of a separate play, the *Iphigenia,* which will not have been without influence on Euripides' treatment of the myth. For with all his different outlook on life, Euripides constantly reverted to themes already handled by the older poet. In drawing his subjects from the vast storehouse of epic myth, Aeschylus here, as elsewhere, made himself the legislator of all Attic tragedy.

It was a wise man who said that literature is only a fragment of fragments. Aeschylus wrote at least ninety plays. Most are ruins, ruins that cannot be rebuilded to any semblance of the unshattered edifice. Seven columns remain—"seven lamps" to light the way to the understanding of the mind of the dramatist whom that great lover of the classics, Lord Macaulay, so loved as to declare that, Homer only excepted, he was immeasurably superior to every other poet of antiquity.

Not that I have fathomed the depth of the riches of his mind and art. But I count myself happy to have lived long enough to have tried to discover their meaning for human life. For it is worth while to live if only one may catch some reflection of the splendor and the nobility and the majesty of the thought, clothed in the imperial vesture of a sovereign style, voiced in the solemn cadences of harmonious rhythm, that mark the work of Euphorion's son, first of the three greatest religious poets of the world.

CHAPTER II

THE SUPPLIANT MAIDENS

Since of itself antiquity is an indifferent guaranty of worth, it is unmeet for a Grecian to indulge in the luxury of that intellectual dishonesty which stamps as excellent, because it is ancient, any expression of the art of the Greeks. Cant may not be granted license to put an aureole on the past. And yet, on the other hand, condescension toward the primitive is ungracious in the case of the earliest manifestations of genius of a people dowered by nature with large capacity for development. If priority in age may justly attach an unique historical interest to *Ferrex and Porrex*, the oldest surviving tragedy of English literature, antiquarian zeal and sentiment alike may well be stirred by the oldest extant tragic drama of the world. The primitive will always claim its votaries; and rightly, when the ultimate perfection of an art may be discovered afar off in its first essays. A fragment of early Mycenaean pottery may possess a charm not to be outrivaled by a Pan-Athenaic amphora. Not always does the eye delight to linger on the shore where the sea breaks in full splendor—it seeks the far-out heaving swell as it gathers strength for its final triumphant onrush.

The genius of a poet in its setting majesty discovers itself best to him who has discovered the first gleams of its rising. Aeschylus is a poet whose development may be traced from youth to age with some sense of security, indeed with a greater sense of security than is possible in the case of Sophocles or of Euripides. We have lost Sophocles in his first manner, the manner in which, as he himself (perhaps playfully) tells us, he imitated the pomp and elevation of his predecessor; lost, too, it would seem, are the examples of his second style, marked by "harsh incisiveness and artificiality;" and there remain only those works that illustrate his art in its maturity. As for Euripides, his variation of attitude, his self-contradiction, the collision of his religious and his skeptical spirit, make well-nigh impossible any curve of systematic advance. If we indulge the wish to exchange the *Suppliant Maidens* of Aeschylus for his lost *Niobe*, *Weighing of Souls*, or the Lycurgean trilogy, our possession of the less famous play at least enables us to gain a better comprehension of the growth of the author's genius from the period of its earliest budding to the period of its ripest bloom.

Yet the antiquity of the *Suppliant Maidens* is not its sole title to fame. Its author, at the very outset, proved himself one of the greatest religious lyric poets of his people. Not in the *Agamemnon*, not indeed in any other poetical monument of Greek literature, with the possible exception of the *Hymn to Zeus* by the Stoic Cleanthes, is there discoverable anything that outranges the sublimity of the invocation to the High God, whose power and majesty form the burden of the prayer of the suppliant virgin daughters of Danaüs.

Though the deep will of Zeus be hard to track,
    Yet doth it flame and glance,
A beacon in the dark, 'mid clouds of chance
    That wrap mankind.
Yea, though the counsel fall, undone it shall not lie,

Whate'er be shaped and fixed within Zeus' ruling
   mind—
Dark as a solemn grove, with solemn leafage shaded,
    His paths of purpose wind,
    A marvel to man's eye.
Smitten by him, from towering hopes degraded,
    Mortals lie low and still:
Tireless and effortless, works forth its will
    The arm divine!
God from His holy seat, in calm of unarmed power,
Brings forth the deed, at its appointed hour![1]

The *Suppliant Maidens* need not, therefore, fear
comparison with the first fruits of the modern drama.
Rather, indeed, the comparison forces home the truth
that history is also a record of the interruptions to
progress and of the delays in the continuity of human
effort.

In such a retrospective, if not elegiac, mood we are
tempted to wonder what would have been the history
of the earliest classical tragedy of modern times, had
its first craftsmen known at first hand the Greek
originals, even as represented by the immature stage
reached by the *Suppliant Maidens;* and not been
forced by fate to discern afar off their true image
through their diminished reflection in Seneca, the
exemplar to our forefathers of the spirit of the Greek
drama. For Seneca was more philosopher and moralist than artist. Stoic that he was, he failed to realize
the difference between horror and tragic 'fear,' between passionate emotion and tragic 'pity.' Designed for the closet, and thus freed from the obligations of the acted drama, his tragedies disdain the
relations of character to action, tear passion to
tatters, and revel in the agonies of suffering that no
Greek had ventured to display in visible presence.

---

[1] *Suppl.* 87-103, translated by Morshead.

But it is foreign to my purpose to defame the Roman who first in poetic form unlocked to the Renaissance the treasure house of mythology enstaged by the tragic poets of Greece. Nor would it be done with good grace. For was it not Seneca who directed the author of our earliest English tragedy to the story of the sons of Oedipus that was first put into dramatic form by Aeschylus? Seneca's influence was not long dominant in England. The robust native sense of our English ancestors soon rescued the English drama from his authority, which in other lands long held undisputed sway.

Overshadowed by the fame of his later work, Aeschylus' *Suppliant Maidens* has suffered undue neglect. No other extant play of all Greek tragedy has experienced more of the injustices of time. If Aeschylus at large is, in many respects, the most difficult of all the Greek tragic poets, the *Suppliant Maidens* outdoes even the *Libation-Bearers* in presenting textual problems that put the acumen of the keenest critic to its fullest tension. Long neglect in ancient times, due in large measure to the loss of the music of the choral odes, has worked such havoc with the tradition of the text that even professional scholars have been repelled from that closer study of the play which alone reveals, along with its many demerits, an antique charm and beauties peculiarly its own. I cherish the admirable theory that no emendation should be admitted solely because it is possible. Yet here emendation is as exasperatingly necessary as it is exasperatingly uncertain. When I survey my own printed text, more conservative than many another editor's, I am appalled at the warning indications of a departure from the reading of the manuscripts. Fortunately, in my case, the signs of danger are not asterisks; otherwise the reader, on taking up a book plentifully supplied with such stellar ornamentation, might well exclaim with a famous German scholar *"Was soll diese verdammte Astronomie?"*

It is a noteworthy feature of the dramaturgy of Aeschylus that he did not confine his handling of certain myths within the confines of a single trilogy. With the story of Iphigenia he dealt twice; twice also with the story of Io and from the same source: first in the *Suppliant Maidens*, later in the *Prometheus Bound*.

In the *Prometheus Bound* the Argive maiden Io, in the course of her fateful wanderings, comes to a cliff in farthermost Scythia where the Titan is riveted in chains of adamant—he, fixed in his agony, she, in her agony, traversing land and sea: victims both of the passion and the power of Zeus. The roving glance of the Henry VIII of Greek mythology had rested on the fair daughter of Inachus, priestess in the temple of Hera, the spouse of Zeus. On his passion followed Hera's hate, an age-long hate, projected even to pursue the far-off descendants of her maiden votary. Hera transformed the girl into a heifer, and in that guise, distraught in body and in mind, she was driven throughout the world, guarded by many-eyed Argus, set over her as herdsman by the rancor of the Queen of Heaven. In the earlier play Io is imagined as completely animal. In the later play, where she appears before our very eyes, she is seen with only a conventional indication of her beast-like form. The difference points at once to a regard for scenic possibilities and to the distinction, noticeable in early

vase-paintings, where the purely animalistic type is
gradually supplanted by the partially human form.
In the *Prometheus Bound* Io herself with maidenly
reserve recounts the tale of her distress to her fellow
sufferer at the hand of Zeus; and he, a god, with foreknowledge from his mother Themis, unfolds to the
girl the perils still in store for her until she reach the
land of Egypt, where she is destined, by the touch
of Zeus, to regain her human shape and give birth
to a prince from whom there is to spring a royal
line. Of that royal line were the Suppliant Maidens,
the heroines of our play, who retrace the history of Io
in the very land of Argos, whence she, their primal
mother, had been driven forth.

In every Greek tragedy it is the part, either of the
chorus, or of one or two individuals impersonating
characters of the play, themselves at the start to set
forth who they are, where they are and why, and
what are their relations to other people involved in
the story; and, at the same time, to indicate more
or less distinctly an actual or impending conflict of
opposing interests. In the earliest tragedy the business of exposition fell to the chorus as the element of
prime importance. This original arrangement survives in two plays by Aeschylus, the *Suppliant
Maidens* and the *Persians*. In all his other extant
dramas the audience is informed of the situation in
more dramatic fashion, either by a dialogue or by a
soliloquy, an innovation probably due to Phrynichus,
an older rival of Aeschylus. At least we have no
indication earlier than Phrynichus' *Women of Phoenicia*, produced in 476 B.C., that the exposition was
not given in the march-anapaests chanted by the
chorus on its entrance, and followed by a choral song,

which might either continue the exposition or be entirely independent.

Exposition is invariably a difficult matter. The characters must be unconscious of the presence of the audience, yet they must set forth naturally what must be told to the audience, some portion of which (in ancient times) was familiar with the story. In our play this is briefly and effectively managed before the purely lyric part begins.

We are the daughters of Danaüs. We implore the protection of Zeus, the protector of all suppliants. We have fled the land of Egypt, seeking refuge in Argos from the pursuit of the sons of Aegyptus who would possess us in marriage from which Right holds them aloof. Argos was the home of our ancestress Io, the object of the passion of Zeus. O realm of Argos, its pure waters, its protecting gods, O heroes beneath its soil, and most of all, O Zeus, receive this band of women and overwhelm in the sea our suitors who follow hard upon us in their swift ship!

But emotion, thus following upon the exposition of fact, must rise to a more sustained flight. The lyric part of the parodos vibrates with sudden alternations of mood—now appeal, now despair, now prayer, now trust in the gods, now the unsearchableness of the mind of Zeus, the all-seeing Father, now lamentation; until at the end the agitation voices itself even in threats: if the celestial gods do not harken to our cry, we will perish by the noose and fare to the god of the nether world, the great hospitaller of the dead; and then Zeus, the very founder of our race, will justly be charged with doing dishonor to our righteous cause.

Action now succeeds to song, action in three separate phases—'acts' would be a misnomer. Danaüs, discovering the approach of an armed host, bids his

daughters place on the altars of the gods the branches
they bear as symbols of suppliance, bids them keep
a modest front in the presence of the strangers, and
take sanctuary with the gods whose images are
grouped on a near-by eminence. When it comes to
parley ,with Pelasgus, the leader of the armed force
and king of Argos, the girls alone, without the help
of their father, undertake to vindicate their claim
to protection. As two Homeric warriors, before they
engage, introduce themselves by proclaiming each
his lineage, so with Pelasgus and the Danaïds. Together they indulge in a veritable genealogical orgy.
The King will not credit their assertion that they,
swart-faced and garbed in outlandish fashion, are
Greeks at all. But he knows something of the story
of Io; they supply the rest—all told in a long-winded,
undramatic dialogue. At last he is convinced. But
his acceptance of their descent from Io and Zeus is
altogether different from a friendly reception. The
dilemma is hard—war with their cousins, the sons of
Aegyptus, on the one hand, and, on the other, recognition of the sacred right of suppliants imperiously
demanded of him by his petitioners. He is assailed,
and cruelly, by doubt. Appeals for compassion, to
the law of mercy, leave him irresolute. King though
he is, it is not at his hearth but at the people's that
his suppliants sit. His power does not extend so far
as to grant them sanctuary without the approval of
the Commons—a naïve touch of contemporary
Athenian political theory. At last he yields, not
because they are descended from Io of old, nor indeed
because of their suppliance, but because they threaten
to hang themselves even from the statues of the
gods—a desecration of the name of Justice and a

defilement of religion. That argument produces an almost instantaneous effect.

Thus ends the first complication and the play is nearly half-finished. The second phase of the action is brief. Interposed between two choral odes, one of seventy-six, the other of eighty-five verses, it is comprised in twenty-five lines, perhaps the shortest 'episode' in extant Attic tragedy. Danaüs is directed by the King to proceed to the city and plead his cause before the assembly of the people. The King promises to lend him his support in person. Meantime the maidens, in one of the sublimest hymns in Greek literature, voice their trust in Zeus. Danaüs returns; to a man the Argives have voted to champion the cause of the Suppliants; whereupon they pour forth orisons for blessing on their kinsmen, defenders of the fugitives.

Never may the wanton lord of war, who reaps a human harvest in alien fields, descend upon their land; never may pestilence empty this city of its men; nor strife stain the soil of the land with the blood of native slain! May Zeus cause the earth to render its tribute by the produce of every season! May minstrels sing hymns of praise at the altars; and from pure lips let there proceed the chant that attends the harp! May the people that control the State guard its privileges free from fear! May they worship for evermore the gods, who protect the land, even as their ancestors did before their time, since reverence for father and mother standeth written third among the statutes of Justice, to whom honor supreme is due!

But no sooner have their prayers voiced their joy than a new peril besets the Suppliants, a new peril charged with dramatic and exciting action. The prudent Danaüs, ever on the lookout for danger, descries the ship of the suitors close at hand. The maidens are filled with nameless anxiety. Their father departs to summon help. They invite death in any form. They implore the aid of Zeus, who holds all things in his balance.—A herald enters, attended by men-at-arms. Now heralds in Greek tragedy are wont to be overbearing, but the herald of the sons of Aegyptus outdoes all his tribe in brutal violence. Just as the frantic Danaïds are on the point of being dragged off, there appears a deliverer in the person of the noble Pelasgus, type of the Greek champion of distress. He drives from the scene their barbarous and impious assailant though he threatens war; and promises the Suppliants a safe dwelling place in Argos. Warned by their father of the perils of their beauty, they accept the protection of the Argives, to whom they pour forth a song of gratitude. The play ends with a strange division of sentiment. The Chorus of the Danaïds hymn the maiden Artemis and deprecate wedlock by constraint. Another Chorus, that of their handmaidens, celebrate the power of love and see in marriage the destiny of women now as in former times.

The Suppliants' case has triumphed. Their claim to Argive descent is acknowledged, the State of Argos has made their cause its own, the Argive king has repulsed the herald of their enemies. The Danaïds have abundantly won our sympathy, as befits the true protagonist of the play. Yet their future fortunes are still in the balance. Danger has threatened but it has not yet come to the uttermost. Sinister presentiments darken the final scene. The Egyptians will soon land in Argos to support by force the pursuit of their cousins. An inconclusive conclusion imperatively demands a sequel. An Aeschylean trilogy is thus, at the start, shown to consist of a group of dramatic units, each of which, as the extant *Orestea* proves, is structurally complete in itself, yet each only a fraction of a greater whole.

By itself the *Suppliant Maidens* is a mirror of the primitive right of refuge. It proclaims the sacredness of far-off ties of kinship and the compelling power of hospitality. It is Greek humanitarianism arrayed against barbarism. The sequel was a tale of war and love; but its reconstruction is as hopeless as it is tantalizing. In the *Egyptians*, the second play, if Hermann is right, the Argive champions of the Suppliants suffer defeat in battle; Pelasgus is slain, and Danaüs, though he has gained the throne, is compelled to marry his daughters to their detested suitors. It has been suggested that Pelasgus was not slain, but that he and the Argives effected a compromise between the opposing parties, the issue of which was the marriage of the cousins. This, however, leaves Danaüs without any capital position, and this position he must have had in order to give his name to the Danaoi, the primitive inhabitants of Argos. From the play itself only one word is preserved; though there are bits of flotsam among the unlocated fragments that seem to seek harborage therein.

Nor are we in much better case as regards the final play, the *Danaïds*. In the first member of the trilogy, the women, despite their number, voice the spirit of an undivided group. In the last member a division has been worked by love. Hypermestra alone refused to obey the injunction of her father that his daughters kill their husbands on the marriage night. That murderous deed afforded a theme both for many lost Greek tragedies (and comedies) later than Aeschylus, and for the Roman poets, whose fancy envisaged the scene with express and emotional detail. As for Aeschylus himself, in his *Prometheus Bound*, he lets the Titan foretell to Io the main fact unincumbered with attendant circumstance.[2]

Fifty maidens shall return to Argos, not of their own free choice, but fleeing marriage with their cousin kin; while these, their hearts ablaze with passion, like falcons following hard on doves, shall come in pursuit of wedlock unlawful to pursue. But God shall grudge them enjoyment of their brides. Pelasgian soil shall offer the maids a home, when, in the watches of the night, their husbands have been slain by a deed of daring wrought by women's murderous blows. For each bride shall reave her lord of life, dyeing a two-edged sword in his blood. But one among the maidens shall love's desire so charm as not to slay her mate: rather the edge of her resolve shall be blunted; for of two evil names she will make choice to be called coward rather than murderess. She it is that shall give birth in Argos to a royal line.

From the *Danaïds*, which dealt, if not with the deed, certainly with its consequences, only two fragments of any importance remain. One perhaps comes from a 'waking song' after the wedding night. The other presents Aphrodite defending the cause of Hypermestra before the court appointed to pronounce upon her rebellion to her father's command—*patria potestas* here strained to the uttermost. She who had been swayed to spare her husband, Lynceus, not by pity, but by the power of marital love, is championed by the goddess of love in person.

The holy Heaven longs for Earth's yielding breast,
Earth inly yearns to feel the fond embrace,
Heaven then descends in genial rain,
Quickening Earth's womb, that bears, to bless mankind,
Demeter's gifts, and yearling flocks that graze.
From that moist marriage-rite the woods put on
Their pomp. The fault of Earth and Heaven is mine.[3]

---

[2] *Prom.* 858-869.   [3] *Frag.* 44, translated by Lewis Campbell.

Love, deified as the force pervading all nature, will not desert the woman who has unconsciously surrendered to its cosmic energy. This tiny fragment, the Bridal of Heaven and Earth, recaptured in spirit by Shelley, proves the truth of Ruskin's words: "It is the crowning virtue of all great art that, however little of it is left by the injuries of time, that little will be lovely." Possibly the drama ended with the consecration of shrines to Aphrodite the Bringer of Victory and Artemis Peitho after the acquittal of Hypermestra, whose union with Lynceus was to provide Argos with its race of kings. The satyric play *Amymone*, named from a Danaïd rescued from the violence of a satyr by Poseidon, himself enamored of the girl, is lost.

No Greek myth covers such a stretch of time and has such an extensive geographical and genealogical range as the myth of Io and her descendants; and no other is so replete with difficulties. It seems to be compacted of two elements, one purely Argolic; the other came into existence when the Greeks became acquainted with the religion of Egypt.[4]

On the Argolic side, the myth presupposes the ancient worship of the gods in animal form. Io, of the myth, beloved in bovine form by Zeus, is in reality only 'ox-eyed' Hera herself, the great goddess of the Argolic plain. Io, the priestess in the service of the spouse of Zeus, was in fact evolved by the myth out of the theriomorphic Hera and at a time when the old-time belief in animal deities had lost its force. When Io, as a person, became independent of Hera, her prototype, the love of Zeus remained;

---

[4] See especially Eduard Meyer's study of the Pelasgians in the first volume of his *Forschungen zur alten Geschichte*.

and because of his love she incurred the enmity of
Hera, and by her or him was turned into a cow, and
driven from the land guarded by Argus of the many
eyes. Danaüs must have belonged to the Argolic
story.

His daughters, all save one, murdered their husbands in the wedding night. Students of folk-lore
dispute whether the Danaïds were primarily personifications of the springs or fountains of the thirsty
land of Argos, or bloodthirsty demons of a story,
such as appears in many countries other than Greece.
Poetry is not conterminous with myth. Nor is it, as
poetry, concerned with any ultimate explanation of
the product of mythopoetic fancy.

Connection between Greece and Egypt dates
from a very remote period, certainly as remote as the
middle of the second millenium before Christ.
Evidence of later contact is possibly warranted by
the fact that on an inscription of Rameses III of the
twentieth dynasty (about 1200 B.C.) mention is
made of a people called Danauna, which the king
boasts to have driven from their islands. It is perhaps no idle fancy which connects these Danauna
with the Danaoi, who, according to Greek fancy,
took their name from the father of the Suppliant
Maidens of the play.

When Egypt was opened to the Greeks of the
historical period they found there a highly developed
worship of the gods in animal form such as had long
disappeared from the religion of their own land, but
of which they may have still retained a dim memory.
They saw the Egyptians worshipping Isis in the form
of a cow, and Apis in the form of a bull engendered
by a flash of light and born of a virgin cow. Because

of their belief that the gods of other countries were only their own gods under other names, these early Greeks identified Isis with their own Io, who had been driven forth from Argos. The land of Egypt was then discovered to be the final stage of her manifold wanderings. Various localities, such as the Ionian Sea, the Thracian or the Cimmerian Bosphorus, suggested themselves as places for her passage from Greece to Egypt. The rest of the geographical details were supplied by the interest in far-off countries that attended Greek ˙colonization in the seventh and sixth centuries.

Now after Io had been transformed into a cow by Hera, she was approached by Zeus in the form of a bull. The legend on one side being purely animalistic, her offspring was an animal, even this Apis, the sacred bull of Egypt. But the legend had also its human side. Io had been retransformed by Zeus into a woman, and had human offspring, Epaphus by name. 'Epaphus' has thus a double aspect, as bull and as man, since he is the child of the cow-woman Io.[5]

---

[5] The interpretation of the name Epaphus, long the battleground of scholars, is too intricate for more than passing mention here. Two explanations have been offered, neither of which is convincing.

1. The name is Greek, derived from the myth, as set forth by Aeschylus, that Io's son was born upon his mother's restoration to human shape by the touch (ἐπαφή, ἔφαψις) of Zeus. It has been shown by Maass (De Aeschyli Supplicibus commentatio) that the Greeks were familiar with the idea that the pains of women in labor were relieved by the laying on of hands, and also that metamorphosis was believed to be accomplished by touch. Since 'Epaphus' should signify 'he who touches,' not him 'born of touch,' as Aeschylus takes it, Maass derives the name from Zeus Epaphus, an appellation comparable to Zeus Paion, Zeus Apemius, designations which he restricts to the medical sphere. In his admirable study Epaphus and the Egyptian Apis, Linforth would substitute Hera Epaphus for Zeus Epaphus. But apart from the departure from the myth in the intrusion of the goddess hostile to Io, this explanation is

Epaphus, according to the myth, married Memphis, a personification of the city where the sacred Apis was especially worshipped. His daughter was Libya—hence the interest of Cyrene in the story. Libya had a son Belus, whose name, recalling that of the Aramaean god, indicates connection with the Semites to the north. Belus' sons were Aegyptus and Danaüs, the one bearing the ancient name of the Nile; the other being the name-giver of the Danaoi in Greece.

The problem was therefore how to get Danaüs from Egypt to Greece in order that he might there become the eponymous founder of the Danaoi. To this end the Egyptian and the Argolic myth were united. The daughters of Danaüs had killed their husbands in Argos; so their suitors, now become the sons of Aegyptus, were imagined to have pursued them, attended by their father, across the sea. Aegyptus, it is generally reported, remained behind in the land of his own name. How Danaüs, an emigrant, got possession of the kingdom of Argos, Aeschylus at least does not tell us. But later writers did not fail to grapple with the question.

---

equally open to the objection that an hypostatized Epaphus should be a mythical healer by virtue of his touch. To the Epaphus of the Io myth no such magical power was ever attributed; unless indeed he can be ultimately equated with Apis, the seer and leech, Apollo's son (*Suppl.* 262). 2. The name Epaphus, a phonetic approximation of the Egyptian Pe-Hapi, itself gave rise to the myth of the miraculous birth. On this showing, then, the Greeks will have had two names for Apis, one Apis outright (Herod. 3.27), the other Epaphus. It is improbable that the differentiation is due to a desire to safeguard confusion of Epaphus with the Greek Apis, who appears now as the son of Phoroneus, the ancient Argive king, now as Apollo's son; and for whose name connection has been sought in ἄπιος (ἤπιος), or in Apia, the ancient name of the Peloponnesus, from ἄπ 'water' (cf. Messapia).

Some part of the Oriental coloring of the play the poet may have derived from the tales of travelers and merchants who had visited Egypt. But, for its substance, the sources were literary. Hesiod's *Catalogues* seems to have yielded little. The epic *Danaïs*, a poem nearly half as long as the *Odyssey*, furnished him with the main material. Though of its six thousand five hundred verses, only a few remain, it is tolerably clear that this poem coördinated the various scattered elements of the myth. Even if Argive acquaintance with Egypt and its religion dates as far back as Psammetichus I and not Psammetichus II, who is generally believed to be the prince whose Ionian mercenaries inscribed their names on the rock at Abu Simbel, ample time must be allowed to intervene before the epic could fuse the Argolic with the Egyptian legend. The *Danaïs* will not therefore have been composed until well into the sixth century. Of the early lyric poets, only Archilochus, of the early historians, only Hecataeus, touched on the story. It was recast for the stage by Phrynichus, whose *Egyptians* and *Danaïds* will have anticipated Aeschylus.

Two aspects of the story engaged the attention of antiquity at large. First, the murder of their husbands by the daughters of Danaüs, secondly and later (at least the evidence is not earlier than the *Axiochus* of Plato), the punishment of the murderesses in the lower world, where they were condemned forever to draw water in leaky vessels. The murder formed an integral part of Aeschylus' dramatization of the myth. The expiation of the murder apparently stood outside his scheme.

When the scene of the action is laid in Grecian lands, the tragic poets did not scruple to import from abroad women (but not men) to form their choruses. In the *Suppliant Maidens*, however, the Chorus consist, not as in the *Women of Phoenicia* by Phrynichus and by Euripides, of Orientals, but of heroines of Hellenic stock, though their ancestors, for five generations, had been settled in the delta of the Nile. To match such antiquity abroad the poet devised a like antiquity at home. The fugitive Danaïds land on the eastern shore of an empire stretching far to the north, to the Strymon, and reaching to the western sea; an empire, whose king is Pelasgus, son of a son of Earth, and mythical ancestor of the Pelasgoi, that ancient people whose primal home was the Thessalian plain but who were extended to be the original inhabitants of a great part of Greece. Pelasgus owes his presence to no other cause than that the name 'Pelasgic Argos' was transferred to the Peloponnesian Argos. Pelasgus himself had been preceded by Palaechthon and by Apis, all three mythical personages, and thus matching Epaphus, Libya, and Belus, the three who intervene between Io and Danaüs.

Legends of such sort know no date. The *Suppliant Maidens* revels in timeless personages and eponymous heroes, to us mere creations of that primitive exuberant Hellenic fancy which defied the unknowable, but to the poet still, for the most part, undistinguished from the substantialities of veritable history. To the Greeks, as long as their science did not dispel the illusion, legend was in essence historical fact. To the imagination of Aeschylus a horned Io, or an Io completely bovine, presented no difficulties. The time was still distant when the wandering maiden was to be consciously resolved into the wandering moon. Nor was he staggered by the numerous progeny of Danaüs and Aegyptus or by the circumstance that sex was so nicely apportioned by fate that just fifty daughters of one brother were the objects of the passion of just fifty sons of the other. (The names of the mothers, if known to Aeschylus, were mercifully suppressed by him, but not by the mythographers—the later Greeks know everything.) Mythical folk have mythical offspring. It was just fifty children that Selene bore to Endymion. Are not the innumerable waves typified by the fifty Nereïds? And did not Priam have fifty sons and fifty daughters? No poet could foresee that an unpoetical age was to discover in that number only the relic of a primitive calendar.

Now of the numerical constitution of the chorus before Aeschylus we know nothing; but to him, in the *Suppliant Maidens* at least, it was a happy coincidence that the myth gave to Danaüs fifty daughters, a number exactly equal to that of the chorus of the dithyramb, from which tragedy itself had sprung. His later choruses consisted of twelve singers; this early chorus, of fifty; and since each Danaïd is said to have an attendant, the supernumerary chorus at the end of the play was exactly equal in number to the chorus proper. The Aeschylean orchestral space, thus crowded with singers and with the Argive men-at-arms, presented a splendid spectacle; and it had full need of the amplest space that Allen claims for it.[6]

----

[6] J. T. Allen, *The Orchestra-Terrace of the Aeschylean Theater* (1922).

Genetically, a Greek tragedy consists of a series of choral songs to which have been added, before and after, divers epic, non-lyric elements. The history of the tragic art records the advance of the later non-lyric element at the expense of the original lyric element. It was Aeschylus who was chiefly instrumental in inaugurating this momentous change. In his earlier plays, as in the case of none of those of his successors, there is a clear preponderance either of the lyric or of the epic type. The *Suppliant Maidens* is 'lyric,' the *Persians*, *Prometheus*, and the *Seven against Thebes* are 'epic.' ('Lyric tragic drama,' as it is known in Shelley's *Prometheus*, did not exist in ancient times.) In the poet's later *Orestea*, the two distinctive types are no longer apparent: the two elements coexist, both equally developed, though the *Agamemnon* and the *Libation-Bearers* contain extensive choral odes, unequalled for their architectonic majesty in the whole range of dramatic art. Best of all the extant plays, the *Suppliant Maidens* represents the primitive character of Greek tragedy. It has no 'hero.' Chorus and heroine are one. The fifty daughters of Danaüs think and act as one. They are in reality only a "multiplied heroine." About three-fifths of the play is choral, while the interposed narration or dialogue serves no other purpose, except toward the final crisis, than to carry the slight action. Beyond question the play stands nearest to the period of the single actor. Sophocles, on the occasion of his first appearance as a tragic poet (in 468 B.C.), introduced a third actor. But we have no warrant that Aeschylus' capital innovation of the second actor was coincident with his first attempt to gain the tragic prize (in 499 B.C.).

We do not in fact know whether, among the plays
whose titles are recorded, there may not be some of
the single-actor period; but I should be loath to
hazard a guess as to which, if any, of the lost plays
is so archaic.

Greek tragedy normally presents the spectacle of
greater men and women whose words and deeds
provoke emotional or intellectual reflection in an
obligatory body of spectators, representative of a
mass, and themselves part of the play. This group,
the chorus, is, as it were, also interposed between the
impersonated characters and the larger audience in
the theater. It is usually a passive agent: it sym-
pathizes, it counsels, it warns; but it does not usually
initiate or carry through any significant action. It
consists of subordinate persons, in Aeschylus normally, without exception in Sophocles, and in
Euripides, even in the *Bacchae*.

The earliest and the latest play of Aeschylus are
unique exceptions to the rule. In the *Suppliant
Maidens* and in the *Eumenides*, the Chorus, consisting
in one case of human, in the other of divine women, is
the main personage, is passionately interested in its
own cause, and is intimately engaged in the action
from start to finish. And because it is not a passive
agent, but itself acts, the old-time notion that the
Greek chorus is the "idealized spectator" here breaks
down absolutely.

The prominence of the chorus in the *Suppliant
Maidens* is not due to an abnormal situation or to
the plot. It is the survival of primitive tragedy, in
which the group uniformly played the chief part.
Many later tragic choruses appear in obedience to
command; some appear out of curiosity; others, for

no explained reason at all—there must be a chorus,
behold it marching into the orchestra! To a greater
degree than even in the *Eumenides*, the chorus of the
Suppliant Maidens itself carries the main action. Its
very dominance works against the development of
the other persons in the play. Danaüs, for all that
he is a prudent father, is reduced to relative obscurity. His main part is to keep a good watch and be
ready with sage counsel and consolation. In the long
colloquy between the King and the Danaïds when
their identity is at stake, he is not allowed a single
word. Not that, as daughters, they fail to observe
the commandment they themselves proclaim, the
commandment to honor one's parent, but as chorus,
they may not relinquish to a subordinate person
their proper function as bearers of the main action.
Besides, an eponymous hero is not a creature of much
flesh and blood.

Un-Hellenic in garb, the Danaïds are at least in
part un-Hellenic in temperament and character.
They are entirely familiar with the Greek pantheon;
yet they need to be instructed concerning the significance of the symbols of the gods whose images are
grouped on a collective altar, placed so close at hand
as to provide a sanctuary. In his characterization
of these women, the poet endeavors to preserve the
essential integrity of their maidenly nature and yet
join the Oriental with the Greek. The peculiar woofs
that drape their forms, their cheeks burnt by Nile's
sun, are only indications of a strangeness that extends
to their style of passion and even to their language.
Only Clytaemestra can rival their intense and determined will. Yet, unlike the heroine of the *Agamemnon*, they know terror as it is known only

to the women of the *Seven against Thebes*. Their
song ranges through every scale of emotion,—hope,
despair, defiance, frenzy, courage; they trust in the
gods, yet they threaten even High Zeus himself.
They oppose the Argive king with an insistence
foreign to the women in the Theban play. As elsewhere Aeschylus shows character by effective contrast, so here their impetuosity is set against the
indecision of the King. Clytaemestra would have her
husband believe that in anxiety for his life she had
attempted to take her own. But these maids would
do that which had never been done in Grecian lands.
They would make the very altars of the blessed gods
their scaffolds. These maids, who all had the will
thus to hang themselves, had also, all save one, the
will to kill their husbands; and the one who would
not was to be the ancestress of Perseus, of Heracles,
and of the Danaan kings.

It must be confessed that, because of a certain
indistinctness as regards the circumstances antecedent to the play, the poet has not made it altogether
clear why the Danaïds should profess such violent
detestation of their cousins. It is, in fact, this very
indistinctness that is the sole argument for placing
the *Suppliant Maidens* after, and not before, the
Egyptians. Certain it is, however, that the loathing
shown by the maidens for their suitors is not due to
scruples as to religious defilement through marriage
within a forbidden degree of consanguinity. At
Athens only children of the same mother were forbidden by law to marry. It is, therefore, inconceivable
that Aeschylus should have ignored the facts at
home, where even half-sisters and half-brothers
might freely marry; and improbable that he should

have been ignorant of the facts in Egypt, where the
marriage of Isis with her brother Osiris reflected the
human custom whereby a brother might marry his
sister-germane or his uterine sister. Nor is adequate
stress laid on the horror of marriage with near kinsmen, had it been the cause provoking the insistent
and furious denunciations of their suitors by the
Danaïds.

To Bachofen[7] these denunciations represent the
protest of gynaecocracy against the encroachment
of a later system of social organization. Gynaecocracy, he maintains, includes the right of women not
to marry, or, if they are willed to marry, then to
choose their own husbands. Mother-right, which the
Swiss jurist silently equates with gynaecocracy, prescribes the reckoning of kinship and succession to
property through females only. Bachofen admits
that the idea of gynaecocracy had disappeared from
memory in the time of Aeschylus and that it was an
audacity for the poet to represent it. But it was a
motive rich in contrasts—the defense of the right of
the heart against a loveless union. The sons of
Aegyptus seek to invalidate the ancient prerogative
of women; through marriage with their cousins they
would win power for themselves; they perished, slain
by their brides, champions of the older order. Their
murder is an incident in the contest of related families
and an echo of savage times long overpast.

The Danaïds' opposition to marriage with their
kindred is, according to Ridgeway,[8] the protest of

---

[7] Bachofen, *Das Mutterrecht*, p. 92.

[8] Ridgeway, *The Origin of Tragedy*, p. 190, on the basis of *Suppl.*
333-339, 387-391. In *Laws* 725, where Plato touches on certain hardships
resulting from the law concerning heiresses, he does not admit the
injustice of regulations that form the point of Ridgeway's argument.

a considerable section of the community that still
remained hostile to (assumed) relatively recent
Athenian legislation which had made an heiress a
mere appendage to the estate, and, unless her hand
was otherwise disposed of by her father's will, obligated her to marry her next of kin, who, to this end,
might, if married, put away his own wife. The
Danaïds denounce union with their cousins as unnatural because they stand for exogamous marriage,
which is based on a social system that traces descent,
and prescribes succession to property, through
females; whereas the sons of Aegyptus represent the
doctrine of endogamy, which established itself at
Athens in the course of the fifth century. The latter
assumptions of the Cambridge scholar are too
far-reaching for discussion here. As regards his contention that the Danaïds stand in the position of
heiresses according to Attic law, it is to be objected
that their father is *alive* and is himself unwilling, in
this play at least, for his daughters to marry the
sons of Aegyptus (v. 227); that, at best, the girls are
therefore only presumptive heiresses; and that the
sons of Aegyptus do not themselves explicitly claim
that they, as next of kin, have the right to marry
their cousins. Or will Professor Ridgeway claim that
in the original story Danaüs was dead and that
Aeschylus has wrought confusion by bringing him
to life?

Wilamowitz is of the opinion that the play presupposes a contest of arms, waged in Egypt,[9] between

---

[9] Wilamowitz, *Aischylos: Interpretationen*, p. 15, thus explains the
verses of the epic *Danaïs*:

καὶ τότ' ἄρ' ὡπλίζοντο θοῶς Δαναοῖο θύγατρες
πρόσθεν ἐυρρεῖος ποταμοῦ, Νείλοιο ἄνακτος.

the families of Danaüs and Aegyptus; that the
Danaïds had fallen into the power of their cousins,
from which they had escaped; and that, like the
Amazons, whom they resemble in aspect and in
nature, they are absolutely averse to wedlock. The
comparison with the Amazons had long before been
made by Bachofen, who had also noticed that the
Danaïds seem to be likened to them in a fragment of
the lyric poet Melanippides of the time of Euripides;
though the similarity goes no further than an un-
feminine love of hunting—a love that is, however,
shared by Cyrene, the heroine of Pindar's ninth
Pythian ode. It is true that, at first sight of the
Suppliants, the King likens them in appearance to
Libyans, to Egyptians, to Cyprians, and finally to
Amazons. But nowhere else is there any hint of their
similarity to the mythical "mateless, flesh-devour-
ing" warrior-women, whose hatred of men was born
of an age with large capacity for wonder and large
zest for wonder. Once fancy had created fighting
women (a breed not unknown in our own time), it
was but a step to make the Amazons loathers of men
as husbands. As for the slaughter of their husbands
by the Danaïds, that was done, not at their own
insistence, but at that of their father.

To my thinking this much at least is clear—the
very style of their vehement and passionate detestation proves that the maidens fear and hate the
brutality of their cousins because they are the object
of their wanton pursuit. Incessantly and explicitly,
they stress the unholiness, the violence, the lewdness
of suitors who would wed them by force; and to their
own loathing is added the unwillingness of their
father to have them submit to an enforced marriage.

It would be unprofitable to dwell at length on the defects of the play, defects indicative of its early date. It lacks life, it is meager in forward action, it is unable to make the action organic, it is slow in movement. It unduly expands certain parts in order to fill time. Its weakness in psychological analysis results in failure to draw strong characters except in the case of the choral protagonist. It awakens no other sympathy than that of pity.

Two instances of dramatic helplessness are worth mention. At verse 710 Danaüs sees the Egyptians drawing close ashore. He would hurry to the city to summon help, yet, despite the imminence of the danger, he delays no little time to enhearten his daughters by words of comfort and by a lengthy description of the difficulties which a ship has to encounter in making anchorage. The passage has no dramatic necessity and serves only to create an interval between two choral odes. The other case shows that the poet has not yet learned the art of managing his two actors—later he has abundantly shown that he could write a good play with no greater number at his disposal. After the Herald has been repulsed, the King offers (at verse 957) the Danaïds a home within the city—either in dwellings of separate sort or in a kind of municipal lodging-house. Unwilling of themselves to decide the question, they beg the King to send for their father to instruct their choice. Scarcely has the King quitted the scene when Danaüs enters, and much too soon for him to have received the summons. Yet, once on the scene, he does not settle the moot question at all: instead he delivers a fine harangue on the dangers incident to the beauty of his daughters. The whole matter of the lodging-place is no more than a scheme to get Danaüs back. But he could not reappear until the actor who had been playing the Herald had time to dress up as the father. Danaüs and his body-guard were needed to join in the procession at the end; for Aeschylus affected pomp and ceremony here above all. In stage effect as in language he loved the grand style.

But this, and like inartistic handling of a dramatic situation, has only a certain historical interest when measured by the steadier art of the later works. Even as it stands, the *Suppliant Maidens* is rich in vividness and variety of spectacle, rich in its power of portraying vibrations of emotion, rich in its capacity of sustained lyric energy.

"*Poeta nascitur non fit*" rings truer of a lyric poet than of a dramatic poet. Behind Aeschylus, it is true, lay the lyric art cultivated for a century and more; and now, in his own time, wrought into its fullest perfection by Simonides and Pindar. Yet by grace of God and in his own right, he was a great lyric poet at the start. Only gradually did he learn to manage his exits and his entrances and attain to the full excellence of dramatic craftsmanship.

The lyrics soar, whether as the expression of alternating emotion, or in passionate argument, or even in the tale of Io distressed and coursing through the world. Nor does the burden of profound religious truth impede their strong flight in the Suppliants' praise of Zeus.

From him our race did spring;
Creator he and King,
Ancient of days and wisdom he, and might.
As bark before the wind,
So, wafted by his mind,

Moves every counsel, each device aright.
    Beneath no stronger hand
    Holds he a weak command,
No throne doth he abase him to adore;
    Swift as a word, his deed
    Acts out what stands decreed
In counsels of his heart, for evermore.[10]

Yet this Zeus, whose wisdom and power are celebrated as if by a Hebrew prophet, is the Zeus whose passion brought humiliation and sorrow upon Io, as the story is told in full in the *Prometheus Bound*. Is the High God of Greece so made in the image of man that he can be both brutal and beneficent?

The question is vital for Greek religion. In its acutest form it permeates Greek thought from the sixth century before Christ nearly to the end of the pagan world. Xenophanes' protest against anthropomorphic gods is echoed by Euripides, by Plato, and the Christian Fathers. But Aeschylus is not troubled in soul by the thought that underlies the passionate argument of the Ionic moralist. He will not deliberately, with Pindar, fling from him the evil tales of the gods. Nor does he, with Euripides, assert that, if the gods do evil, they are not gods at all. Sophocles evades the direct issue. Aeschylus deals with the gods at close range, and of set purpose involves himself in themes that test the divine justice. To him the tales about them are wrought into the very fabric of the myths, which, as a dramatist, he must use as the material of his art. In these myths he must somehow find his idea of God.

In the *Prometheus Bound* it is his purpose as a dramatist to arouse pity for the victim and detestation of the god who inflicted upon Io such cruel

---

[10] *Suppl.* 592-599, translated by Morshead.

suffering. When his aim is to depict the cruelty of Zeus, Io staged in visible presence was a living and moving incrimination of the god. When also, as a dramatist, it is his aim to depict the fortunes of Io's descendants seeking safety in her primal home, Io was a name wherewith to evoke the compassion of Zeus, the guardian god of all suppliants. Her sufferings lived in the memory of her offspring, yet they are summoned from a past whose very remoteness is felt to have assuaged their bitterness. The pain and the offense are gently minimized. Zeus is now the healer of pain. Even as long ago he brought deliverance from her pangs to the object of his love, so now he will prove himself the deliverer of her descendants.

Lofty as are his religious ideas, Aeschylus is first and foremost a dramatist, not a religious teacher or a prophet whom we must approach with a certain ceremony of mind. He operates with divine as well as with human characters; he is not bound by any ecclesiastical prescription to any fixed conception even of the one highest god, toward whom his religious aspiration darkly moves. Once Zeus enters into the domain of mythology, ever fluctuating, ever inconsistent, for the depiction of character he is no more than human. Through mythology, which is also theology, Aeschylus arrives at religion, not the religion of the formal national worship, but the religion that transcends all cult. Out of the defilements of mythology in which Greek religion was involved to him, as to us, he dimly discerns the good. He knows how to depict the birth and growth of sin, but he does not grapple with the origin and nature of evil as such. He does not, like Sophocles, find in the sufferings of the innocent part of the unintelligible mystery of human things, unintelligible, yet to be borne with resignation and fortitude. Nor does he directly encounter the question of the irreconcilability of a good and an evil God. He discovers how the evil of gods and the misery of men at last issue in goodness and in happiness. The Zeus of the *Suppliant Maidens* thus wears another aspect than the Zeus of the *Prometheus Bound*. Into the mouth of these young girls of the story, the poet puts thoughts that far surpass the utmost range of their religious experience, the vision of a glorified Zeus, whom they invoke as "King of Kings, among the blessed most blessed, power most perfect among the perfect," "Zeus, through endless time, the lord." Poetry and religion are not the same. The dramatist does not always lay bare his inmost faith. Yet this soaring vision of the majesty of the Supreme God—the god also of the myth of Io—is his and his alone. It is the searching of the spirit after God if haply he may find him.

CHAPTER III

THE PERSIANS

The Chorus, who represent the Council of the Persian realm, chosen to that high office by virtue of their rank and years, appear before the palace of the Great King at Susa. Disquieted by the absence of all news of the force led against Hellas by Xerxes, their youthful king, Darius' son, they hearten their spirits by calling to memory the gallant commanders of the vast host that had been collected from every part of the empire. The flower of the Persian land has departed. Asia, their foster-nurse, laments; parents and wives, as they count the days, shudder at the lengthening delay. Yet there is no cause for despair. The host of Persia is not to be withstood. Valiant of heart are her sons, and their chief, the impetuous lord of populous Asia, is himself the peer of the gods. Since ancient days Fate enjoined upon the Persians the pursuit of war upon the land; and now, of late, they have learned to look upon the domain of the broad-wayed sea when it is smitten by the tempest's blast.—"Yet the insidious guile of God, what mortal man shall escape it? Delusion, with semblance of fair intent, lureth man astray into her snares."

Thus at the outset the souls of the Elders are shaken by a religious fearfulness.

Atossa, the Queen-mother, appearing in royal splendor, at once confirms their gloomy apprehensions. Heretofore she had been confident that fortune would remain constant. But in the night just passed a disturbing dream has shown her the vision of two fair women, sisters of the self-same race: the one, symbol of the free Greeks across the sea, the other, symbol of the Asiatic Greeks under Persian rule. Xerxes, her son, yoked both to his chariot: one was submissive, the other in her struggles hurled him to the ground. Waking, Atossa would make sacrifice to avert the evil portended by her dream. On her way she beheld an eagle fleeing for safety to the altar of Phoebus: its head torn by the talons of a falcon, chasing in hot pursuit.

Bidden by their Queen to interpret these portents, the Ancients counsel her to make libations to Earth and the Departed and thereby to beseech the spirit of her dead spouse Darius to withhold in the nether gloom all ill and to send back all good for herself and her son. On the point of departing on her mission of supplication, Atossa suddenly inquires in what region of the earth this Athens lies of which she had heard report, and who is set over its men as lord and master. Scarcely has she been answered than there enters a Courier, speeding in hot haste from Xerxes' shattered army now painfully nearing the last stage of its homeward march. "Our whole armament is lost!"

Smitten with dismay at the news of the disaster, Atossa is long silent. When her misery at last finds voice, she puts the tremendous question "Who then is *not* dead?" Comforted to learn that her son at least still lives, her questioning draws from the messenger the details of the catastrophe at Salamis: the death of the leaders, the false message conveyed to Xerxes that the Greeks had purposed to escape by

stealthy flight, the annihilation of the Persian fleet
in the narrows, the sufferings endured by the troops
following Xerxes through Boeotia and Thessaly, their
losses as they sought to win a passage over the melting ice of the Strymon, their hardships in Thrace,—
"few there were indeed that escaped and reached the
land of hearth and home."

All too clearly did Atossa's dream portend misfortune and all too lightly did the Elders read its
meaning! Nevertheless she will sacrifice as they
had counselled, not now to avert the coming of a
dreaded evil but in the hope that the future may hold
something auspicious in store. Her intended sacrifice is (unexpectedly) directed to a libation to summon the spirit of her consort from the grave, if haply
he may provide relief for her and hers in this crisis
of fortune. Darius' ghost, startled by the invocations,
the shrill cries of the Elders and their stamping on
the earth to evoke his presence, rises from the tomb,
his head crowned with the royal tiara. The Elders,
overcome by their former awe of their august
sovereign, can make no answer to his inquiry why he
has thus been called forth from the shades. From the
lips of his Queen he must therefore hear the tale of
the calamity visited upon his empire under the rule
of their son. Warning his people never again to take
the field against Greece, he predicts the disaster of
Plataea soon to overtake the Persian forces still in
that land; and then returns to the gods beneath the
earth among whom he enjoys an honor equal to his
earthly estate. Atossa quits the scene to comfort her
son in his distress. Her purpose is not realized.
Xerxes appears with a scanty retinue, a fragment of

his army; and he and the Chorus close the play with an alternating chant of misery and lamentation.

The *Persians* is at once patriotic and religious, a combination of qualities rare enough in literature and dangerous enough for the unity of interest vital to the successful conduct of a tragic drama. It is significant that two of the most powerful human emotions have fostered so few truly great poems in literature. Love of God and love of country have each inspired much verse; yet little is charged with the proper magic of the true poet's art. The sentiment underlying each would seem too elemental to need reinforcement from without. The veil of beauty is not readily cast upon sacred song; and the express didactic and spiritual element, vital to its very nature, tends to bear down so heavily as to weaken, if not to destroy, the power of the wing.

What here holds true in the somewhat restricted province of religious poetry, holds true also, but to a less degree, of that form of secular poetry which has been inspired by love of fatherland. Of the mass of 'patriotic poems' in English, the most charitable criticism is that they are admirable in intention, not without edification, but otherwise intolerable. Few would maintain that our "National Song" climbs to a lofty poetic height; indeed, there are intimations that we might do well to reform it altogether. Our British kin, for their part, are not altogether satisfied with the afflatus of "God save the King." The French, and perhaps the Germans, have an advantage, in this regard, over English-speaking peoples. The King of Prussia, halted before Mainz in the "Year II," declared: "The Marseillaise is worth two armies to our enemies." Two of the best patriotic lyrics in any tongue, "Ye Mariners of England" and the "Battle of the Baltic," owe their fame to their union of poetic spirit and patriotic fervor; yet Thomas Campbell was otherwise a poet without great distinction. These two poems, and perhaps Drayton's "Agincourt," Burns' "Wha hae," Scott's "Innominatur" ("Breathes there a man with soul so dead"), Wordsworth's "Poems dedicated to National Independence and Liberty," Henley's "England, my England," and some score other lyrics, are the best put forth in the three hundred years in which British patriotism has been carried to the realm of pure poetry. "The Battle Hymn of the Republic" combines patriotic and religious fervor to an unique degree.

But apart from lyric, in which patriotism or religion finds its absolute, its most direct expression and burns with its purest flame, there is also historical tragedy, where patriotism must be knit with circumstance. Shakespeare dramatized long stretches of English history in epic fashion for his countrymen, as Aeschylus dramatized, and likewise in epic style, one flaming moment of the national unity of Hellas. In *Henry V*, *Henry IV*, *Richard II* patriotism is an ever present undertone and fires the verse of many a stirring passage. Later patriotic tragic drama followed somewhat other lines than Shakespeare's. Yet it is difficult to discover in Shakespeare or in any later dramatist a fair parallel to the one surviving historical tragedy of Ancient Greece; and of all the dramatic histories of Shakespeare only those are nearest akin to the *Persians* which picture the wars of his countrymen against the national enemy of the fifteenth century, and not the factional strife of the Red Rose of Lancaster with the White Rose of York.

The *Persians* is in fact quite unlike any other historical tragedy of the world. Not indeed because of its subject, of necessity rooted in a particular place and time, but because of its setting, the differences that result from that setting, and because it was composed so shortly after the heroic struggle it commemorates and by a combatant. Imagine, for a moment, an Elizabethan play on the destruction of the Armada written by a participant only eight years later: the scene laid in Spain before the disaster, the pride in the vast armament, the high hopes of victory not unmixed with anxiety for the success of an expedition beyond the sea, the arrival of tidings of ruin, the reaction upon Philip and his people. But all so fashioned that the audience, some part of which had fought under Drake off Plymouth and Gravelines, could yet transcend the limits of race and put themselves for the hour into the place of the characters and comprehend their way to think and feel. The characters would be so idealized that, although Spaniards, they would be only dramatically Spaniards—Medina Sidonia or even Philip, English at bottom but masking under Spanish guise. The English spectators in the Globe Theatre or even at Whitehall must, too, have in imagination a proper dramatic sympathy with the defeated enemy, though they had in fact wished that enemy the pain and ignominy of defeat. For tragedy must body forth pity in its interplay with fear: pity and fear, the two cathartics of the soul—pity for a people misguided to defeat; fear lest a like fate overtake the conquerors. Did not Scipio weep over fallen Carthage

and repeat from Homer, "The day shall come when
sacred Ilios shall fall"? Such a play as we have
imagined, would indeed have been filled with exultation, with the spirit of magnanimity, but with no
undertone of derision or contempt. For contempt or
ridicule of a defeated adversary would destroy the
very purpose of tragedy.

The imaginary parallel has been drawn from the
distant past. It had easily been possible to draw it
from the events of our own time. But the parallel
itself is specious. The Spanish peril of the sixteenth
century was unlike enough to the Persian peril
twenty centuries earlier. The recent victory over the
Armada may have prompted the famous passage in
Richard II, and less probably that in *King John*.
But of the two hundred and twenty recorded chron-
icle plays in English, only a few, such as *The Rise of
Cardinal Wolsey*, *Sir Thomas Wyatt*, *Sir Thomas
More*, *Gowry's Conspiracy*, and of Shakespeare's
tragedies, only *Henry VIII*, deal with recent events,
and none of these can claim as its theme an event
of widely national importance. Our English ancestors dramatized the whole of English history from
the time of mythical Lear or even from that of King
Brute; yet their chiefest interest lay in the story of
actions which, at the farthest, a man's grandfather or
great-grandfather might recall—the reigns of Henry
VI and Richard III. The *Persians* deals with almost
contemporary history. Its poet had himself been an
eyewitness of the battle of Salamis. His audience had
themselves defended their country in Athens' wooden
walls. If Dryden had followed Rymer's advice and
written an *Invincible Armada* in imitation of Aeschylus, it would have been written in cold blood.

Masefield's *Philip the King* consciously or unconsciously follows that advice, but it was composed three centuries and more after the event.

Contemporaneous or recent history is full of peril for the dramatist, above all if it centers about his native country. Nor was the danger less great for the Greeks than for the moderns. If the triumph over Persia in 480 and 479 B.C. was so momentous as to induce the poet to desert for once the national legends of the immemorial past that he might compress into a single play the story of the victory over an age-long enemy, the difficulties might well seem insurmountable. He might indeed count upon a peculiar sympathy on the part of his audience, but by what craftsmanship could he adequately represent their heroic deeds in the actual presence of the men who had fought at Salamis? The shadow could ill be substituted for the substance. No enthusiasm recalled by mimetic art could hold poise with the intensity of the actual exultation of the Athenians on that day when they saw the Persian fleet hacked to pieces in the narrow strait. They had seen Xerxes, the Great King, seated on his throne on Mount Aegaleos overlooking the scene of the rout of his proud fleet. A dead day cannot live again.

Thus menaced by the challenge of fact and of the emotions it awakened, for the tragic poet, careful of his proper art, there was also an insidious danger challenging that art. To revive at least some part of the high vitality consequent upon a national victory would be artistically within his powers. But the patriotic impulse might not weigh too heavily upon the purely aesthetic element. Intemperance of exultation, or downright bombast, in an attempt

to rival the emotion called forth by the actual victory,
might win the applause of the crowd. And for other
temptations to overstep the modesty of nature, dramatic devices were all too ready at hand. One such
device at least Aeschylus has employed to bring
down the house at the expense of dramatic naturalness. Atossa is assumed to be entirely ignorant even
of the situation of Athens and of its government; and
for no other purpose than to be instructed that its
people are the vassals of no lord and master.

The *Persians* is far from revealing its author at
the topmost pitch of excellence. A contest of opposing wills, such as is pictured by Herodotus—
Xerxes for, Artabanus against, the expedition to
Greece—was impossible if the unity of the theme was
to be preserved. But the actual defects are many and
important. The internal movement is halting, the
parts are not naturally articulated, the location of the
action shifts from council hall to Darius' tomb
without proper definition of distance, there is an
overweight of reflection, expectation is raised that
certain things are going to happen, but which do not
happen. Nor has the poet escaped the danger of
carrying a double motive—religion and patriotism—
that underlies the play. Nevertheless, taken all in
all, the *Persians* is one of the most impressive
achievements of dramatic art and well worthy of its
high theme. That theme, a national triumph of surpassing importance, was itself hazardous; and at his
disposal Aeschylus had only a chorus with its leader
and two actors. With a minimum of machinery he
has constructed one of the greatest battle-pieces of all
literature, "the one great tragedy of the world on a
recent historical occurrence." Nor has it lost its

potency even now. The text of Rhys Roberts' address on Patriotic Poetry, delivered during the World War, was the shout raised by the Greeks as they moved out against the Persian fleet.

> On, ye sons of the Greeks! Fight for the freedom of your fatherland, for the freedom of your sons, your wives, the shrines of your ancestral gods, and the tombs of your forefathers. Now we battle for our all.

It was a stroke of genius to set the entire scene not in the land of the victor but in the land of the vanquished. Aeschylus might not, as the Elizabethans, shift the scene from one combatant to the other, and at the same time preserve that unity of action which was the lifeblood of tragedy, at least before Euripides. Greek tragedy was too static to admit of these violently hurried alternations of scene that delighted the spectators under Queen Elizabeth. The advantages of placing the action at Susa, in the heart of the Persian empire and immediately after the disaster to the army of Xerxes, are unmistakable. On the one hand: the repercussion of the defeat on the defeated; the consternation, the lamentation, pride overwhelmed, the agony of a nation, the blasted fame of the author of its ruin, the searching to fathom the moral cause of so appalling a reverse, the discovery that man's presumptuous folly and not the malignity of Fate had wrought so tremendous an overthrow.

Nor, on the other hand, was the negative gain less by reason of a distant setting to ensure dramatic perspective. The suppression of impertinent details, the entanglement of circumstance, the contentions in Greece at large and the factional differences at Athens, the mutual jealousies and recriminations of the allies, then as now, drowning the memory of the

paean of triumph, the inequality of achievement of
individual commanders in the battle (for praise of
one had spelled dispraise of another)—all these pit-
falls were avoided and an ideal picture presented
when the victory was reported far from the scene
where it had been won.

The *Persians* is essentially epic in spirit rather
than dramatic in action, but only if 'dramatic
action' is baldly conceived as equivalent to bodily
movement. Nowhere in the range of ancient tragedy
is the part of the Messenger more necessary to depict
events that could not be represented on the stage.
In surging sequence and without the accessories of
scenic apparatus, Shakespeare could set forth the
moving accidents of war on land and sea. Even the
resources of the modern stage would have been taxed
to the uttermost to give verisimilitude to the scene
that Aeschylus must depict in retrospect; and Greek
tragedy, it will be remembered, never sought to stage
even the contest of land forces which a later art could
present only in miniature, mere fractional engage-
ments of armies, the picture of whose total engagement challenged the craftsmanship of Victor Hugo
and of Tolstoi. By the very law of its being, Greek
dramatic art was prevented from realizing even the
partial truth to nature presented by the isolated collision of armies upon the stage: the partial truth to
nature, for such collisions are but the sections of the
larger contest that lies beyond the vision of any actual
participant. Of course the film, with its visualiza-
tion of such topical events as the Battle of Jutland,
has here put the stage out of business. But even here
the dangers of nearness in time make themselves

felt: the film is said not to square with the testimony of eyewitnesses of the battle.

Narrative and descriptive report had then, of necessity, to take the place of visible physical action here, as in the *Seven against Thebes*. But in the *Persians*, Aeschylus succeeded in avoiding the monotony that was to disfigure the later play. Here, by a plausible fiction, the Courier is conceived as an eyewitness of the whole course of events—the rout of the ships and the agonizing march homeward of the troops under Xerxes, whose distressful appearance at the end confirms the tidings appropriately placed in the mouth of his messenger.

It was indeed a stroke of genius to place the scene of the play before the council hall and tomb of the Great King. But it is not Aeschylus to whom is due the credit of avoiding the difficulties of staging the action in Greece. Only four years before the *Persians*, Phrynichus had dramatized the victory at Salamis in his *Women of Phoenicia* and had won the prize; and no less a person than Themistocles had, as choragus, defrayed the special cost of the performance. It was thus a contemporary of Aeschylus who first (so far as we know) realized the truth, so vital to dramatic art, that nearness of scene is not a guaranty of excellence, either of perspective or of proportion. To compensate for the normal remoteness of time, Phrynichus substituted remoteness of place. The indebtedness of the poet of the *Persians* to his rival seems to have extended even to details. Glaucus of Rhegium, a writer of the fourth century before Christ, and apparently the first express student of tragedy, asserted in his book *On the Plots of Aeschylus* that the poet had 'made over' or 'com-

posed on the model of' (παραπεποιῆσθαι) the play of
Phrynichus. The statement cannot be tested because the older play is lost save for a few lines, one of
which anticipates the opening verse of the *Persians*.[1]
Further evidence of the debt of Aeschylus to Phrynichus has been sought in the account of the flight of
the land forces under Xerxes, and the entire passage
(vv. 482-514) has been regarded as a *rifacimento* of
the earlier play, designedly intended as a "parallel
though dependent handling of the story."[2] Whatever the extent of the verbal similarities between the
two poets, there were important differences of larger
scope which mark the distinctive quality of Aeschylus. He introduces us to the Councillors deliberating
as to the fortunes of their King. Phrynichus, on the
other hand, began with a speech of a eunuch who was
arranging the cushions for the session of the Council
—the first known occurrence of the 'prologue' as a
dramatic device; for the so-called 'prologues' of
Thespis resist all exact definition. In Phrynichus the

---

[1] Τάδ' ἐστὶ Περσῶν τῶν πάλαι βεβηκότων. Aeschylus' οἰχομένων
('gone' and 'gone to their death') carries an equivoque absent in
βεβηκότων. In like fashion Euripides in his *Philoctetes* altered the diction of Aeschylus' more literal expression in his play of the same name:
φαγέδαιν' ἀεί μου σάρκας ἐσθίει (θοινᾶται Euripides) ποδός.

[2] Verrall, *The Bacchants of Euripides and other Essays*, pp. 283-308·
While I cannot admit as equally cogent the various considerations (style,
vocabulary, meter, punctuation, historical presentation) adduced in
favor of this contention, it remains a fact that the shift (v. 482) from the
naval to the land forces is (and has always appeared to me) surprisingly
sudden and ill-motived. The mention there of the army would seem to
include the entire Persian army and was so interpreted by the Chorus
(v. 798); yet it is not till much later that we hear from the ghost of
Darius that Persian troops were still in Greece, the troops that were to
be engaged at Plataea. The dramatic reservation of that crowning
disaster for Darius' prophecy has been purchased at the expense of
historical perspective.

Chorus was formed of Phoenician women who be-
wailed the loss of their husbands and sons, forced to
fight in the Persian galleys at Salamis. The author of
the *Capture of Miletus* was familiar (he had learned
it to his cost) with the art of drawing sympathetic
tears. In Aeschylus the Chorus consists of the regents
of the Persian realm who must themselves hear the
news of the ruin of their country. More significant
still was another divergence. Phrynichus started
with the announcement of the disaster to the
Persian fleet. He thus anticipated the tragic event
so exactly as to leave little chance for complication or further expansion except through lamentation. He preoccupied the rest of his play for one
emotion. Aeschylus deferred the crisis until he had
definitely engaged our dramatic sympathy for the
hopes and fears of the Royal Council and for the
anxiety of the Queen-mother as to the fortunes of her
long absent son. Tidings will never come, the delay
is agonizing. Yet confidence will not altogether
surrender to foreboding—Persia's wealth is vast as
her armament; but that armament was launched
against a foe beyond the sea, a foe that had
checked even the might of Darius at Marathon.
Before Aeschylus' play opened, Persian pride had
already in fact been broken with her ships; but the
poet has so skilfully managed the machinery of suspense that the play is one-fourth over before the
Courier bursts in with his appalling news. These
improvements of its model by the *Persians* warrant
the guess that Aeschylus remodelled a play defective
dramatically but distinguished for its choral parts:
for Phrynichus was famous for the sweetness and
tenderness of his lyric strains. If Aeschylus did so

make over the *Women of Phoenicia*, it was only the
inferior skill of its author that gave his rival the
chance to win a higher dramatic value for his piece;
as Aeschylus was himself to provide his successors
with opportunities he himself had not realized: the
encounter of the two brothers in Euripides' *Women
of Phoenicia* was an opportunity missed by Aeschylus
in his *Seven against Thebes*. Poetical genius may show
itself as well in opportunities discovered as in difficulties surmounted. It is therefore small wonder
that it was the play of Aeschylus and not that of
Phrynichus (whose lyrics were famous, at least in
the time of Aristophanes) which was represented at
Syracuse on the wish of King Hiero, patron of poets
and victor at Himera over the barbarians of the
West on the same day as that on which, according to
popular fancy, the barbarians of the East met their
defeat at Salamis.

The reworking of plays is an old story, poet has
pillaged poet since recorded time. Neophron's *Medea*
is reported to have been made over by Euripides.
The comic poets contain at least a dozen references
to purloining of others' literary property. Guilhem
de Castro's *Jeunesse de Cid* was refurbished by
Corneille. *As You Like It* was adapted from Lodge's
Rosalynde (1590); *A Winter's Tale* is based on
Greene's *Pandosto* (1588); *The Life and Death of
King John*, on *The Troublesome Reign of King John*.
The dramatists of the Restoration would better
Shakespeare—a battle of pigmies with the giant:
D'Urfey with his *Injured Princess* (*Cymbeline*),
Dennis with his *Fatal Resentment* (*Coriolanus*),
Dryden with his *Tempest*. Fletcher's mechanical
The Chances was "altered and corrected" by the

nimble wit and roystering obscenity of the second Duke of Buckingham. Dryden's famous *All for Love*, despite its simple psychology, is the most beautiful of these adaptations; but it is rather a transposition of the tone of its model to a more somber key in which sentiment takes the place of passion. There is a difference, however, between these modern refurbishers and Aeschylus. They altered many years after their originals; Aeschylus followed only four years after Phrynichus.

Since its major theme was a description of the victory at Salamis, the play was exposed to the dangers of monotony. Before the arrival of the Courier there had been sufficient variation of tone; thereafter, in his report of the battle, there was need of diversity. First, the announcement of the disaster, with a minimum of exact circumstance, attended by the cries of despair on the part of the Elders. Then, when Atossa has broken her agonized silence, it is she alone who guides the Courier to his detailed story—the roll of dead chieftains, the numbers of the two fleets, the particulars of the rout, the destruction of the Persian nobles stationed on Psyttalea, the despair of Xerxes, his command for instant flight, the cruel march homeward of the land forces. Throughout, whether the life-like narrative is expanded or condensed, the style responds to the theme, and for sustained dignity and elevation is unmatched in the poetry of war. Lepanto, Trafalgar, Navarino produced no bard to rival Aeschylus. In prose, there is Tolstoi, artist and soldier in one, with his *Sebastopol* and *War and Peace;* but here the confusions of war's realities disturb the unity of effect.

The play was more than half finished when the
full tale of Salamis was told. The plot was now in
danger of being becalmed. A meaner poet had raised
a tempest of terror, consternation, grief. Aeschylus'
fertile imagination answers the challenge. He raises
a fresh wind. He has recourse to a procession of
incident, gradually rising in intensity, that shall hold
the interest of the spectators to the end. He allows
full scope for lyric reflection on the desolation of the
Persian wives and mothers, and he is aware that
narrated action, to be apprehended only by the eye of
the imagination, must now give place to visible action
charged with tragic tension. The House of Death
must be startled to share the consternation of the
world above. The living must be instructed by the
dead. Darius, summoned in spectral apparition from
the grave, rises troubled from the tomb. The ghost
of Hamlet's father will not rest by reason of the
outrage done to his body in life; the ghost of Darius
quits the shades by reason of the misery of an empire.
More tragic, too, is the supernaturalism of the
ancient dramatist. Darius, evoked from Hades to
bring relief to the desperate condition of his realm,
announces a yet greater calamity to befall his people.
The wisdom of his advice to wage no further aggres-
sion against Greece was a slight compensation for the
revelation that Plataea was to be the scene of the
crowning disaster—because Persian armies had given
to the flames the altars of the gods and had dashed
from their pedestals the holy images. Marathon lay
in the past and is mentioned only as a warning and a
signal foreboding disaster. Salamis in the present
with good reason is placed at the center around which
the main action revolves. Plataea is foretold. Thus

skilfully has the poet ensured variety as he con-
denses the course of the entire war and pictures the
triumphal issue of that war's long agony for his
people. The final scene is un-modern, and perhaps
wearisomely elaborate to our taste. But the Greek,
untroubled by our anxiety to get away once the end
of action has come, refused to hurry. The wretched
Xerxes, whose mental blindness made of him a broken
man, is reserved for the emotional climax. De-
spoiled of his glory, in tattered garments, his quiver
empty, the veritable epitome of ruin, he gives the
final impact of the disaster, heretofore heard only and
not seen.

Fortunately for the forward movement of the
play, the supernaturalism of Darius is not omnis-
cient. It is a moot question whether his power to
foretell the future is because he is dead or, as is more
likely, because he was sagacious and prudent in life.
At any rate, his wisdom is limited. He knows nothing of the doings of his successor on the throne; so
that Atossa has to disabuse his mind of the possibility that it was pestilence or faction that had
prompted her desire to seek his ghostly counsel. If
the Queen in her report conveys no new information
to the audience, her disclosure of the ruin wrought
by Xerxes affords the poet the opportunity to let
Darius hear of the folly of his son and then interpret
the cause of the catastrophe.

The raising of the Great King from the lower
world has been called the greatest ghost scene in all
literature. If surpassed at all in ancient tragedy, it is
surpassed only by the apparition of the ghost of
murdered Clytaemestra in the latest of Aeschylus'
own dramas. It is a mark of the genius of the poet

that with a solemn religious tone he joined the art
of producing sensational effects wherein only Euripides was to attempt to rival him; for the simple,
yet profound, art of Sophocles, disdaining such
machinery, concentrated its power on the portraiture
of the characters of living men. Notwithstanding the
thrilling emotion produced by the ghost scene in the
Persians, it is not vital to the conduct of the main
theme. It causes no change in the subsequent action.
In fact, Aeschylean tragedy realizes some of its most
telling effects by interruptions to the plot proper—
witness the introduction of Io in the *Prometheus* and
of Cassandia in the *Agamemnon*. Nevertheless,
powerful as is the scene, its portraiture of the character and reign of Darius is a dramatic falsification
of the truth.

Poets are not to be brought to the bar of historical
justice, nor is their art to be fettered by rigid adher-
ence to reality. "Poetry," says old Thomas Rymer,
"requires the *ben trovato*, something handsomely
invented, and leaves the truth to History." We
would only show that the principle of contrast by
which Aeschylus worked in his delineation of character is here stretched to its utmost tension. In
order to magnify the father at the expense of the son,
Xerxes is represented as disobeying Darius' express
command to undertake no war against Greece. Yet,
as Herodotus informs us, thrice daily did Darius hear
from his slave the words bidden him to speak:
"Master, remember the Athenians." In the indis-
crimination of their grief the Chorus lay all the
blame on Xerxes for the failure of an expedition
against Greece undertaken contrary to his father's
will. To the elders, Darius was the divine counsellor

of the Persians, a hater of war, yet, when he warred, he brought back his men, unworn and scatheless, to happy homes. Marathon is indeed in the mind of Darius when his ghost declares that neither he nor any of his predecessors had ever brought upon the State so great a disaster as the defeat at Salamis. But when he inveighs against the impious recklessness of Xerxes for venturing to trespass on the domain of Poseidon by bridging the Hellespont, he is conveniently oblivious of the fact that he had been guilty of a like offense in crossing the Bosphorus on his expedition to Scythia, an expedition that had cost him the lives of a good part of his men. Xerxes' guilt in disturbing the laws of nature was equally his father's. It ministered to Athenian pride to listen to the boast of the Chorus early in the play that Persia had taken to the sea when its proper home was the land; for no doubt the Athenians looked upon the Aegean much as Britons do, or did, look upon the ocean—it was their sea. Popular belief regarded it as a contempt of nature when a land power would make of itself a sea power. The Cnidians wished to make their country an island in order the better to oppose the attack of Harpagus. From the Delphic oracle came the answer:

Fence not the isthmus off, nor dig it through—
Zeus would have made an island, had he wished.

To enlightened Athenians this transgression of nature had seemed no offense at all, nor would their commanders have been deterred by such a childish superstition. At bottom, the objection to bridging the Hellespont is an item in the history of human thought that regarded human skill or art as the foe of nature. Another example we shall encounter later

in the Cynic belief that Prometheus by his invention
of the arts destroyed the happiness of the human race
he had thereby sought to benefit. Aeschylus is not
of design an obscurantist, but for dramatic reasons
and because he would let the envy of the gods fall
only upon the head of Xerxes, he distorts or omits
facts. Set him against Herodotus, point after point,
and the contrast is luminous. To the poet, Darius
wrought no evil; to the historian, he was guilty of
barbarous cruelty to the Ionians. To the one,
Darius did not himself cross the Halys River; to the
other, he was present in person as leader in his campaign against the Scythians.

Unique in containing the most authentic description of a battle scene ever written by a poet, and by a
participant, the *Persians* is thus one of the most un-
trustworthy documents by reason of its contempt
of fact. Our confidence in the integrity of the historical element must be abandoned except in the case
of the well-circumstanced narration of the contest
at Salamis and of the choral ode, which, unpoetical
in its over-wealth of geographical detail, is, in its
panoramic marshalling of the conquests of Darius,
a threnody on the ruin of his sea empire. The main
events of the war, the names of the Persian princes
and of some of the Persian commanders, were of
course known to Aeschylus. But of the personality
of the main actors in the contest he knew nothing or
next to nothing. Atossa's dream, the oracle revealed
by Darius, many of the high-sounding polysyllabic
names of the captains, and much else are only creations of fancy superimposed on a foundation of fact.
In his other extant dramas Aeschylus depicts the
fortunes of single families through successive genera-

tions. In the *Persians* nation is pitted against nation physically and morally. The personages are not transcripts of reality. They simply had to conform to certain general notions about Persia, its rulers, and its people. Most of the ideas put into the mouths of Persians are universally human. Only one idea has any specific analogy in Persian tradition. The ghost of Darius, on departing to the nether world, leaves with the Elders the injunction of Sardanapalus: "Amid trouble give joyance to your souls while today is yours."

To the Greeks at large, Persia was synonymous with arrogant confidence bred of wealth and numbers. This note pervades the play: Xerxes' gold-bespangled palace, his host richly arrayed in gold; the vast wealth of his empire; the Queen-mother would know whether Athens has sufficient store of riches to support her in the contest. By an audacious etymology the very name 'Persian' is connected with Perseus, Danaë's son, engendered by Zeus in a shower of gold. (Possibly the Achaemenidean princes may at the time have favored the kinship for diplomatic reasons.) As the poverty of Greece is thus silently contrasted with the riches of its enemy, so the cardinal Greek doctrine of sophrosyne is opposed to the limitlessness of Persian hybris. "Learn to know thyself" says the Greek, that is, realize the limitations of thy mortality, know that thou art a feeble creature born only for a day. The Persian Elders declare that Darius and Xerxes are "gods," that Atossa is "mother of a god;" before her they prostrate themselves.

Of the Oriental potentates, Atossa is the most truly human. She is Queen, but more than Queen—

she is mother and wife. Interposed between son and
husband, she it is who must first hear the news of
Xerxes' defeat and report it to Darius risen from the
grave. Years have schooled her to the vicissitudes of
life. Shaken with terror while she is still uncertain
whether her son still lives, her silence has an awful
dignity. Her dread of the instability of her empire
does not lack suitable motivation. Prosperity may
be overturned by great riches. When fortune smiles,
fortune, she thinks, will remain forever fair, but when
everything goes ill and full of terror, it is a visitation
of Heaven—an attitude of mind like to that of the
Persian troops who, when they found the Strymon
miraculously frozen before its time, only then turned
to pray. Once the disaster of her son is known in its
terrible completeness, Atossa shows her fine feeling:
she will not now come with the pomp that had attended her first entrance. Her mother-love prompts
her to defend her son against her spouse—Xerxes fell,
not of himself, but by reason of his evil counsellors.

But even an historical play would not be Aeschylean were it not also religious. Not in the distant past
only, but in the living present, does the poet discover
God working in the affairs of men. Whether the un-
truth to historical fact is conscious or unconscious,
the religion of the *Persians* is better than its history.
That the poet should represent the vengeance of God
descending on Persian arrogance and impiousness
was humanly as inevitable as that Greece should be
pictured as defended by the powers of Heaven. Nor
is this any special and peculiar trend in Aeschylus'
total conception of things, so far as he had any such
conception. Have not victors always regarded their
cause as just and themselves as ministers of the

divine righteousness? In his other extant dramas the
poet has shown an unbroken consciousness of the
dominance of God in the world. But there is no
reason to assume that the religious conception of the
war entertained by his fellow countrymen did not
reinforce Aeschylus' individual belief concerning the
nature of the Divine as it was gradually shaping
itself to the image of a single, all-wise, all just and
perfect, power, of which the name "Zeus" was but
the symbol.

When I endeavor to represent to myself the effect
produced by the play upon the ancient audience, I
seem to realize that its two voices cannot have been
equally apprehended then and that these voices
speak a somewhat different language now. Our
view must of necessity be somewhat foreign to the
men of Salamis. To the spectators crowded upon the
rocky slope that looks down upon the precinct of
Dionysus, the drama spelled pride, exultation, and
thanksgiving in varied degree according to their
nature. They will not have been altogether heedless
of the deeper import of a play their cheers helped
on to victory, even as they had swelled the mighty
chorus as their fleet bore out against the enemy.
Nevertheless, it would pass all bounds of probability
that the crowd should completely realize that the
artistry of their warrior-poet had the deeper significance which it was his purpose to discover in so unexpected and overwhelming a triumph. Only the judi-
cious might observe the means whereby dramatic
sympathy was assured to the characters who impersonated the leaders of a national enemy visited with
the humiliation of defeat. It will not have escaped
their notice that the poet showed a due measure of

restraint on occasions when he might have cheaply purchased applause or otherwise stirred patriotic sentiment: he did not break the divisions of the Courier's report with lamentations of the Persian Elders—Atossa alone must bear the burden of sorrow and regret; he did not permit the Elders to pursue their first reproach of Xerxes with further incrimination until Darius has enlightened their judgment as to the true culpability of his son. He did not lay excessive emphasis in word upon the relation of punishment and guilt. The eye was assured of that which needed no special reinforcement through the ear. No criticism of the play is more vicious than that of an English editor which discovers in the lengthened antiphonal dirge at the end no other purpose than to make the Great King an object of derision. That final scene of agitation, dramatic as well as lyric, meant to be heard not read, fulfilled the law of Greek taste that demanded a fuller ending which should set forth the emotional reaction following upon the main crisis. Voltaire indeed objected to a like ending of the *Oedipus Tyrannus*, and modern playwrights, sensing the impatience of a modern audience, make short work when once the issue is decided. With this difference between ancient and modern dramatic craftsmanship I am not primarily concerned. I am, however, concerned with an interpretation which brands as 'comic' a scene that presents the full repercussion of a crowning disaster upon a barbaric and emotional people that made a luxury of lamentation—but in ways not altogether alien to the Greeks themselves. Throughout, Aeschylus sounds the note of magnanimity toward the national enemy: easier no doubt for the victor, yet still

a testimony that even a combatant would not hate
or belittle a defeated foe.

Only the men of Marathon, Salamis, and Plataea
who sat among the audience and whose vision out-
ranged the scene of those victories could read the
deeper meaning of the poet. In the exultant paean of
the victors and in the anguished cries of the defeated
they heard voices unheard by the crowd—the peril
of self-exaltation, the feebleness of man, the muta-
bility of human things. Salamis was itself a warning
for the victor also. "Zeus is a chastiser of presumptuous thoughts and he correcteth with heavy hand."
Froude speaks of the "daemonic heroism" of the
men of the time of Queen Elizabeth. Daemonic
heroism in the face of greater odds had been displayed by the men of the time of Aeschylus. But
their poet does not fail to show that it was not their
prowess, but the gods themselves, that had given them
the victory.[3] With them the gods were confederated
to break barbarian arrogance. Nation and individual
citizen, then as now, must reverence sophrosyne.

The treatise ascribed to Plutarch under the title
Of the Malignity of Herodotus reprehends, among
other offenses of the historian, his exaltation of the
part played by Athens in the struggle against Persia.
"Who won the war?" is no new question. It is as old
as Waterloo, as old as Salamis and Plataea. Yet
inter-cantonal or factional jealousies find no echo
in the *Persians*, though it was written by an Athenian

---

[3] So with Henry V when the victory was won, says Holinshed:
"The King commanded euerie man to kneele down on the ground at this
verse: *Non nobis, Domine, non nobis, sed nomini tuo da gloriam*, which
doone, he caused *Te Deum* with certeine anthems to be soong: giving
laud and praise to God without boasting of his owne force or anie
humane power."

for Athenians and to commemorate a victory preëminently Athenian. Aeschylus surveyed the issue
not as a partisan but as an Hellenic patriot. The
glory of all should not be surrendered to the glory of
one. Some fifty commanders of the Persians are
mentioned by name, not a single leader on the Greek
side; though there is a covert allusion to the stratagem of Themistocles which caused the Persian crews
to wear out their strength in the night just preceding
the battle. Athenians were not absent from Plataea,
yet they find no place in Darius' prophecy:

For so great shall be the mass of clotted gore spilled by
the Dorian lance upon Plataea's soil that heaps of dead
shall make known, even to the third generation, a voice-
less record for the eyes of men that mortal man needs
must not vaunt him overmuch.

The *Persians* is fired by the spirit of Greece willed
to stand together, united as never before and never
afterwards in its history. For once its people sought
to cohere. Aeschylus' play finds them at a moment
when the centripetal force of that people was not
surrendered to those centrifugal tendencies, which,
if they were the source of the varied individuality of
the various states, were yet the cause of the ultimate
fall of the nation. The *Persians* is inspired by the
consciousness of a common heritage of liberty as
opposed to despotism. It is the voice of national
intrepidity in the face of overwhelming odds and of a
national faith upborn by the conviction that an
adequate return is vouchsafed to man's resourcefulness in a cause, not man's alone but God's. Patriotism is united with religion in the white light of poetry.
Yet their union here is a different thing than in the
Roman, whose patriotism was itself a religion.

Aeschylus' play is for us in part a document of that age-long contest between East and West which, even now, is still unended. We feel today the pressure of that contest; yet we feel it less than the men of Aeschylus' day who had seen with dismay the growing menace of Persia—its overthrow, first of Croesus, then of the Greeks in Asia and in the islands of the Aegean. Phrynichus' *Capture of Miletus* had pictured in anticipation the misery that would befall each and every Greek city once the storm should finally break, as break it did when Aeschylus was still in the vigor of martial manhood.

It is no new truth that we can judge Euripides better now than could his contemporaries. So too, perhaps, even better than Aeschylus' audience, can we, after the long interval of time, interpret the solemn earnestness and simple piety that animate his play. And far better than the poet can we understand the historical, if not the moral, significance, of the victories he commemorates. Persian prestige was not in fact destroyed until the fourth century. But had Persia triumphed on sea and land, and held its conquest in the fifth century, Greece had been orientalized. Then Aeschylus' voice had been quelled. There had been no age of Pericles, no Sophocles, no Euripides. The Parthenon had never been restored. Thucydides had written no possession to instruct all time. Plato had seen no vision of the Good that is one with God. Aristotle had not been the master of those who know. Alexander had had no world to conquer. The fierceness of *Roma victrix* had not been tempered by the arts of Greece. And the language of Greece had not been the language of the Evangel.

CHAPTER IV

PROMETHEUS

In his attack on paganism Tertullian shows Christ foreshadowed to the heathen world as the martyr of humanity. *Verus Prometheus, Deus omnipotens:* "Omnipotent God, your true Prometheus," mangled by the revilings of the unbeliever Marcion. The secret of Christianity (said the convert Heine) is the deification of suffering. The Fathers of the Church discovered in the agonies of the Titan a mystical symbol of the passion of the Redeemer of mankind. The daughters of Ocean who compassionate Prometheus became to them precursors of the mourners at the foot of the cross. The thief of fire pointed to the Saviour of the world.

If Milton's conception of Samson—overcome, led bound and made of his enemies the scorn and gaze, yet defiant in his fortitude and his soul's loftiness—was stimulated by his recollection of the Aeschylean drama, no less may the poet of *Paradise Lost* have drawn from the same source some part of his representation of the defiant heroism of the arch-enemy of mankind, grander than his Hellenic model because he had no reliance on hope, less grand because he was swayed solely by ambition. To Calderon the fire brought from heaven by Prometheus is the light of knowledge and the Titan himself the incarnation of the ideal striving of mankind.

Long before the eighteenth century, which witnessed the overthrow of Aristotle's doctrine that poetry is the imitation of nature, Julius Caesar Scaliger had proclaimed that the poet is an *alter deus*. Shaftesbury's utterance that the poet is "a second maker, a just Prometheus under Jove," was hailed with enthusiasm by the ardent spirits of the *Sturm und Drang*. The poet fashions from his own head and brain. Genius is God and God is the supreme genius. To the age of Rousseau it was as the creator of the race of men that Prometheus made his chief appeal. So the young Goethe would create, even as Prometheus who fashioned men from clay and fire. The young Goethe, to whom the world was God and God the world, and who rejected the solace offered by a sentimental theism, saw in Prometheus a rebel against a personal deity who hearkens to the prayers of men. To him, as to Rousseau, God is to be fathomed not by dogma or by mystery, but by the emotions that lie at the root of all religion. To Goethe grown old, Prometheus had become the personification of doing, not dreaming, good to his fellow-men.

Herder, whose eye was always fixed on the progress of the human race, sought in the myth of Prometheus an emblem of "the continued striving of the Divine Spirit in man for the awakening of all his powers." In 1797 Vicenzo Monti in his *Prometheo* likened Napoleon to the Titan, each a liberator from tyranny. To Byron, on the contrary, the destiny of Bonaparte was to desolate; of Prometheus, to be the giver of life. Byron's earliest English verses were a translation of a chorus of the Aeschylean play, which, in his day, boys at Harrow read thrice a year. In a letter of 1817 he confesses the possible influence of the tragedy on all or anything he had written.

Manfred voices human pride rebellious against
Divine providence. In the poem entitled *Prometheus*, the hero's adversary is the incarnation of hate,
the hero himself,

> A symbol and a sign
> To Mortals of their fate and force;

the hero, who was martyred for humanity, and of
whom the poet says

> Thy Godlike crime was to be kind,
> To render with thy precepts less
> The sum of human wretchedness,
> And strengthen Man with his own mind.

It was said by Gissing that only by laughing a
little at suffering is it possible for us to live our own
lives. No such creed was possible for the poet who
felt himself to be

> A nerve, o'er which do creep
> The else unfelt oppressions of the world.

Shelley's ecstatic idealism was born amid the con-
vulsions of the French Revolution. Confident of
human perfectibility, persuaded of the ultimate
triumph of liberty, equality, and fraternity, he lived
in the light of an imaginative existence compacted
of perfect morality. He would build a fairer world
out of the ruins of a world wrecked by the oppressors
of mankind. To his iconoclastic vision the race of
men had become the multitudinous slaves of a
personal God, a tyrant, whose empire was founded
on traditional authority, on loyalty to dogma, and
on fear, the keeper of hell. Only Prometheus, the
champion of humanity, refused submission to crime
enthroned in brief omnipotence; for submission had
been the death-seal of man's captivity. Through the
slow years of countless ages he endured infinite

suffering of body, and a yet keener agony of soul
as the Furies, minions of the tyrant, summon from
the future the phantasmal shapes of the misery in
human history: prophets done to death because they
had dared proclaim the truth;

> A youth
> With patient looks nailed to a crucifix;
> Who made his agony
> The barrier to our else all-conquering foe.

To Shelley, Christ is the antithesis of God, who is
half the tyrannical Lord of Hosts, half Satan himself.
Prometheus triumphs because he has subdued himself. Misery taught him wisdom, expelled his disdain
and hate; he would recall the curse he had pronounced against his torturer for whom now he has
only pity and grief. Released at last by Heracles,
when Jupiter has been dethroned by Demogorgon,
his own son, the Titan beholds a new world founded
on love, liberty, and communion. Knowledge
wielded by Prometheus is the instrument to liberate
mankind; and to knowledge has been joined gentleness, virtue, and endurance.

To Edgar Quinet the children of men are the
children of Prometheus; and, as in Shelley, Prometheus is agonized by the spectacle of their sufferings.
On Caucasus he beholds Golgotha. Paganism is
overthrown by Christianity, itself to be transformed
in the revolutions of time.

Victor Hugo found in Prometheus a sort of divine
Hamlet with the vulture gnawing at his vitals. To
Lipiner, the Titan is the power that breaks the last
terror threatening the human race—omnipotent,
implacable Fate. Prometheus shatters the delusion. Fate does not exist, only character exists.

Nietzsche's conception of the superman as the consummation of humanity was anticipated by Spitteler, whose Prometheus, proudly reliant on his own personality, will be what he *is:* he will follow the God who dwells within him; he will triumph over himself, renounce earthly happiness, and minister to a great cause solely for its own sake.

To the romantic poet, fascinated by the vision of man's creation by Prometheus, the Promethean spark, breathed into his own soul, typifies his own creative energy. To the humanitarian poet who finds himself, or mankind at large, reflected in resistance to oppression, the myth is a symbol of revolt against tyranny—tyranny of a religion of the intellect throned in authority, tyranny of the injustices of the governors of men, tyranny that stifles the life and thought of him who would shape the world to better things. But more august than the figure of the rebel emerges the figure of the sufferer whose agony was his glory; who, undismayed, overcomes self and his miseries present and to come, because he is self-sustained against all foes by the consciousness of the supreme justice of his cause.

But it is not only poets that have repaired to the inexhaustible treasure house of the myth. Euhemerism, ancient or modern, rationalized the Titan into an historical personage, now a governor of Egypt, now an astronomer, now the founder of alchemy. For the vault of the Sistine Chapel, a Prometheus was designed for a pendentive by Michelangelo. Bouré's bronze chains him on Mount Caucasus. Palavicino in his sonnet addresses El Greco:

> Thou rival of Prometheus in thy portraiture,
> Mayst thou escape his pain, yet seize his fire.

Prometheus was a theme for the art of Beethoven and Liszt. The Stoics, and after them Bacon, discovered in him that Foresight which proved their conception of the Providence that rules the world. To Schopenhauer he is the symbol of the foresight distinguishing man from the brute, the power to think beyond today that brings with it the torture of anxiety. Prometheus is now the type of human reason that would measure the immeasurable, the craving intellect that would climb to Heaven's heights and lay hold on the Divine. Now he is the prophet of the Unknown God whom the Athenians ignorantly worshipped. Now he is the Divine Love. Now he is Eternal Man. Now he expiates his knowledge with Averroes, Giordano Bruno, Galileo. Now he voices the torments of men agonized with other eagles rending their breast. From a concrete person of the myth the Titan has passed into a lifeless and controversial abstraction.

A dynamic, a far-flung myth. Chained to his rock Prometheus traverses space, outranges time. In successive incarnations he forces himself upon the intellectual and moral imagination, an invincible attraction as the generations come and go. Many and strange are the fires burned on the altar of the Athenian potter god; yet, as Bacon says in his *Wisdom of the Ancients*, the fable "demonstrates and presseth many true and grave speculations." The Aeschylean drama has been the *primum mobile* whereby the fable, rooted in a remote antiquity, is coëval with every age.

Not, however, that the infinite riches of the myth at large were compressed within the little room of the single trilogy of which only one member exists entire. The *Prometheus Unbound* is known only in small part; and scholars and laity still dispute whether *Prometheus Pyrphorus* opened the three-part drama as the Fire-Giver, or, as the Fire-Bearer, concluded the whole with the inauguration of the torch race by which the Athenians did honor to the god of their potter guild.

Certain features of the story, seized upon by his successors, Aeschylus could not but reject as alien to his dramatic purpose. He knows everything of Prometheus as the inventor of the arts and sciences; nothing of Prometheus as creator of the human race, a legend far older than his time and commonly associated with that of the gift of fire to man. The Titan's championship of mankind had need of no reinforcement by reason of his compassion for the children of men, the work of his hand. Nor was the poet concerned with the myth at large that sought to explain the evil of the world through the instrumentality of Pandora, by the gods dowered with every gift for man's undoing. The gloomy fashioner of that myth, anguished at the crushing reality of the misery that had befallen man since the Golden Age, and reflecting the spirit of the Boeotian peasant, distrustful of gods who had broken him with toil and trouble, saw evil even in Hope that remained within Pandora's casket, Hope that misguides man to folly and vain ambitions. To that version Aeschylus implicitly opposes his conception. Prometheus, the well-wisher to man, planted blind hopes within his breast that so man might not foresee the doom of death.

The crude stuff of the myth lay to hand in Hesiod. In the *Theogony* Prometheus sought to deceive Zeus in the division of sacrificial offerings; and in his wrath the god took fire away from man. But the trickster stole the fire and in requital was fast bound. An eagle gnawed at his liver, which by night grew again to its former bulk. Heracles shot the eagle and released the Titan, not without the will of Zeus, eager to magnify his son's fame. In the *Works and Days* the account is slightly different. Zeus in his wrath hid the bread of life from man because Prometheus of crooked counsel had deceived him. Therefore he sent misery to mankind and hid fire. But Prometheus stole it *again* from Zeus. Both accounts agree that it was because of this deed that Pandora was created by Hephaestus as a beautiful bane to bring evil upon mankind.

This, the oldest extant form of the myth, is devoid of a truly moral content. Innocent man is made to suffer because the crafty son of Iapetus stole fire in his behalf. Aeschylus, discerning in the myth a tragic significance, raised the question of the Divine justice and the Divine government of the world. But, for all its depth, his play is one of the simplest of all dramas; indeed in certain aspects of its simplicity it is absolutely unique. The action proper is confined to a single spot. The hero is immobile; chained to his rock, he is more awe-inspiring than an unfettered sufferer. There is so little play of circumstance from beginning to end that the movement is of the slowest. There is no subtle complication of plot, no *metabasis*, no reversal of fortune. There is only one character and that is subject to no development.

In substance, too, nothing is more rudimentary. Prometheus has robbed the gods of fire, their proper prerogative, and he has given it to mortals. This offense is the precipitating motive of the play. At

the command of Power and Force, the minions of
Zeus, now become master of the gods, Hephaestus,
though unwilling to bind a kindred god, is compelled
to rivet the Titan to a desert rock. One weapon only
is in the control of the prisoner—he knows a secret
menacing the sovereignty of Zeus. This secret he will
not disclose until Zeus free him from his bonds. Un-
daunted by the threat that his enemy will visit upon
him torture more appalling than his chains, he refuses
to unveil the mystery, and is hurled to Tartarus.

Everything else is virtually foreign to the theme
proper. The daughters of Ocean, who, frightened by
the reverberations of Hephaestus' hammer and impelled by sympathy, visit the hero on his rocky
height; Ocean, who counsels submission to the will
of Zeus; Io, distorted in mind and body, an enforced
wanderer through the world, victim of Zeus' lust and
Hera's hate; Hermes, breathing forth the savage
threats of the omnipotent lord of Olympus—all these
personages come and go either directly because of
Prometheus or because of their spiritual kinship with
him. The play must be of the normal length, the
interspaces must be filled. Art has been forced to
yield to necessity or, rather, it coöperates with
necessity. But variety has been secured, a certain
element of progress has been won, for a scene otherwise
fixed; and a standard has been gained whereby to
measure the different aspects of the hero's sense of
injustice, the inflexibility of his purpose, and his
supreme power of will. Nor has the poet failed to
seek variety by other devices. He alternates the
description of Io's future with her past wanderings.
He understands the virtue of retardation by making
Prometheus disclose to the daughters of Ocean the

fatal secret only after he had at first deliberately withheld it from them. He produces the impression of the infinite duration of Prometheus' sufferings, though this description is compressed within a play that is a unit as regards time. He has in fact divorced the action of the trilogy from the strict regulation of time.

But it is not merely its structural simplicity that constitutes the uniqueness of the drama. Other plays show Olympian visitants to the scene of action. In the *Prometheus* the dramatic personages are all divine. Even Io, though a mortal in contrast to the immortals who have wrought her ruin, is the daughter of a river-god. The human race is represented only through her and through its spokesman, the hero of the play. In creating divine *dramatis personae* Aeschylus had no true rival except himself. The *Eumenides* was to give visible presence alike to the gods of bright heaven and primordial powers housed in nether darkness. A master of thrilling spectacular effect, Aeschylus did not fail to suit to their nature and function the appearance and the appurtenances of the portentous beings of the play. The merciless executants of the will of Zeus, terrific incarnations of brutal violence, order the rebel to Zeus' will to be clamped to a lonely and naked rock with adamantine chains. The daughters of Ocean are swung into the scene upon an aerial car. Ocean himself bestrides a four-footed bird which he guides by force of mind. Nature itself is made confederate to the awfulness of the dramatic impersonation. The huge bulk of the Titan is hung aloft in mid-air, the sport of the winds, sleepless through unceasing pain, now burned by the bright blaze of the sun, now frozen by the frost of

morn. Solitude has its consolation, but loneliness is
appalling. Abandoned at first by every living creature in the world, the Titan can find communion only
with the everlasting elements, the azure vault of
heaven, the multitudinous laughter of earth's waters,
and the all-seeing Sun. At the end heaven and earth
and sea are convulsed in turmoil. The hurricane is
let loose, the earth rocks, the waves of the sea strike
the very stars. The Titan, undismayed, triumphant
in defeat, is plunged into the yawning chasm that
consigns him to the nethermost region, as far below
the earth as high heaven is above the earth. Never
was there such a terrifying appeal alike to eye and
imagination.

The play has not won its present fame without
detraction in the past. In its matter, in its form, the
very things that mark its uniqueness, the French
censors of style of the eighteenth century discovered
a violation of the vital principles of dramatic craftsmanship. Not that these Levites of the Ark of taste
were insensible to the splendor of the language, the
powerful imagery, and the grandeur of the senti-
ments. But to them the play violated nature as it
violated art. The characters were superhuman,
grotesque; there was no proper intrigue; there was
episode upon episode; there was nothing proved. The
thing in fact had neither subject nor design. It was
barbarous to the disdainful caprice of Voltaire. To
Fontenelle it was a dramatic monstrosity, the work of
a madman of a lively but ill-regulated imagination.
La Harpe, the disciple of Voltaire, denied it (as even
the *Bacchae* of Euripides) the very name of tragedy.
Italy echoed France; and Metastasio has no other
name for it than sheer buffoonery.

In the Battle of the Books the nobility of Homer's naturalness was often accounted indecorous by the guardians of taste under Louis XIV. A century later the virtues of the *Prometheus* were obscured by Gallic intolerance of defection from self-created canons of dramatic propriety; and even in the present day not all French critics acquiesce in its merits without protest. M. Faguet sees in the play only a long and magnificent effusion of lament. But to the neo-Hellenism of the end of the eighteenth century, as to the Romanticists, the irregularities of Aschylean genius needed no championing. Sympathetic imagination reacted against the frigid authority of rationalism; and a drama once called "altogether monstrous" was seen to embody the spirit of emancipation against tyranny: its artistic symplicity symbolized nature oppressed by convention; it was the medium for the broodings of a great soul over the tremendous problems of human destiny and divine providence.

Vital to the understanding of the play is the idea that the security of Zeus' empire is imperilled and that the duration of his rule is destined to be brief. The Titans who had championed the ancient rule of Cronus had been subdued and hurled, along with Cronus, to the depths of Tartarus. On Atlas, Prometheus' brother, had been loaded the vault of heaven. Typhos, another brother, the last of the rebellious brood of Titans to use force, had been crushed, yet Aetna still bore witness to his rage, impotent indeed against his conqueror yet destructive of the level plains of fair-fruited Sicily. Prometheus himself, who had helped Zeus to establish his sovereign sway, had used no force, but now, for his theft of fire, is pinioned in torment upon a bleak cliff beyond the reach of the human race for whom he agonized and whose compassionating laments resound through the world.

Yet the victor has two causes for dread. The one he knew—the curse imprecated against him by his sire, whom he had dethroned, even as that sire had himself deposed his father and received his curse. For the dynasty of the Olympians is linked by a chain of malediction; even as the generations of men are exposed to ruin through the magical potency of the curse.

The other cause for Zeus' dread was locked in the breast of Prometheus, the last rebel to his rule. From Earth, his oracular mother, the Titan had learned a secret, which, so long as it was undivulged to Zeus, prolonged the insecurity of the tyrant's sway. The lord of heaven and the lord of the waters were each enamored of the sea goddess Thetis, whose son, it was decreed by Fate, should prove mightier than his sire. Zeus, could he but learn the secret, had the choice: win Thetis and lose Olympus, or lose Thetis and retain his sway.

The curse and the secret thus coöperate, each foreboding danger. The curse of Cronus was a part of the Titanomachy, the secret was directly imported into the plot by Aeschylus to serve the purpose of introducing both an element of suspense and a complication ultimately to be resolved. At the outset Prometheus darkly indicates his knowledge of Zeus' purpose, fraught with danger to his Olympian sovereignty. Later, he discloses it to Io with the assurance that Zeus cannot escape the fatal consequences of his purposed union with Thetis except he secure timely knowledge of the secret by releasing its possessor. Zeus' security is thus dependent on the will of the Titan, who wields a moral weapon that shall ensure, together with his freedom, his proper justice from his enemy. But what Prometheus has imparted to his fellow sufferer at the hands of Zeus, he will not impart at the command of Zeus' messenger; and his persistent refusal, in spite of the threat of new torments, is the direct cause of the catastrophe. The motive of the secret, thus defiantly and unflinchingly guarded, controls the movement of the play.

Now this secret, of which Prometheus is made participant by his oracular mother, was originally foreign to the legend of the Titan and his rebellion against Zeus. And, it would seem, the oracle did not in the beginning refer to Zeus at all. Designed only to explain the superiority of Thetis' son Achilles to his father Peleus, it was shifted to the Promethean myth by Aeschylus or, more probably, by one of his predecessors. Pindar still recounts it solely in connection with the wooing of Thetis by Zeus and Poseidon. The importation of the new form of the legend into the play of Aeschylus supported his identification of Earth with Themis—"one form she hath but many names." The source of oracles is Earth, in whose bosom lies hid the future. Earth is Prometheus' proper mother, mother of all Titans. But, as the legend declared that it was Themis, the goddess of Right, who had declared the decree of Fate in reference to Zeus' union with Thetis, it was the easier for the poet to assimilate Earth with Themis, a syncretism known to Attic worship and not therefore derived from the play. But the introduction of the motive of the secret, so menacing to Zeus' continued

sway, has other consequences. As the poet envisages
the situation, the dominion of Zeus is imperilled in the
present or in the not too remote future, if, by his
union with Thetis, he beget a son who shall dis-
possess him of his empire. Yet the revelation of the
secret was withheld for thirty thousand years, the
period of the Titan's bondage, from which he was
released only in the *Prometheus Unbound*. The knot
is untied only after aeons have passed over the head of
the sufferer. Thus does the poet, by his sovereign
right as poet, bridge the gaps of time. He contracts,
he expands, time at will.

Further, the disclosure of the secret was to effect
Prometheus' freedom. Yet, in the ancient version
of the myth, a version followed also by Aeschylus, it
was Heracles who, by the will of Zeus, shot the eagle
and released his prey. If the disclosure of the secret
sufficed to release Prometheus, there was no need of
Heracles; if Heracles sufficed, there was no need of
the secret—double motive for the fact of release. If
the two explanations still subsisted in the sequent
drama, their mutual accommodation remains another of the many obscurities that darken the path
of our understanding of the *Prometheus Unbound*.

Over the Aeschylean drama there broods a spirit
of mystery confederate with its mysterious praeter-
natural personages. Its grandeur is due not solely
(with Coleridge) to its sublime simplicity, nor yet to
its magniloquence (a virtue which Horace did not
neglect in his incomplete view of the poet's fame), but
to the altitude and the profundity of its vision,
wherein it surpasses all other tragedies of the
ancient world. Aeschylus was primarily neither
theologian nor philosopher. Throughout his entire

career he was a playwright contending for a tragic
prize to be awarded by a select body of his fellow
Athenians. In him unite the two currents of purpose
in earlier literature: Homer's desire to please,
Hesiod's will to instruct. On the surface his dramatic art might not be so charged with subtleties as
to overpass the intellectual range of his audience; yet
the myth, as it took sensible shape under his hands,
might be made the instrument whereby he might
darkly shadow forth his broodings over God and
man. His soul was somehow occluded in his work.
In that dark brooding over eternal things, a brooding
Hebraic rather than purely Greek in essence, lies the
true preëminence of the poet in his religious aspect.
Therein lies also in some part the essential obscurity
of the *Prometheus*. We cannot altogether disem-
barrass ourselves of the suspicion that the informing
spirit of the Promethean fire has not brought illumi-
nation to its interpreters. If the poet might not, or
could not, resolve into clarity his own vision, it is
small wonder that they have embroiled with successive confusions the purpose of the play. Was
Prometheus the victim of transcendent injustice or
did he deserve his fate? Was he a miscreant or a
martyr? Or was he neither? One precious scroll
from the final play, recovered from an Egyptian
mummy-case, might quiet all anxious questionings.

The guilt of Prometheus, measured from one
base, is unquestionable. He was a thief, the thief
who had stolen fire, the prerogative of the Olympians, and given it to mortal man. He had thus con-
founded the world of the gods and the world of man;
for Moira, the dispensation of things, had established as unassailable the realm of the immortal gods

upon which mortal man might not encroach save to
his loss.   On Zeus' apportionment among the several
gods of their several rights and functions, fire had
been assigned to Hephaestus.   Prometheus, therefore, deprived Hephaestus, the son of Zeus, of his
special prerogative. His purpose, too, collided with
the will of Zeus to destroy the existing human race
and plant another in its stead. At the outset of the
play the former offense is placed in the forefront;
later, it seems to lose its preëminence as the hero
himself narrates the varied blessings he conferred on
man. No other impulse prompted his action than to
benefit mankind. But Tartarus, too, may be paved
with good intentions.   If his chastisement seems to
us, as to the victim, to exceed the measure of his
offense and thus to disable the justice of a moral
equilibrium, it must be remembered that ancient
thought looked rather to the quality and station of
the offended power than to the nature of the offense
or to any good motive prompting the offense. Nor
must we forget that the impression produced by the
severity of the Titan's punishment is alleviated by
his certain knowledge, and therewith by that of the
spectators, already fortified by acquaintance with
the myth, that in the course of myriad ages he was
to be released from his torments.

On other counts, too, Prometheus may be incriminated. Did he not play false to his kinsmen the
Titans, warring against Zeus? Only when he had
learned from his prophetic mother that victory in the
contest for Cronus' throne would be decided by craft
and stratagem and not by violence, only then did he
range himself on the side of Zeus, and then himself
rebel against the conqueror. He had assisted in

establishing a new and a better order of things, yet impatient of its delays, he arrogates to himself the right to oppose it. He fails to realize the antinomy of conflicting duties. He fails to recognize his obligation to the new ruler of the gods, of whose ultimate purposes he divines nothing. He follows the devices of his own will. He lets his sympathies usurp the place of an all-surveying reason. He ignores the fact that harshness attends reaction. He is the type of that hasty judgment of the Greeks of history who aimed to secure an ideal individual justice won at the expense of ordered law. He has no other thought than of his own aims and of his own merit, which he recounts at length in the satisfaction of his egotistic pride. Persuaded of the nobility of his intentions, he seduces himself into the deception that his rebellion was founded on a higher justice than the justice of Zeus, whose victory over the ruder forces of an earlier world was itself the moral sanction of his success. And is it not urged against him even by the friendly daughters of Ocean that he was deceived in his very reliance on mankind? "Didst thou not," they argue, "didst thou not behold the feeble helplessness, like unto a dream, wherewith the purblind race of creatures of a day is bound"?—even as the modern poet asks to what purpose shall the heavenly torch pass to men eternally doomed to blindness. "Never," conclude the Chorus, "never shall the plans of mortal men transgress the harmony of Zeus," a conception, it may be remarked, as foreign to the intellectual range of these maidens as, on the other hand, it is akin to the philosophy of Heracleitus.

Nor is this all. Even the excellence of Prometheus' benefactions to mankind has not passed un-
challenged. There are critics, holding with the Cynics
and Rousseau, who discover in the arts and sciences
only the corrupting influence of a culture that robs
man of his pristine felicity. Prometheus, it is
claimed, though he taught man "number, most
excellent of arts, and the combining of letters, and
Memory, mother of the Muses, artificer of all
things," taught him otherwise only what aids man's
physical well-being: carpentry, shipbuilding, knowledge of the stars helpful to the husbandman and to
the sailor, the use of horses, medicine, the mantic
art, the working of metals erstwhile hidden in the
earth. To what end does it advantage man to wrest
from nature gold and silver and bronze and iron
which she has taken such precaution to hide in order
that he might not discover them to his undoing?
With all his benefits Prometheus left man unac-
quainted with the art of civil government—as
Plato, for his part, did not fail to observe. Shall it
profit man to cultivate the arts and learn the ways
of luxury if he has not learned withal how to govern
himself, and also above all how to be good?

On this showing, then, the Titan, who, in his
fatuous self-delusion thought to build well, built but
ill. Nay more, he is disclosed as the architect of evil
for mankind. Prometheus, who prefigured Christ
to the Christian apologist, finally emerges, by the
extreme limit of oscillation, as the veritable Satan
of Schoemann.

In resentment at so transparent a paradox,
effected without self-suspicious caution on the part of
of its author, we are tempted to the belief that man

has been dowered with reason only to work the works of folly. The contrast between the Satan of Milton and the Prometheus of Aeschylus has nowhere been more compactly or more eloquently marked than by Mrs. Browning:

Satan suffered from his ambition, Prometheus from his humanity; Satan for himself; Prometheus for mankind; Satan dared peril which he had not weighed; Prometheus devoted himself to sorrows which he had foreknown. "Better to rule in hell," said Satan; "better to serve this rock," said Prometheus.

Now if I have read aright some part of the multitudinous books about Prometheus, I find that it is almost invariably the professional scholar, devoted to the "idol of his tribe," who in modern times has discovered that our admiration of the hero is admiration of a miscreant, antipathetic to us and likewise to the ancient audience; and that his beneficent works for human happiness were only the fruit of the forbidden tree. It does not count for little that even those interpreters of the play who defend the justice of Prometheus' punishment have themselves been forced to confess that their primary moral impression had uniformly been that of the justice of his cause. And this, too, is the essential moral impression of poets. Poets may be incurious of the subtleties of philological eristic, but they are wont to see into the heart of things. Primary moral impression wears the aspect of the logic of human nature and is not the product of an age schooled to look with sentimental sympathy on humanitarian intentions. Or has the ancient poet in very truth created a mirage that has obscured the vision of generations? Can it be that we are mocked of the dramatist who, true to his art, must recommend the sufferer to our sympathies, yet also and of set purpose excites those sympathies for the moral cause for which he suffered? If we are thus deliberately mocked, his play is only a dramatic study of tragic endurance, akin in its sublimity to that of Milton's Satan, and of the perversity of a casuistry that would justify the means by the end. If we recoil with the consternation of surprise at such a conclusion, it is no defense to invoke as parallel the peripeteia by which Euripides in his *Ion* leads us to expect one ending yet effects another. Aeschylus is not concerned here with the mere machinery of dramaturgical device.

The issue for the *Prometheus Bound*, but only for that play of the trilogy, is inescapable. Dramatic consistency demands that if the character of Prometheus is depressed, the character of Zeus must be elevated; raise Zeus, we lower Prometheus.

We shall not suffer ourselves to be persuaded that Aeschylus saw only evil in Prometheus' works. We shall not be misguided by the dream of a primal felicity that first haunted the vision of the poet of Ascra, the vision of that Golden Age under King Cronus when man was dear to the blessed gods and knew naught of sorrow in his soul; when he was not the thrall of toil and trouble and miserable eld, but died as if overcome by sleep. Nor, on the other hand, shall we permit our knowledge of fact to be falsified by the emotional unreason of Rousseau. Departure from the primitive stages of human society does not spell human misery, nor will the Eternal Wisdom have had man unlearn his primal happy ignorance to the end that he win knowledge fraught with sorrow. In the dark spaces of time to which Aeschylus transports us in imagination, Prometheus found man in a savage state, but found him also potentially capable of civilization, a civilization happily epitomized by those arts and sciences which were to ensure alike the existence and the maintenace of a well-ordered constitution of human society. Aeschylus is a realist in the reconstruction of the past, a problem that had engaged the attention of the Orphics and is implicitly correlated with the myth of the Ages of the World. To him man has not lost perfection; he progresses toward perfection because of, nay despite, the blind hopes planted in his breast. But the sovereign of the gods, flushed at his recent victory, wished, like Lycurgus, to destroy existing things and build anew. Zeus' power was not partnered with compassion for the human race; Prometheus had confidence that man could transcend his imperfections. Our admiration is not lessened because the poet, obedient to the ways of ancient thought, attributed to the work of a single supernatural being those ameliorations of man's primitive state which were won by man himself, by his blood and his tears through the long ages of unrecorded time.

But if Prometheus is guilty, Zeus is also guilty. Implicitly and explicitly is he charged with offense. He brings awful suffering of body and yet more awful suffering of mind upon the mutineer who would reform the world against his sovereign will; yet he does not disturb the reforms effected by the rebel. Tyrant-like, he keeps justice in his own hands, and his arbitary pleasure takes the place of law. Tyrant-like, he keeps his thoughts to himself. His servitors, Power and Force, are fit symbols of their lord. He had brought disaster upon Io, whom some critics

would even make a sinner because she had withstood
his will. He had done violence to his father, he had
usurped his throne, and plunged him into Tartarus.
And it is by reason of this filial injustice that Zeus
is expressly marked as feebler in power than the tri-
form Fates and the ever-mindful Erinyes, symbols
of the primeval moral governance of the world, and
far outranking the Olympians in antiquity.

Of the cardinal virtues, nearest to the heart of the
Greek lay justice. Like Achilles, Prometheus is stung
to impetuous wrath by his sense of the injustice visited upon him. Zeus owed his throne to Prometheus:
he requites him with ingratitude. Prometheus had
subordinated self to the well-being of mankind. Of
his own free will he had offended, persuaded of his
righteous purpose. But his reason did not lapse in
foreseeing harm to himself. He did not expect absolution because of the rectitude of his intention. But
for all that he could foresee the future, his thought
had never compassed in its utmost reach such agony
as had been heaped upon him by the very god who
had received good at his hands.

The representation of Zeus as an evil god touches
close upon an argument different in kind from those
mustered heretofore, an argument in which some
scholars have sought sanctuary in order to defend
their incrimination of Prometheus. It is their contention that it would have been morally impossible
that an Athenian audience should ever, without
offense, have suffered so flagrant a defamation of
their most high god. Because the Athenians, by the
very fact of their prepossessions, would have resisted
depreciation of Zeus, therefore, it is argued, Zeus was
in reality not depreciated at all. Comedy of course

has its proper liberty and license of irreverence. But it would be inconceivable that the solemn religious festival dedicated to tragedy should have been tolerant of an impiety which deliberately disowned the supreme god of the national faith by representing him as a cruel, a jealous, and a vindictive tyrant. Systematic blasphemy may not with impunity mar the face of the Divine; and not even the magnificent fiction of the Marathonian warrior-poet could have rendered righteous the sacrilege of Prometheus' mutiny against the will of the omnipotent father of gods and man.

Now I am far from denying the supreme audacity of Aeschylus' handling of the traditional mythology, which is, however, only the vesture that veils religion. The full tale of his audacities is ignored by many students of his art. He was audacious in putting the Queen of Heaven on the stage as a priestess collecting alms; he was audacious in troubling the divine serenity by making a blustering attorney of Apollo; he was audacious in making Thetis upbraid Apollo for bringing death upon her son, yet at her marriage he had prophesied for her a future charged with no distress; he was audacious in unveiling the awful majesty of Zeus: for he dared, as did no other tragic poet, to present the actual person of the great god.

It is an unbefitting argument that in our play Zeus was swayed by malevolence in the form of personal animosity to Prometheus. It is an impertinent argument that certain contemporaries of the poet may have regarded Zeus as a tyrannical ruler; though it well may be that his portraiture of a tyrant has been drawn from the history of his own time and that it purposed to keep alive Athenian

detestation of despotic rule. I have not one jot of
sympathy with the plea that Aeschylus was himself
disaffected to the Olympian religion, and had in mind
to display the crudities of a popular superstition re-
tentive of outworn conceptions of the gods in order
thus to evaporate Zeus into a poetic fiction.

The interpretation of the play is exposed to one
peculiarly subtle danger in its estimation of Zeus. On
the one hand, the moderns insensibly tend to think
of the high god of Greece in his loftiest aspect and
thus to equate him, though afar off, with the high and
lofty One that inhabiteth eternity. But far more important is the difficulty of supposing that the Greeks
could rid themselves of that maturer conception of
Zeus of which Aeschylus was by far the noblest ex-
ponent, the Zeus who to him is the "most blessed
of the blessed, power most perfect of the perfect,"
the Zeus who teaches mortals that the way to wisdom
lies through suffering, the Zeus whose infinity of
power and majesty is compressed within the tiny
bulk of the monosyllable that voices his name. But
the Greeks did not in fact so stabilize the head of
their pantheon as we stabilize our God. Their profounder thinkers did not always equate Zeus with the
Godhead, the Supreme. Elsewhere, in Aeschylus
at least, 'Zeus' or 'the gods' only sometimes ap-
proximates 'God.' In the *Prometheus Bound* Zeus
is only a god, never God. Intrude the mature conception of a spiritual Zeus into the Zeus of a rudimentary world, and you destroy the integrity of the god
of the play. Zeus cannot be at once the Zeus of a
high spiritual conception, the abstract head of the
celestial order, and at the same time the Zeus of the
Olympian world just freed from physical disorder and

conflict. It must be the earlier god who is expressly incriminated by the poet; if it were the great god of a later age of thought who is incriminated for mere dramatic effect in order to raise the scale of our sympathy for Prometheus, we might well hold with Renan that the Greeks lacked moral seriousness. But there is nothing permanently wrong with the Greek conception of the moral constitution of things: our abhorrence of Zeus is only an abhorrence of the Zeus of a pre-civilized antiquity. It is not just to brand the Titan as criminally insubordinate to the rule of an all-wise and perfect divine being. As well hale a man to court for violation of an unenacted law. At best Prometheus is an offender only because he has not bowed the knee to a provisional rule of might, the only rule in existence on the rise to power of Zeus, whose beneficence was to be made manifest only in the onward course of time.

Calamity, in Greek tragedy as in life itself, is often visited upon the individual who, with never so fair a motive, sets his will to counter authority, human or divine. Nevertheless it is also true that change of spirit may come upon the power which crushes him who translates into act his rebellious, but virtuous, purpose. Greek tragedy is not so closely engaged with the significance of an act as to let recognition of desert vanish because of insubordination, and to confess no true sympathy for the righteous intention of the agent. Antigone is broken, but Creon is broken, too. Sophocles will not solve the problem, as it concerns his heroine, by reference to the gods at large or to an informing cosmic will. Not so with Aeschylus. By some bold stroke, alike dramatic and satisfactory to the moral sense, he will effect an equilibrium between virtuous motive and the opposing force; and thus win something of that composure which makes the *Oedipus Coloneus* unique among the dramas of Sophocles.

The Zeus of the *Prometheus* is not a celestial being absolute and independent of all time: he is insulated in a definite time. He is not the god of yesterday, today, and forever. He came into being like the cosmos itself. There even existed legends that he suffered death. Parmenides conceived of the rise and fall of the gods. It is not for nothing that the personages of the play, his minions included, expressly declare that his rule is harsh because he has just attained to power. Modern poets see in Prometheus the opponent of age-long tyranny. Aeschylus sees in him the rebel to tyranny just established. Zeus has not yet learned, as later in his treatment of Ixion who first shed human blood, the truth that underlies the utterance of the Sage of Greece, the truth that pardon is better than punishment. The Zeus of the *Prometheus* is, in fact, deliberately pictured as far older than the Zeus whom Homer makes compacted of majesty and human frailties. Is not Homer ignorant alike that the son of Cronus laid violent hands on his own father and that he had won his way to power? The Zeus of the Aeschylean drama is the Zeus just emerged from battle with the Titans. The savage spirit of the Titanomachy pervades the opening play of the trilogy. As the poet's imagination has taken wings and traversed with Io and Heracles the uttermost regions of east and west, so too does it dare to envisage the infancy of the world of gods and men. Aeschylus is the poet

Of old unhappy far-off things
And battles long ago

against the recital of which in the symposium Xenophanes so earnestly protested. I cannot deny to his Athenian public the power of sympathy to follow in the track of so large an imagination. The strife of god with kindred god—for Prometheus, it must be remembered, was close akin to Zeus— thus resolves itself into no permanent impiety. What had been blasphemy in mortals is only protest against a power not yet shaped into the image of veritable divinity. Is not another religion conversant even now with threatenings against God and saint? In Spain believers in the one true God have threatened him with apostasy if He sends no rain. The Neapolitans have burst forth in angry clamor if the blood of St. Januarius is not liquefied on the minute. Not until nearer Aeschylus' own time do we encounter a more reasoned impeachment of the justice of the Olympian Father: "Thou rulest the world and knowest the might and heart of each and every man. Yet thou now dost dare to measure by the same standard the sinner and the righteous."[1]

For all its implicit extension of time, the *Prometheus Bound* is set in a definite period of the past; and in it the cause of the Titan, not the cause of Zeus, holds preëminence, and by dramatic right. The *Prometheus Unbound* presupposes an infinite advance of time and of moral vision. With man it is the revolving years, with gods it is aeons, that bring healing. The myriad ages have broken the body and the pride of the Titan held in agonizing distress. He has realized his fallibility, he has been schooled to unlearn his obstinacy, his arrogance, and his defiance

---

[1] Theognis, 373 ff.

of the god who has now been transformed into the moral ruler of a world itself transformed. Shelley would not weaken the fable by any subjection of his defiant hero, and so his unchangeable evil God must perish. To Shelley there can be no moral compromise. Other moderns are loath to draw within the circle of their vision the *Prometheus Unbound*. Truncated as is the trilogy, these atomists would cast out of sight even the poor remnants of that tragedy in order that they may preserve unimpaired the image of an unshaken and defiant will supported only by the justice of its cause. Not so the Greek poet, whose religion bore on its very surface the proof of long centuries of growth, a growth of which his trilogy is an epitome, even as Greece, as was said by Bourgainville, is the universe in small. There are not wanting elsewhere in Aeschylus indications of the conception of the perfectioning of the crude mythological Zeus into the Zeus of a spiritual religion. In the *Agamemnon* the poet coördinates the moral superiority of the god with the fact of his succession to the older regents of the world. Aeschylus is in fact an evolutionist as regards both gods and man. The *Prometheus Bound* is thus a dramatic study of antagonistic characters in far-distant time and situation, not a portrayal of the absolute or final nature of the adversaries. Within the limits of a single play Aeschylus always shows his characters as intellectually consistent, and never in process of development. If ever they are impermanent, they change only in the further course of the trilogy, whose slow and orderly advance is symptomatic of that change. As Prometheus had been softened in course of time, so a change has come upon his antagonist who is under bonds to Fate. Right has been added unto might. Mercy and equity temper the omnipotence of Zeus; he has learned to recognize the inherent justice of Prometheus' championship of man now ennobled through the providence of the ancient rebel to his rule. Whatever we do not know about the manner and order of the reconciliation effected in the *Prometheus Unbound*, we know this: Zeus' wrath against the Titans had ceased, his clemency had unlocked for them the gates of Tartarus, and from the nethermost abysses they come to form the chorus of the play, which issued in the release of their brother Titan. The eagle is killed by Heracles at Zeus' command, Chiron's voluntary death is a vicarious punishment to atone for Prometheus' now recognized offense, and the hero puts upon his head a garland of osier, emblem of his fetters, and bids men, for whom he had so cruelly suffered, wear this wreath in recollection of his bonds. But his humbleness was not a surrender of the justice of his cause. The day had come when, as he had prophesied, Zeus would lull his stubborn wrath, and mutual eagerness would unite them in bond and amity.

So far as was possible within the limits of his art, Aeschylus sought to discover a moral solution for the contradictions of his theme. He would resolve the unreason of a savage antiquity, allay the perturbation of spirit excited by a spectacle of moral contradictions. The tension of a moral antinomy must be relaxed. A final accommodation must be secured whereby confidence should be reëstablished in a world founded on a principle of righteousness for gods as well as men. This pacification will have been the natural expression of the poet's religious convictions.

Aeschylus sought the unity of the Divine will, a unity that should replace diversity through the medium of reconciliation that would restore a moral equilibrium. In the *Eumenides* he achieved the seeming impossible by transforming Spirits of Wrath into Spirits of Blessing; and he likewise knit closer the bond between Zeus and Fate. The *Prometheus Unbound* is the spiritual predecessor of the *Eumenides*. The old order surrenders to the new order. Out of the welter of dynastic revolutions in the older race of the divine regents of the world, out of the fierce contentions of primordial unmoral powers, out of the gods' jealousy of mankind and mankind's progress, achieved through rebellion and infinite suffering, emerges at last a new world. In place of struggle, peace; in place of discord, harmony.

CHAPTER V

THE SEVEN AGAINST THEBES

The fate that controls the life of books has given the fame of Oedipus into the custody of the sweet singer of Colonus. Who, unless he be schooled in the lore of ancient literature, remembers that a Meletus once wrote an *Oedipodea*, or that Theodectes, a poet esteemed by the author of the *Poetics*, once composed an *Oedipus?* What would it not advantage us to regain the *Oedipus* and *Antigone* of Euripides that we might match them with the plays of Sophocles? And what would we not give if an Egyptian tomb might, even yet, release from its darkness the drama of Aeschylus, wherein he first gave tragic setting to the legend of Laïus' son, unhappiest of men, slayer of his father, successor to his father's bed, brother alike and father of his own children?

The story of Oedipus has a place among the most ancient of the heroic legends that cluster round the princely houses of Greece. The hero of the *Odyssey*, descended into the dolorous regions of death, sees among the fluttering ghosts the wraith of the wife of Laïus, wife, too, of her own son, the son who took his father's life. Not until the *Thebaïd* and the *Oedipodea*, the post-Homeric epics that first dealt expressly with the legend, did the history of the line of Oedipus receive that expansive treatment which made it the treasure house for Corinna's lyric, the *Seven against Thebes*, and for a long line of poets whose plots were to charge the epic narrative with tragic pity and fear.

It is Aeschylus who has the distinction of realizing for the first time the dramatic possibilities of a story which, after his time, was to be the theme of that supreme monument of closely-woven artistry, the *Oedipus Tyrannus*.

In 468 B. C. the veteran poet had suffered defeat at the hands of Sophocles, his youthful rival on his first appearance in the tragic lists. In the following year, however, Aeschylus reasserted his preëminence, winning the prize with a group of plays consisting of the *Laïus*, *Oedipus*, *Seven against Thebes*, with the *Sphinx* as the satyric drama. The trilogy, so far as we can judge, combined the subject of the *Oedipodea* with that of the *Thebaïd;* though the two epics, which connected Theban with Argive myths, may have overlapped in their handling of the legend. The *Oedipodea* probably dealt by preference with the earlier history of the family of Oedipus, the crime of his father and the death of his sons, each by the other's hand. The more extensive *Thebaïd* supplied the incidents of the contest between Argos and Thebes. The *Epigoni*, latest of the epics in this field, will have had as its special theme, the second, and successful, attack on Thebes by the descendants of the seven Argive chieftains, who, also under the leadership of King Adrastus, had failed in the first expedition. The first expedition, known as early as the *Iliad* and the *Odyssey*, lies at the foundation of the sole surviving member of the Aeschylean trilogy. The two expeditions have as their theme the first great war waged in Europe, a war that was a struggle for supremacy between the two dominant States of Greece in the legendary, not mythical, period; between powers which were often arrayed against each other in historical times. The contest had the further attraction for the imagination that it seemed to reflect the glories of a greater war, waged across the Aegean by all Greece for the possession of the fairest woman of the world. Yet it is not impossible that the story of the first contest between Argos and Thebes may have been even older than the war between all Greece and the kingdom of Priam.

Now the myth of Laïus, Oedipus, and his sons and daughters, had, at the outset, no connection with the story of the first conflict between Argos and Thebes. But once the myth of Oedipus was united with that story, it was extended to embrace also the second expedition. The fusion of the two elements—the story of the house of Oedipus and the story of the contending States—was effected at an early period, so early in fact that we learn of the attack of the seven Argive champions only in connection with the rivalry of the two sons of Oedipus. Thus compacted, it was a tale, which for poets (but naturally not for vase-painters) vied in popularity with the tale of Troy and of the house of Agamemnon. The tragic poets were unwearied in discovering new incidents, new complications, new opportunities for the representation of character, in a cycle of stories that embraced no less than four successive generations of the same family. Apart from our trilogy, Aeschylus drew from this repository of legend the plots for his *Nemea*, *Argives*, *Eleusinians*, and *Epigoni*. Of Sophocles' seven extant plays no less than three deal with the Oedipodean cycle, which also inspired his *Epigoni* and *Alcmeon*. The latter, a satyric drama, took its title from the son of Amphiaraüs, the noblest of the Argive champions.

Euripides, in the *Women of Phoenicia*, groups in a single play the major incidents of the story as he fashioned it for his dramatic purpose: the blinding of Oedipus and his imprisonment; the attack on Thebes, the quarrel of Oedipus' two sons, Eteocles and Polynices, in the presence of their mother, the posting of the seven champions at the gates of Thebes, the self-sacrifice of Creon's son to ensure victory for his country, the single combat of the brothers, Antigone's defiance of the decree that Polynices' corpse remain unburied, her refusal to marry Haemon, and her resolve to share her father's exile. In Euripides' *Suppliant Women*, the chorus is formed by the mothers of the seven chieftains who were slain and whose burial, refused by the Thebans, was assured by Theseus. Euripides' *Alcmeon* is lost, as is that of his contemporary Achaeus, author also of an *Adrastus*. The *Parthenopaeus* of Astydamas the Second, a lineal descendant of Aeschylus, was so famous as to win for its author a statue in the Dionysiac theatre ten years before the Tragic Three were accorded a like honor.

It is characteristic of the art of Aeschylus, reflecting the processes of his mind, that all his dramas of the Theban-Argive cycle were closely knit in trilogies; his successors, whatever their varied handling of the legend, always dealt with it in independent plays. Aeschylus sought to concentrate attention on the march of a moral idea, in its successive phases, through three generations of a sin-laden family. His successors sought to concentrate the resources of their craftsmanship on momentous events in the life of an individual member of the race. The controlling religious and ethical motive of

Aeschylus is not restricted to any narrow limit of time or concentrated to a single dramatic crisis. In Sophocles' *Oedipus Tyrannus* it is the hero's search for the truth about his birth that controls the tragedy from beginning to end, and all comprised within the limit of a single day. In Aeschylus that discovery was only one testing moment in the fortunes of his ill-starred line. Laïus, elsewhere in Greek tragedy, is only the father of Oedipus and slain by his son; and his deeds are recovered to memory only to explain the fate of that son. In Aeschylus alone did Laïus, as tragic sinner and sufferer, occupy a place of prime importance.

The reconstruction of the first member of the three-part drama is almost entirely guesswork. The *Laïus* will have dealt with the murder of the king, who gave his name to the play; but we have no means of determining where the *Laïus* ended and the *Oedipus* began. No doubt Aeschylus dealt at length with the events which Sophocles compressed in the *Oedipus Tyrannus*. Differences of detail there were, but of no signal importance. In Aeschylus, Oedipus slew his father at the crossroads at Potniae and not on the way to Delphi, as Sophocles relates, therein perhaps following a later version of the story. In Aeschylus, Oedipus was buried at Thebes, and not in Attica in the sanctuary of the Eumenides, a variant version adapted by the Athenian poet in the *Oedipus Coloneus* to enhance the glory of his home. Most significant in the development of the legend is that Aeschylus seems to have been the first to make the children of Oedipus the fruit of his incestuous union with Jocasta.

It is proper to Aeschylus' handling of a theme running through an entire trilogy to look before and after, and to view the present in the light of the past. The last member of the trilogy interprets the whole. In the final, and sole surviving, drama we get information of capital importance for the poet's working of the legend. In the *Seven against Thebes*, after Eteocles rushes from the scene to encounter his brother in mortal combat, the Chorus, foreseeing all too clearly the bloody issue, raise a song of terror at the power of the Avenging Spirit of Oedipus who had cursed his sons and doomed them to perish each by the other's hand.

O house of misery, wherein new woes are blent with woes of old! Aye, of ancient time is the transgression I recount, and swift its retribution: yet unto the third generation it abideth. Thrice with prophetic voice did Apollo declare unto Laïus at Delphi, earth's central shrine, that he must die without offspring would he save his realm. Yet Laïus, overborne by the perverse counselling of his nature, begat doom unto himself, even Oedipus, the son who slew his sire; the same who sowed his seed in a hallowed field, his mother's womb, wherein he was nurtured to life—and he came to endure a growth of blood. It was madness that linked the infatuate pair.

The divine command thus laid on Laïus was not the wanton exhibition of the envy of the gods at human happiness. It was provoked by wanton sin on Laïus' part. In the extant play Aeschylus himself does not recall it, as he does recall the forewarning; but from another source we learn that Laïus, enamored of Chrysippus, the beautiful son of Pelops, had carried off the boy and therewith brought down upon himself the curse of the father—that he should die childless or be slain by his own child. Apollo's warning, what was it but the divine reinforcement

of the imprecation of man? Thus Laïus' sin, abiding
even to the third generation, still lived in the sons of
Oedipus, joint heirs of the curse of their father,
himself begotten in defiance of the god. The second
play in the group will have dealt with Oedipus' victory over the Sphinx, that "deadly beast whose prey
was man," with his marriage to Jocasta, with his
discovery that he had been exposed as an infant by
his father, and that he had unknowingly slain his
father and married his mother. The cursing of his
sons and their mutual hostility will also have found
a place in the *Oedipus*. Hatred between the brothers
will thus have been already existent before the action
of our play begins.

The cause prompting Oedipus' passionate resentment against his two sons is not fully explained in the
extant drama: all that the text warrants is that, after
their father's fall from power, they had failed to
minister to his needs with loving tendance. From
other sources of the legend we learn, however, that
he cursed them either because he was ill-fed or given
to drink out of a cup unlawful for him to use by
reason of some religious inhibition. The *Seven
against Thebes* makes no allusion to the tradition that
the sons were to rule alternately, each for the space
of a year ("divided reigns do make divided hearts").
All that is said, or to be inferred, on this score is that
each sought for himself alone the sovereign rule, to
which each had inherited an equal right, and that
Eteocles had refused to yield to Polynices, who took
refuge as an exile with Adrastus, king of Argos. Our
play, with its scene laid in Thebes and with Eteocles
as the defender of the town, presents that prince, in
his own judgment, as the rightful possessor of the

monarchy, while the cause of his rival, equally confident of his right, is studiously minimized. Whatever his past, Eteocles is made the proper subject of our present sympathy. He is pictured as a patriot battling for his fatherland; Polynices, as a traitor to his country because he had induced Adrastus to lead an army against Thebes to bring him to his own again. Apparently, according to Aeschylus, the brothers are twins; certainly neither is married in the *Seven*. In our poet's *Epigoni*, however, each had a son who renewed the strife of the fathers. No more luminous example can be found of the elastic nature of heroic legend and the opportunity therewith opened to the elective affinities of the dramatist. The *Seven* is intelligible only if Eteocles and Polynices had no sons—the race of Oedipus perished with them, his daughters being virtually non-existent. The *Epigoni* is unintelligible if the brothers left no male descendants.

Whether the Prometheus-trilogy is earlier or later than the *Seven against Thebes* is disputable. Certain it is, however, that the latter play provides us with the earliest datable example of a tragic drama introduced by a speech spoken by a dramatic personage before the appearance of the chorus. From the year 467 B.C., at least in the surviving dramas, Aeschylus definitely abandoned the archaic fashion of beginning his plays with a processional chant by the chorus setting forth the existing situation; nor does the more ancient type ever recur except in the archaizing *Rhesus*. This innovation in technique is significant: the chorus, now no longer the controlling element in the plot, need not hereafter come upon the scene until the situation has been sufficiently explained, either by the hero of the piece or by one or more subordinate characters. The change was furthermore a patent indication that henceforth greater stress was to be laid on the depiction of character, even at the expense of continuity of action. With the *Seven* the portraiture of character assumes an importance hitherto unknown. The *Suppliant Maidens* had in its chorus a multiplied heroine; the *Persians* had only interlocutors and no single controlling personage. The *Seven* presents us with the first proper hero in the history of tragic art. It is the earliest extant drama in which a truly human personage stands out with the clearly marked lines of individuality. Not indeed that the figure of Eteocles is drawn with the minute deftness of later art; but he is preëminently a real character, and as such demands a closer consideration, not only because he is none other than himself, but also because his sin touches on the tremendous question of Fate.

The *Seven* has no great variety of spectacular situation, the chief action being concentrated upon Eteocles. It has no subordinate interest, even of character. Not until the appearance of the Herald (admitting that the scene is genuine) is there any marked differentiation between Ismene and Antigone, such as is visible in the contrast between Darius and Xerxes. Dominating the play up to the moment of his death, Eteocles appears before us in four distinct scenes, in each of which his attitude toward his native gods is a feature of capital significance: at the beginning of the play, when he sets forth the situation; in his altercation with the Chorus; in his reception of the Scout's detailed report of the disposition of the Argive assailants at six of the seven gates; and,

finally, when he resolves to confront his brother at
the seventh gate.

At the outset, in the speech that opens the play,
the youthful prince displays in the presence of danger
a full consciousness of his responsibility as commander now that the enemy is threatening its supreme assault. He is in complete control of all those
faculties that are necessary to form a prompt and
well-advised decision—he is cautious, yet resolute;
intrepid, yet calm. He is stirred by one passion
only—to succor the altars of his country's gods and to
safeguard his motherland, that dear nurse of all her
sons, who reared them with nurturing care when in
childhood they crept upon her kindly soil. Thus far,
thanks to the gods, fortune has inclined to the side
of the defenders of the town of Cadmus (Thebes is
never called by any other name); and the ultimate
success of its champions, if success is to be theirs, will
be due to the gods; defeat, on the other hand, will be
laid to his sole charge by the citizens, whose threatening murmurs and laments will voice no other name
than "Eteocles."

His courage is not daunted when the Scout confirms the imminence of the danger. Seven valiant
captains of the Argives have dipped their hands in
bull's blood and sworn that they will ravage the city
by force of arms or imbrue the land with their own
blood. They breathe the spirit of iron resolve, glowing with valor, as lions with battle in their eyes.

So long as Eteocles heartens the citizens of every
age to defend their country and their country's gods,
there is no hint of the dark background of his birth,
none of his father's curse, none of the hatred of his
brother, whom he does not even name, but whose

presence with the invading army he must at least sur-
mise. But once the Scout has quitted the scene, and
before the tumultuous arrival of the Chorus, in the
first soliloquy of extant Greek tragedy, Eteocles
voices his inmost thoughts in a prayer fraught with
the burden of the curse imprecated by his father
against his brother—and against himself.

> O Zeus and Earth, and ye gods that guard our city,
> and Curse, the potent spirit of the vengeance of my sire!
> Do not, I entreat ye, extirpate in ruin utter and complete,
> with ravage by the foe, a city that speaks the speech of
> Hellas, and our hearths and homes. O may never they
> constrain in slavery's yoke a land of freedom and the
> town of Cadmus. But show yourselves our strength. Me-
> thinks it is our common cause I urge. For a State that
> prospers pays honors to its gods.

The sentiment concluding Eteocles' invocation
has no special significance for the understanding of
the quality of his religious temper. That it is to the
self-interest of the gods to assist their votaries because of the expectation of adequate requital is
written large in the undeveloped ethics of Greece as
of Palestine, and such political religion is known elsewhere to Aeschylus as an attitude of suppliants for
Heaven's help.

It is another aspect of the prayer, unique of its
kind, that invites attention. Zeus we know, as also
the collective gods, as protecting powers. To Aeschylus, Zeus is the one god who may not be excluded from
the invocation. Nor need the association of Earth
with the other divinities move our surprise. Not
because Aeschylus, by one of his heterodoxies, elsewhere made her the mother of Zeus, has she her place
in the fourfold appeal. Men swear by her and by
other gods in Aeschylus and in the Athenian court-

room. The words of the Scout have brought into the
immediate consciousness of Eteocles the presence of
his brother in the invading force and therewith the
curse pronounced by his father. The peculiarity of
Eteocles' appeal lies in the approximate equation of
that curse—properly relevant only to his race—with
larger, more universal powers concerned with the
welfare of the State. Oedipus' curse, like any other
curse, was an emanation of will power, but here it has
acquired an independent existence and is treated as
divine. It is an agent, "identified with the power of
vengeance which it summons into being;" and it is
capable, together with actual deities of Greek worship, of receiving man's homage. With the other
gods, normally beneficent, is thus associated a spiritual potency, normally evil and here to be depre-
cated, and to the end that it may champion the
cause of Thebes against its enemy. This curse is
an Erinys, a daemonic power, divine, yet unlike either
god or goddess; it whispers ever in the ear of the son
of Oedipus, but not until the critical moment in his
career does it take voice so as actually to influence his
destiny.

Eteocles' stoutness of heart in the presence of
danger stands in direct contrast to the terror of the
women who form the Chorus. For Aeschylus works
by violent contrasts. In place of the normal solemn
entrance song, these women here enter in wild confusion, voicing their alarm in verse which, in the
sweep of its stormy rhythms, is an echo of their
frantic excitement. They see the dust raised by the
advancing army; they hear the rattle of its spears,
the clang of its shields, the din of its chariots. Maddened by fear, imploring succor in an agony of

distress they rush from altar to altar, supplicating now this, now that divinity—not mere stone images with their insignia, but the very gods in immediate reality of divine presence.

Their tumultuous outcries soon reach the ears of the Prince, who has been busied with the final preparations for defense against the enemy without the walls. His first duty is to quell the disorder within. Hot with anger he bursts upon the panic-stricken women with savage reproaches:

Insufferable creatures! Is it to encourage your defenders that ye thus shout and shriek? The breed of womankind is past all endurance in adversity as in prosperity. Has woman the upper hand,—'tis insolence past living with; but, if seized with fear, to home and city she is still greater bane.

In the thrust and parry of opposing speech the women plead in excuse their trust in the protecting power of the gods before whose altars they have prostrated themselves—"the might of Heaven is above all; and ofttimes in the midst of his distress it uplifteth the helpless even from cruel woes when clouds are lowering over his eyes."

Eteocles' attitude in this scene has often been misinterpreted. Because he is brusque, ironical, scornful, he has been stamped as irreligious. But his attack is on the women, not on the gods they supplicate. He does not grudge their honoring the powers of Heaven: it is their terror and the untimeliness of their prayers that he deprecates. "It is the part of men to offer sacrifice when they make trial of the foe; your prayers put craven hearts into your champions. The food of Ares is the blood of men and frantic shrieks will not avert your doom. If you will pray, pray that the walls hold proof; for the gods are wont to abandon a captured city"—a sentiment expressly drawn from ancient belief at large, and no warrant for a personal irreligion on the part of Eteocles.

In the very midst of his rebukes the women are again overcome by an appalling sense of fright; and it is only with difficulty that they are induced to make the enheartening prayer "May the gods fight on our side."

Designed to set in bold relief the courage and patriotic zeal of Eteocles in contrast to the timidity of the Theban dames, the whole colloquy so rings the changes on the same theme, is so over-elaborated, that it produces an atmosphere of fatigue. The scene is terminated by Eteocles' own prayer for victory. He departs with the significant announcement that he will post at the gates six defenders, with himself as the seventh.

Phrynichus' *Capture of Miletus* may have given fictive reality to the horrors of a city overmastered by a brutal soldiery, and Euripides was to let the agonies of the capture of Melos find an echo in his *Women of Troy.* Aeschylus himself may have heard from witnesses in the Persian wars some of the awful deeds with which the clairvoyant imagination of the Theban women invests their choral song now that they are left alone. They are minded to do the bidding of their Prince; yet the terror finds no rest. They see, they hear, the tumult raging in a sacked city; man slays man, plunderers seek their prey; mothers, bedabbled with blood, hold their babes to their breast; the city is polluted by smoke; garnered wealth is swept away in streams of wastefulness;

women are dragged off by the hair; maidens suffer
the shame of a conqueror's bed. Mad, inspiring to
frenzy, defiling all holiness, is War.

The fortunate, but not well-motived, coincidence
of the return of Eteocles and the Scout at exactly
the same moment prepares the way for the celebrated
marshalling of the chieftains, a scene that restores
the sense of Theban security that had been imperilled by the song of the terrified Chorus. Placed
in the center of the play, clothed in the gorgeous
vestment of ornate magniloquence, this passage
forms the distinctive feature of a drama, of which
its author in the *Frogs* declares that it was "full of the
War-god." The passage is indeed unique, even in a
literature showing a preference for those epic epi-
sodes which are a horror to Gallic sensibilities.
Gallic taste pronounces, as useless, scenes devoid of
movement, for, to that taste, the soul of movement
lies in intrigue, and intrigue lies in a combination of
actions. Nowhere else does Greek tragic art show a
more marked proof that a Greek audience, careless
of rapidity of advance, could be content to linger
with delight on formal description and narration
of the pomp and circumstance of war when embroidered with invention and enriched with the splendor
of stately and majestic diction. Greek tragedy,
dealing with one luminous point in the career of its
hero, allows scope for an elaboration of accompanying circumstance foreign to the modern stage.
Beauty, not reason, is, to the Greeks, beauty's own
justification.—In several hundred verses the Scout
reports in due order and in broad epic style the
several Argive assailants, each assigned by lot to the
gate he is to attack. At the mention of each, Eteocles,

in duly but not equally balanced speech, names his
Theban antagonist; while the Chorus interpose a brief
lyric, now an imprecation on the enemy, now a prayer
for the victory of their defenders. There is no physical
action except the departure for his post of each of the
champions named by Eteocles—and even this meager
movement is ruled out by Wilamowitz, who would
have the six defenders already at their posts.

Like the Courier in the *Persians*, the Scout possesses, and justifiably enough, dramatic omniscience.
Since his departure at the opening of the play, he has
been able to see and hear every occurrence outside
each of the seven gates. Eteocles, for his part, gives
good reason for his selection of the Theban warriors
to oppose the commanders who are to lead the
assault. The son of him who guessed the riddle of the
Sphinx is quick to interpret to the advantage of his
cause the threats and boasts that pass the lips or are
blazoned on the shields of the Argive assailants. On
the buckler of Tydeus is a sky ablaze with stars, and
in their center is the moon, the eye of night: night
shall fall upon his eyes. Typho, the monster, is
fashioned on the shield of Argive Hippomedon;
Hyperbius, the Theban, bears on his shield the figure
of Zeus: the battle of the men will be decided even
as the contest of the gods. All the Argives, save one,
are defiant, overweening, insolent, voicing their
prowess in speech blustering like Marlowe's brag-
gadocio warriors. Each Theban is modest, courageous, pious—and each far less interesting than his
antagonist. The wicked seem, through their vigor,
to have the prerogative of being more intensely alive
than virtuous folk. Throughout, the style echoes
the pomp of the Argive champions.

One Argive champion is unlike his fellow captains
—Amphiaraüs, to whose lot the sixth gate has fallen.
Against his better reason he had joined the expedition, the failure of which had been forecast by his
mantic art. Even in the field he does not hesitate
to condemn, as Summoner of the Avenging Curse and
minister of bloodshed, Tydeus who had urged the
Argive king to the campaign. Nor does he spare
Prince Polynices for his disloyal ambition and his
treason in launching upon his motherland an invading
host. Amphiaraüs is at once seer and warrior—he
knows that he is to be sepulchred beneath a foeman's
soil. His buckler's orb bore no blazon—"for it is his
will not to seem bravest, but to be; and he reaps the
harvest of his mind's deep furrowing, whence his
sage counsel springs." Yet even he, declares Eteocles, even he, though sagacious, just, brave, and
godly, a wise interpreter of Heaven's will, must pay
the penalty of his partnership with impious, bold-
mouthed men.

Cruel is the Fortune that makes the just man companion
of the unrighteous! In every issue nothing is more evil
than evil partnership—the fruit thereof must have no
gathering. The crop of infatuation yields as its harvest
death.

Six gates have now been named, their assailants
and their warders. At the sixth is posted a champion, misguided indeed but whose innate nobility of
soul is not challenged by Eteocles in a speech marked
(it is well to observe) by calmness of discernment
and freedom from all personal passion. Up to this
point the Prince's judgment of men had shown no
finesse, no great variety of relief; here, in the case
of Amphiaraüs, endowed with three of the four

cardinal virtues—sobriety, justice, bravery (instead
of prudence, he has piety), we have a portrayal of
character such as had never been thus far in tragedy.
Yet Amphiaraüs is not an active personage in the
play—for throughout the *Seven* there is no proper
subordinate interest. Everything centers on the
question: will the brothers meet and fulfill the curse
of Oedipus?

By slow and stately progression, not entirely
(despite M. Faguet) devoid of the interest of curiosity, we have at last reached the seventh gate.
That gate, so reports the Scout, is to be attacked by
Eteocles' own brother.

The tragic suspense of the action of the *Seven*
consists essentially in the fact that, as the Argive
warriors are told off, it becomes more and more
evident that Polynices is to attack one of the gates.
When the sixth gate is provided with its assailant,
it is dramatically inevitable that the seventh gate
should be assaulted by Eteocles' own brother. Yet
Eteocles, who, early in the play, has declared that
he will appoint six defenders with himself as seventh,
here seems unconscious of the possibility that
Polynices will himself lead the attack at any point.
Indeed the very mention of his brother's name apparently bursts upon him unexpectedly—dramatic
surprise seems to be purchased at the cost of a
proper consideration of military probabilities. But
this is not the true explanation. In his tragic economy Aeschylus uses the element of surprise to effect
tragic irony. What is evident to the spectator is
unexpected to the person of the action. "Expectation is superior to surprise" both here and in a later
play when Aeschylus was to depict the taking-off of

Agamemnon, which comes unexpectedly to the
Chorus but not to the audience. Absolute surprise,
unmotived by the forecast of the plot, may suit
Euripides. It is not the method of Aeschylus.

It is well to mark the temper of Polynices' mind
and his exact words at this critical moment, when the
conflict of the two sons of Oedipus is foreshadowed,
not brought before our very eyes as in Euripides'
Women of Phoenicia. Polynices prays that he may

set his foot upon the walls of his native Thebes and be
proclaimed conqueror; then, after he has raised a wild
shout of triumph at its overthrow, that he may close with
his brother, and, if he slay him, perish at his side; or, if
that brother escape with life, that he may requite him
in the self-same wise with exile even as Eteocles had dishonored him with banishment.

Polynices' shield has for its design the figure of
Justice, and the legend thereon runs: "I will bring
back unto his home this man, and he shall have a
country, and he shall range in his father's halls."

The specter of the curse that had haunted his
dreams now rushes clear before Eteocles' sight. Now
for the first time is heard the language of purely
human passion, and in a passage scarcely equalled
in ancient tragedy: "O maddened of Heaven and of
Heaven deeply loathed, O steeped in tears our house
of Oedipus! Woe is me! Now indeed our father's
curses bear their fruit in deeds." Furious at Polynices' claim to be championed by Justice, overmastered by hate, Eteocles has now no other thought
than himself to confront his brother. Before, he had
reasoned with the Theban women whose excitement
he would tranquillize; now, in equally rapid dialogue
as then, he resists their pleadings of reason to thrust

from him his evil passion at its birth. He recks not the awfulness of shedding a brother's blood, a pollution that never grows old; he will make no oblation to the gods that the Avenging Spirit may quit the house.—Only here, in the genuine part of the play, is there a true conflict of opposing wills. But Eteocles in the fury of his passion sweeps aside every argument counter to his purpose. Resolved to make harvest of his brother's blood he rushes out with the words "From heaven-sent ills there's no escape."

The agonizing suspense is bridged by a song of the Chorus, who summon from the past the distressful legends of the unhappy race. A Messenger enters bringing joyful news—all goes well at six gates; but the seventh gate, Lord Apollo took that unto himself, fulfilling upon the house of Oedipus the follies wrought by Laïus in days of old. In anxious questionings the women seek the truth. It stands revealed: the city is saved, but the two princes have perished, each by the other's hand. Earth has drunk their blood. Only so much of their father's wide lands will they possess as shall suffice for their sepulture.

The black Curse inherent in the race, the curse of Oedipus, has worked its full completion—his sons have perished by their impious intent. To the anguish of the Chorus is now joined that of Antigone and Ismene when the bodies of their brothers are borne upon the scene. I know not where in ancient literature, except in the *Women of Troy*, is to be found a lamentation more pitiful, more agonizing, more charged with bitter misery, than that of the sisters for their brothers, now reconciled by help of steel, now indeed of one blood.

At the end of all, the Curses raised their shrill song of
triumph now that the race is turned in rout. At the gate
whereat they smote each other, now standeth a trophy
unto Ruin; and victorious o'er them both, the Evil
Genius stayed his hand.

The house of Oedipus has fallen, his sons are dead.
The two sisters chant an antiphonal dirge, Antigone
standing by the bier of Polynices, Ismene by that of
Eteocles. At the very end a Herald unexpectedly
enters to announce that, by the decree of the Cad-
mean authorities, the body of Eteocles shall be
interred with all honor; that of Polynices is to be
cast out to dogs and birds. Antigone declares that no
decree of man shall prevent her from bearing in her
robe the earth to cover the corpse of Polynices. The
Chorus divide in funeral procession, one part following the body of Polynices, the other that of Eteocles.

The tragedies of the house of Oedipus have long
held a position of preëminence in the literature of
Fate. *Die Braut von Messina, The Bride of Lammer-
moor, The Scarlet Letter, Ghosts,* are classed as spiritual descendants of a type first developed by Hellenic
genius. There are not wanting some who, like De
Quincey, hold that a dark fatalism broods over
all Athenian drama and that the portrayal of character, of which will is the "central pivot," could not
find a place therein because man is made the mere
puppet of Fate.

When the religion of the Greeks first lends itself
to analysis, it is certain that they had already left
behind them the conception of the world that
recognizes no purpose or will in the phenomena of
life. In the dawn of Greek religious consciousness,
the world is discovered to be controlled by deities
normally personal. Gradually there emerges the

idea that there is an impersonal power that shapes
the course of things. This idea gains ground more
and more. Behind and beyond man, behind and
beyond the gods themselves, the Greek mind came
to apprehend a transcendent principle manifesting
itself in a mysterious ultimate power affiliating and
controlling all things to the end that the purpose
of their existence should be accomplished and therewith the order of the world preserved. This ultimate
power has various names, but is most often called
moira. *Moira* is properly the "dispensation," or
"allotment," separating one province of life or of
nature from another. Each god, each man, has his
individual *moira*, strictly foredetermined from without, not from within. Neither god nor man is the
absolute controller of his life, though neither is thereby
deprived of his free will. Vigorous as is personification to the Greeks, at bottom Fate is abstract even to
them. It is an external power suffering no inter-
ruption of the moral equilibrium of the world. But
neither *moira* nor *tyche* was conceived to be derived
from the conception of Fate as an all-powerful force
behind all gods and men and ruthlessly predetermin-
ing the life of god and man.

Greek tragedy does not deal with the higher
reaches of theological or philosophical belief. Once,
and for a special purpose, in the *Prometheus*, Aeschylus indeed grapples with the problem of the relation
between the Fates and Zeus. His other dramas represent, however, the plane of the popular religion,
which was not concerned to adjust the distinctive
spheres of free will, Fate, and the gods. Nor did any
downright fatalism overshadow the actual life of the
ordinary Greek as a social or religious being. The

Greeks of the age of Aeschylus never accepted the blows of Fortune or of Fate with the imperturbable resignation of the Mohammedan, subject to a superior will as capricious as it is omnipotent. Greek εἵμαρται does not pair with *kismet*. Fate was a conception with which the ancient world is familiar, and it is written large in Greek literature, as it is in our English literature; but then, as now, it is used in a loose sense without regard to its precise meaning. We lightly talk of Fate, or of ill-starred Fortune, but we are not fatalists at bottom. Nor is even the fatalist consistent in his fatalism. To the Greek, the conception of Fate rarely extended its application beyond the fate of death—whatsoever thou doest, thou shall not escape thy doom. For in this world there are two kinds of beings: the Deathless Ones and man who is doomed to die. The Greek was acutely conscious that the day would come when he should no longer behold the radiant light of the sun; but his sense of the inevitableness of death did not carry with it the idea that he was predestined to die at the very hour when death actually came upon him. Fatalistic the Greek was not, if fatalism, on the one hand, means that in the slightest occurrences of his life, man discovers an immutable result of a series of infinitely predestined causes held together in rigid sequence; fatalistic the Greek was not, if, on the other hand, fatalism invests with the authority of everlasting law any action however inconsistent with man's normal behavior. Fatalistic the Greek was not, because he did not believe that it was no use to struggle in order to prevent that which would happen as the imperative result of causes beyond his control and baffling his power of comprehension.

The spirit that animates the Greek is not a spirit that benumbs man's energies and paralyzes his will. It is a spirit of freedom, of struggle, of joy in the perfect exercise of all his energies, of buoyancy in the face of obstacles, of resolution to master Fortune when Fortune is most adverse. In the indomitableness and audacity of his will, he defies not only man but God himself. Ever alert to seize the proper moment for action, he is the servant, not the slave, of opportunity.

Early Greek tragedy does not, on the whole, seek to enlarge the domain of Fate by making sheer Chance its instrument and letting it control the progression of the dramatic action; and the modern drama has long since broken with those of its forebears in which everything tends to happen *par hazard*. Aeschylus certainly restricts the sphere of *tyche;* but it is also true that before his time the chanceful factors in life, the incalculable, the mere 'luck of things,' played no part in the conception of the Greeks. In Homer there is no *tyche:* things later assigned to its sphere are by him referred to *moira*. In Pindar *tyche* is rather vicissitude than brutal chance, and in him Fortune and Fate are associated. In Sophocles *tyche* does not set aside the divine regulation of the world; it is only, like *fortuna,* the incalculable element in things, which prevents man from seeing that all life is governed by a moral principle. Only in a grosser age were *fortuna* and *sors* practically identified because the sense of their moral difference had disappeared. Sheer brutal chance to the Roman was properly *temeritas*. In Aeschylus' time Fate had not yet abdicated to Chance, nor was the great question yet raised whether the world was ruled by Providence or by Chance. To us moderns

Fate has come to signify, at least in great part, an omnipotent power indifferent to the happiness or the misery of mankind, the blind working of an external force impeding man's judgment, the force that makes man in his futility do the thing he would not and should not do. Through Fate the trifling accidents of life seem to set in motion a ruthless power that determines the issues of our own and others' lives. Through Fate, man becomes the plaything of a stern Necessity, the inner meaning of whose causal relations baffles his understanding.

In Greek tragedy the contest of the hero is primarily with outside forces. The forces of Fate seem isolated, the destiny of man seems superimposed on man. The hero may or may not be subject to the workings of an ancestral curse; yet in either case he appears to be doomed by reason of an implacable destiny, and he meets defeat final and complete.

ἦθος δαίμων ἀνθρώπῳ: character is destiny. Eteocles, for all that he rests under the shadow of the ancestral curse, proves the truth of Heracleitus' saying, not far removed from which is that of Plato: "Your daimon is not apportioned you by lot; you choose your own daimon." We say that lust for revenge on the part of both brothers was the instrument of Fate. Fate has no objective reality, yet its call exercises a magnetic force upon its victim. The voice of his destiny seems to call to Eteocles: "The hour has at last come for the fulfillment of thy father's curse. Fulfill it! Kill thy brother and be slain by him." He translates that subconscious bidding into well-nigh instant act. But he does not, like the hero in Ford's play,[1] juggle his conscience by deliberately

---

[1] Ford, 'Tis Pity: "My Fate's my God" and "'Tis not, I know, my ust, but 'tis my Fate that leads me on."

setting up Fate as his divinity and thus argue himself to be swayed by its irresistible compulsion.

Unquestionably consciousness of 'fatal destiny' is but one moment in the chain of causation. It predisposes to a decision, but it does not create that decision, when man finds himself confronted by the untowardness of circumstance. But the 'fateful' act is directed by man's self; predetermined as he may be, nevertheless he is himself the captain of his soul. Behind the veil of Fate, as Greek tragedy envisages it, there emerges something rooted in personality, in will.

Consider Eteocles up to the moment of the crisis. He has proved himself the incarnation of patriotic zeal; he is resolute, collected; no scorner of the human need of God's help, but insistent that prayer be timely and enheartening in the hour of danger; hating the contempt of Heaven shown by the proud vauntings of overweening braggarts. He is, as a soldier, a rudimentary analyst of the moral values of others' deeds and words. But like Diomed, he is a 'sodeyn man,' hot-tempered, brusque.

The instant Eteocles learns that his brother is to attack the seventh gate, the instant he hears of Polynices' vows of vengeance on himself, and his claim to be led home by Justice, the daughter of Zeus, that instant he is as if transformed. It needed only the opportunity, and there bursts forth, in fierce flame, his lurking passion, his hatred of his brother, the fierce impetuosity he has inherited from his father. For Aeschylus elsewhere expressly recognizes the transmission of qualities from parent to child. In the *Libation-Bearers* (v. 421) Electra declares she has inherited from her mother her implacable spirit. In Eteocles revenge is a passion of concentrated will that marches straight to its goal. He has the solidarity of a character that knows no hesitation, no misgivings. With the sophistry of passion he sweeps aside all opposition. He refuses to come to close grapple with himself. There is no troubled conflict of his nature. Chance, he thinks, has worked so insidiously as to rule his world and wear the aspect of divine design. The very gods seem confederate to his overthrow. Heaven, heretofore benign, has ceased to champion his cause; all the gods demand is the destruction of his house. "Let the line of Laïus be swept to Cocytus' wave by Apollo's hate!"

But Eteocles' reversion to the ancient belief lurking in the background of man's thoughts, the belief that the gods work harm for those whom they will to harm, is not "practical atheism." He is subject to the common confusion of Divine Foreknowledge with Necessity, a confusion that has led to the assumption that between free will and prescience there lies an undetermined contradiction. Interpreters of Aeschylus with a turn for metaphysics expatiate on the question whether or not Eteocles possesses free will. Like the rest of us mortals, he has no absolute free will. He is behind bars he cannot break, he cannot free himself from the facts of birth and untoward circumstance. But relative free will he has. *Sit pro ratione voluntas* he might almost say with the Roman.

Soldier that he is, and possessed of a soldier's inflexibility of purpose, once he knows his course, he feels that it were a dishonest victory over himself were he to refuse to meet his brother to the death.

The son of Oedipus will not quail when confronted
with the challenge of his father's curse, provoked,
as it was, by his, and his brother's, unfilial conduct.
But he is apparently ignorant or unconscious of his
own guilt; nor, as the play is shaped, was there any
place for an adequate presentation of that guilt until
both brothers are slain, and the wrong, as the right,
of each is heard from a sister's lips. The piteousness
of his history is that, like other tragic heroes, under
other circumstances, he had been good. But to the
evil transmitted to him by his ancestors he had added
evil of his own making: his evil charge of his miserable
father. In the testing hour of fortune he cannot renounce an unholy purpose formed in the gust of
passion. Heaven, he says, has abandoned him—
Heaven had helped him had he helped himself.
Eteocles' fate is his very self recoiling upon him to
his undoing—not Fate, but Nemesis.

In the *Seven against Thebes* character is portrayed
as involved in the action, without independent
existence apart from the action; and, if it may be
said to be developed at all, it is developed only in
reference to the action in certain aspects, preëminently moral and religious. In the *Orestea* the case
is different. There, as generally in Shakespeare, the
action is evolved out of character. There, as in
Shakespeare, the greatest characters are in themselves greater than their dramatic semblances. Of
this, Clytaemestra shall be the proof.

CHAPTER VI

THE ORESTEA: I. AGAMEMNON

The *Orestea* is in effect one great single tragedy in three separate parts, each with its own dramatic purpose, yet harmonized by a common inspiration—three great acts of a drama, simple but complex; the whole, as its component members, showing unity of action in rise, crisis, and fall, and progressing in a series of like orderly stages toward a definite dramatic goal. The main crisis of the first and of the second play is only temporary, its finality only relative. The crisis of the third play is the crisis of the whole complex. But because the whole is a complex of three separate main actions, the plot is not of necessity complicated. On the contrary, the movement of the *Orestea* is eminently simple and undisturbed by any subordinate plot. In the *Agamemnon* vengeance is taken on the guilty King by Clytaemestra and her paramour. Their cause is presented, their justification, their triumph. In the *Libation-Bearers* Clytaemestra and her lover are slain by her son. Vengeance follows upon vengeance. In the *Eumenides* Orestes, the avenger, is acquitted and the daimon of the race is laid to rest. The whole is the story of the stormy events in the house of Atreus ending with a final calm. Only when that final calm is attained can the spectator quit the scene, "all passion spent."

The *Agamemnon* virtually forecasts the plot of the *Libation-Bearers*, but it is not prophetic of the *Eumenides*. The second and the third play are closely linked; yet the second does not do more than indicate certain events that are to follow. The *Libation-Bearers* is reminiscent of the *Agamemnon*, the *Eumenides* is reminiscent of both the preceding parts. Yet each of the three factors wears an aspect of isolation by virtue of individual dramatic atmosphere and difference in time and place. The second and the third play are each dramatically intelligible without either of the predecessors. But they are not morally self-complete. The chain that links the three parts is less the continuity of events than the connection of religious and moral ideas. The *Agamemnon* and the *Libation-Bearers* have each a dramatic, but unmoral, unity; unmoral, because the moral imperative is not satisfied at the conclusion of each. The *Agamemnon*, though it presents the vengeance visited on the title-hero, does not fail to end in a forecast of doom. For all the triumph of the usurpers of Agamemnon's throne, there is yet a gleam of hope—Orestes, though an exile, will return as a minister of vengeance. The *Libation-Bearers* looks backward to the *Agamemnon*, and, in its turn, likewise morally demands a sequel. At its end, Orestes' disordered brain envisages the sable-robed demons coiled about with snakes who are to stand as his accusers before the high court of the Areopagus, inaugurated by the daughter of Zeus, the goddess of wisdom, to adjudge his unhappy case. No mechanical articulation could fuse into an Orestean unity Sophocles' three plays on the legend of Oedipus. The unity of the *Orestea* is not truly due to the 'multiplication of a single play.' It is a unity due to internal harmony; each part, for all its definite conclusion, morally unintelligible without the other parts, and

deriving its effectiveness from integral mutual association; the whole illuminated by the beauty of the
parts, the parts illuminated by the beauty of the
whole. If Aeschylus' art at its topmost excellence is
to be seen only in the trilogy of indissolubly connected parts, it is not true, as is sometimes maintained, that his art is to be judged exclusively on the
basis of the three-part drama. The group of which
the *Persians* was the second member would seem to
have no integral unity through sustained connection
of legend.

The march of Aeschylus' genius to its perfection
was slow, but it was uninterrupted. Learning from
others as from himself, he reached the summit of his
development with his latest work. In the *Orestea*
his dramatic technique has reached its maturity:
the plots varied and of sustained interest; the action
diversified and vivid; the *coups de théâtre* striking;
the characters variously and highly colored, stamped
with individuality yet widely human, existing for
themselves, not emanations from the action; the
verse melodious and responding to the lofty message
of the thought it bears; emotion is fused with reason,
leaving a sting in the mind; the rich and stately
language of the dialogue and the majestic lyrics,
unrivaled by those of any of the poet's fellow craftsmen in any age, voice profound searching after God
and his ways with man. The imagination that
conceived a Prometheus in the infant ages of the
world has lost none of its potency now that it
confronts the problem of the descent of sin through
generations of men in the heroic age. A rugged and
massive genius at the outset, as his life was verging
to its close and reflection usurped the place of ex-

perience, a rugged and massive genius Aeschylus remains, still unchiseled to the smoothness of a more delicate artistry. The eagle-bark at blood is there and it still spoils the taste for twitterings.

Most impressive through its dynamic quality is the *Agamemnon*. The intermediate drama yields the main interior crisis of the triad, the scene in which Clytaemestra is confronted by her son. Greatest in its inventive resourcefulness is the *Eumenides*. The final play presented an *impasse* that had defied the utmost powers of an artist less a poet and a patriot than Aeschylus. In varying degrees the separate units of the trilogy, held together by firm bonds at once dramatic and moral, present in their fullest measure, the tragic art of the Greeks, an art at once dramatic, epic, lyric, musical, and sculpturesque. The *Agamemnon* is richest in action. Yet the movement is most deliberate until the crisis. The poet had in fact to grapple with the self-created difficulties of a double-time. He had at once to foreshorten and to prolong the interval between the news of the capture of Troy by Agamemnon and his arrival at Argos. The vindicator of the authority of Zeus, the guardian of the right of host and guest, by which he was commissioned to exact vengeance on Paris for his theft of Helen, must appear in the full flush of victory and meet his death at the moment of his topmost pride for offenses unforgetable, though long overpast, and for offenses present to the eye.

The exposition is the function of minor personages, the Watchman and the Argive Elders, both loyal and attached servants of the King. The first lyrics of the Chorus are needed to interpret and explain the foreboding, partnered with joy, of the lonely watcher

on the palace roof at Argos, who during long months
in the tenth year of the war has been ever waiting
for the flame of the beacon that shall announce the
fall of Ilium, to be flashed across the Aegean by relays
of courier-flame. He has been stationed there by the
command of Agamemnon's Queen, whose "hoping
heart" leaps with the thought that the hour of her
vengeance is near when the Watchman's cry of joy
wakens her from sleep to action. The burden of his
heart he has not dared to breathe aloud even to himself. But the house of his master might tell a tale,
could it but only find a voice.

When Aeschylus needs his chorus, he does not
trouble himself to motive at length the reasons for
its appearance. These old men of Argos, too old ten
years before to join their King when he led his host
against Troy, well remember the omen at the start—
two eagles devouring a hare with young—an omen
presaging both good and evil; good, for the eagles are
their lord and his brother Menelaüs, twin-sceptered
kings; evil, for the goddess, who protects the life of
the things that roam the field, is filled with wrath
against the slayers of the trembling hare. And the
Elders know, as if they had seen with their own eyes,
that monstrous sacrifice of his own daughter Iphigenia at Aulis, whereby Agamemnon had released
the fleet, storm-stayed by the will of Artemis, and
served his own ambition. That pitiful scene, recovered from the past in its heart-rending details, is
moved into the present, and because it inculpates
Agamemnon, justifies to our sympathies the vengeance taken on him by Iphigenia's mother once he
comes within reach of her avenging hand.

In all his plays, however slight the external action, the poet refuses to rush forward to the catastrophe. In the *Agamemnon* he had special reason for delay. He must extend in imagination the march of time between the news of Troy's capture and the arrival of its conqueror. Troy fell during the night in which the play begins. The next morning Agamemnon returns in triumph to Argos, despite the storm that befell his fleet on the way home. In the mimic world of art the hours advance with swifter pace than in the world of reality. To conceal his depredation on the unity of time, the dramatist has recourse to artifices so cunning as almost to escape our observation.

The prolonged doubt and the unwillingness of the Chorus to accept, as evidence of Troy's capture, the beacon-fires and the kindred flames of thanksgiving now blazing at every altar in the city by the Queen's command; her lengthy description in resounding verse of the glad passage of the courier-fires from mountain peak to mountain peak as they overleaped land and sea; her vision of the scene at Troy—the shouts of the conquerors, the screams of the conquered, the repose of the soldiers within the captured city's walls; the vast choral odes, transcending limitations of time, since their burden is a wisdom not of today only, but declared of old—all these are artifices to delay the swift-paced hours. Thus it is that, when Agamemnon appears upon the scene, we have been unconsciously deceived by the inner logic of the imagination and are heedless of the outer logic of fact. The capture of the city has been moved into the past, where it already belonged in the latent consciousness of the audience.

The title-hero does not enter until the drama is half finished. Nor even when he appears with Cassandra in his train, does the action gather speed. The poet will have us climb slowly to the culmination point. He will have us linger over Agamemnon's stately harangue to the Elders, over Clytaemestra's fulsome professions of affection, spun out (so he declares) to rival his very absence beneath the walls of Troy. A rapid dispute between husband and wife ends in his surrender to her will that he enter his palace, setting on costly tapestries the foot that had trampled upon Troy. On his purple path he is lured within and to his death. If by the prescriptions of his art Aeschylus might not let Agamemnon be slain in the open, he had so bodied forth the scene in its reality that we all but see the fatal robe cast upon the King and the murderous ax wielded by his wife. The clairvoyant vision of the captive Cassandra, standing before the very door behind which the deed is done, is structurally only an 'episode' in the forward movement of the action. Yet it is the most stupendous interlude in the whole range of tragic art; both because of the intensity of its emotion and because no other drama of the ancient or the modern world has at its command a traditionary figure akin to Cassandra, endowed with the gift of true prophecy, yet forever doomed to win no credence from the ears of men. She sees Agamemnon caught in the meshes of the robe with which his wife entangles her victim; she sees the uplifted ax; she sees the babes of Thyestes eaten by their father; in frantic appeals, vibrating with reasoned argument, she warns the Elders that the fatal moment is at hand. In vain. Suddenly there rings out from within the cry of

Agamemnon, the most awful death shriek ever heard upon the stage. Elsewhere sights too appalling for the eye are reported; here murder is heard, and with a terrifying immediateness outranging the intensity of any Messenger's description of things seen by the eye of man.

With the main crisis is linked the scene in which the murderess, casting off the mask of her hypocrisy, openly exults in her deed, defends herself, and defies her subjects. The acme of physical action must give place to reflection once the tension is released. The emotional effect of the deed on the doer and on the faithful Elders, aghast with horror, must find place before a new situation is created bringing with it a new crisis. The final scene brings with it Aegisthus, who has left a man's work for a woman's hand. He gloats over the victim, done to death in retribution for the gruesome banquet of human food served to his father by Agamemnon's sire. The ancestral curse launched against Atreus is now discovered to be confederate with Clytaemestra's vengeance on the murderer of her child. Aegisthus' insults to the dead precipitate a struggle. The Chorus, too old to fight in company with Agamemnon alive, would now fight for Agamemnon dead. They are at the point of blows with Aegisthus and his bodyguard, when the Queen, now sated with blood, intervenes; but she has to hear the defiance that, if Orestes still lives, he will return for vengeance.

Such, in brief, is the action of the first part of the *Orestea:* slow in its advance, holding our interest on the stretch, terrific in its main crisis, falling slowly until the excitation of a new tragic moment fore-shadows an inevitable sequel.

In his dramatic handling of the legend of a sin-
laden race, Aeschylus had to mark one crime as the
progenitor of the guilt that reappears from generation to generation. In the history of the house of
Atreus, the primal sin might have been discovered
in Tantalus, the first of the line. In Goethe's play,
Iphigenia would mark her fate as linked with that of
her far-off ancestor in her tremendous line

Vernimm' Ich bin aus Tantalus' Geschlecht.

Nor in the *Agamemnon* is the mention of Tantalus without its sinister suggestion. Yet the poet
refuses to project the evil of the Atreidae so far into
the past as to make the arch-offender that ancestor
of Agamemnon who, in requital for his theft of the
nectar and ambrosia of the immortal gods, was condemned in Hades forever to reach in vain for the
fruit hung above his head and from whose parched
lips the water fell forever back. Nor will Aeschylus
take as his starting point the foul treachery whereby
Pelops, the son of Tantalus, won his bride and his
empire. He deliberately refuses to seek the source of
blood taint in an ancestor earlier than Atreus, the
father of the hero whose evil doing and whose punishment form the theme of the initial member of the
Orestea. To him the first cause was the corruption of
Aërope, the wife of Atreus, by his brother Thyestes,
and the revenge of Atreus. Atreus gave his brother
to eat of the flesh of his own children; and when
Thyestes learned whereof he had eaten, he cursed
Atreus and all his line. Aegisthus, the son of Thyestes, corrupted Clytaemestra, the wife of Atreus'
son Agamemnon, and with that cruel queen formed

the plot to kill the captain of the fleet and the commander at Troy when he should come home.

Aeschylus may well have preferred trilogies whose
parts were intimately connected in theme, for the
reason that his capital interest lay not with man but
with God's relation to man; and only in a drama of
the amplest scope could he find space to trace the
march of eternal justice through long reaches of time.
His successors, "matching drama against drama,"
adopted a smaller unit, the single play. To them the
single play offered a more limited artistic field, which
served them well for the portrayal of the emotional
reactions of the major personages and the transformation of their character under the stress of circumstance. Aeschylus may at times delay the
advance of the action because he desires opportunity
for portraiture; but he is not primarily concerned
with the reaction of events on human personality.
Nor does he show forth complete transformation of
character: it was not his purpose both to follow a
human soul through the various phases of its existence and at the end to depict the last day of a life
when all its issues are compressed into one great final
issue. It cannot be too insistently emphasized that
the personages of the Aeschylean drama, as they
disclose themselves within the limits of a single play,
do not really develop at all. Prometheus at the end,
when he is hurled to Tartarus, is only more defiant
than when he was fettered to the Scythian rock.
Eteocles at the outset is potentially the Eteocles of
the moment of the catastrophe. Despite the alluring
opportunity for presenting the evolution of personality in the course of a three-part drama, Aeschylus
did not let characters in the *Orestea* change much

even when they reappear in a later play. The sheer progression of time, the pressure of the storm and stress of life, alter the situation and are not without their proper effect on the moral constitution of the major dramatic personages. But their character is substantially static. Fixed in advance, it simply manifests itself; as is the case with the characters portrayed by Turgenieff.

Apart from the massed humanity of the chorus, the personages of Greek tragedy show marked differences of social station. On the one hand, there are people who, whatever they were in fact, are depicted as heroic characters, all of princely estate. On the other hand, there are the minor people, who range from councillors to slaves. Messengers and heralds tend to be pretty much the same in every play; they resist transformation into individuals. The messenger has a dash of humorous phrase; he has much to say; he clips off the syllabic augment. The herald apes his master: brutal master, brutal herald; pompous master, pompous herald. Aeschylus shows us the beginning of the art that was to give to humbler folk their proper right of individuality; and in so doing, to bring into higher relief the subordinates who were not merged into the choral group. Herein Euripides only followed the lead of his great predecessor.

Three of these minor personages in Aeschylus have acquired the distinction of human vitalities— the Watchman and the Herald in the *Agamemnon*, the Nurse in the *Libation-Bearers*.

The Watchman is sketched in a few bold lines. Weary of his task, fearful lest he close his eyes in sleep, he hums a stave to keep himself awake. He is

no mean judge of character: in a few words he stamps
the Queen—"woman in her hoping heart, man in
strength of purpose." He is well aware that something is rotten in the State of Argos. He dances with
joy when at last the long-expected beacon-fire blazes
out announcing the fall of Troy. He has thrown a
triple pair of sixes. Soon his beloved master will
come home—yet that homecoming is fraught with
dread for him. He could tell a tale, but "a great ox
stands on his tongue." He is the instrument whereby
Aeschylus (like Ibsen) starts his tragedy in the full
process of catastrophe. Mystery and a moral problem
confront us at the start.

It is the function of the Herald in the *Agamemnon*, as it is that of the Messenger in the *Persians*
and in the *Seven against Thebes*, to set forth events
antecedent to his arrival. But he alone of the three
is a real person, far more real too than the Herald
at the end of the *Seven*.

In moving speech he describes how he had never
hoped to see again his beloved Argos, in whose
kindly earth, all warring past, he may now repose in
peace. Safe returned, he is the forerunner (as he is
the epitome) of the conqueror of Troy. He magni-
fies the glory of his lord, "worthiest of honor of all
men that live;" yet thereby he unconsciously discloses a further incrimination of his king, already
incriminated because of his bloody deed at Aulis.
Agamemnon, sent by Zeus to be the minister of
justice on Priam's city, has leveled the altars of
Troy's gods. He has been guilty of the same offense
as Xerxes. Sacrilege is to be added to his account.
Nor is the Herald's tale without further tragic significance. He exults in his message of triumph; yet

he must unwillingly recount a visitation of Heaven's wrath: the tempest, which, in the night just passed, had raged on the Aegean and swept away a portion of the fleet. Menelaüs had been driven no man knows whither; but Agamemnon has been rescued by the favor of Savior Fortune—rescued to perish in his very home.

The King of Men has a small part in the drama that bears his name, but more rightly had borne the name of his wife. An address to the Elders in reply to their cautious greeting, an address to the Queen in answer to the outpouring of her unctuous salutation, a rapid colloquy in which he is speedily persuaded to submit to her will that he walk on costly tapestries strewn for his path, a prayer deprecating the jealousy of Heaven for the act—and all is done. One scene suffices; then a shriek when he is struck down by his wife.

English tragedy, with Homer, saw in Agamemnon the "magnanimous" leader, ready to "move the question of his place." That nobler aspect of his character, displayed in the satisfaction he offers to Achilles, could find no place in Aeschylus' tragedy. If he is there portrayed in bodily presence as courteous in his kingliness, kindly, beloved by his retainers and the servants of his house, the drama does not fail to discover the prince, as Homer also saw him, compacted of qualities unequal to the burden of his high station as commander of the fleet. Aeschylus represents him as ambitious, proud, weak of will, self-confident, self-duped. He who professes the skill to read men's purposes, is boundlessly ignorant of human nature. He sees himself, his authority, his greatness, always in the public eye. One thought

obsesses him, once he has returned home in triumph.
He it is who alone has conquered Troy. The gods
themselves were only his confederates in executing
justice on the guilty city. He disparages the loyalty
of all the other Grecian kings at Troy—Odysseus
alone excepted. He dwells throughout in unsus-
picious security though his very life hangs in the
balance. The Elders darkly warn him that all is not
well at home—these matters he will settle hereafter
at his leisure. Only his monstrous egotism prevents
him from penetrating the insincerity of his wife,
whose cozening words of affection mask her bloody
purpose. An unconscious hypocrite himself, he is
fooled by a hypocrite. No word is passed between
husband and wife concerning their daughter whom
he had slaughtered—no reproach, no censure. Were
Clytaemestra's design not already perfected, she had
not refrained from casting in his teeth a deed that
for her was the great justification of his taking-off.
For all his fair words on the hardships of a captive's
lot, he has no compunction to bespeak the care of his
unloved wife for his lovely captive who is to dwell
within her home. He would have his name seasoned
pious with the world's regard. He preaches on the
danger of excess, yet he surrenders himself to its
perils, hoping by invocation of Heaven to ward off
Heaven's wrath. He would be no Oriental potentate,
yet he consents, after a faint struggle, to walk on
purple to his palace home. Lord, if this be sin, pardon this my sin!

Agamemnon is cut down at the supreme moment
of his glory. Clytaemestra's ax gave him no pause
to take to himself the lesson of the poet that wisdom
comes through suffering by ordinance of God.

But Aeschylus has not failed to reconcile us to his awful eclipse. If Agamemnon does nothing, before our eyes, that morally justifies his murder, that moral justification is rooted in a foul deed of long ago and in his recent desecration of the temples of the city his arms had overthrown. There is one further incrimination that demands his punishment. He is responsible for the young lives destroyed in an unrighteous war. Countless Grecian homes have to mourn the loss of those they loved; they had sent them forth in their youthful bloom: they received back ashes in place of men. Mutterings fill the town: "our sons have fallen to avenge another's wife"— perfidious and adulterous Helen. Such inculpation of a commanding general is a novel argument in antiquity, and unusual even in modern times. But it is moral, not tragic, guilt, and therefore suited to the impassioned lyric reflection of the Chorus, but unsuited to dramatic argument. Nor does Aeschylus refer to it more than once.

It is not to be gainsaid that in the earlier plays of Aeschylus the action produces the character. In the *Agamemnon*, however, the tragic situation is controlled by character. The drama bears a title imposed by the hero's fame in Homer; but it is Clytaemestra who dominates the dramatic movement. Her character is the very pivot on which the action turns. Insignificant in the *Iliad*, her part in legend had been extended in the Peloponnese, until, together with Oedipus, she has become the supremely regnant personality of the Greek tragic drama.

Aeschylus might have followed the lead of Homer, and represented Agamemnon as slain by Aegisthus, who hated the King because he had corrupted the

King's wife and because of the wrong done his own father by Agamemnon's father; but in that case the theme of the drama had been a brutal murder done in part for revenge, but primarily for the possession of a woman and a throne. In that case Agamemnon's fall had awakened no other feeling than compassion. But in making the wife kill her husband, Aeschylus transformed the deed into a crime of tragic value.

As a great nature gone astray, the Queen must win at once our sympathy and our abhorrence; our sympathy, because of the provocation to her deed, our abhorrence, because of the deed's enormity.   In the part of the play preceding the murder, the Elders set forth, unconsciously to themselves, the main reasons that induce that crime; the latter part, which presents the deed as it reacts on herself, affords her scope to plead her cause with her own lips. But she must, by word as by deed, so remove herself from the sphere of sympathy that we may view with less repugnance the vigor of that primitive tribal law which surrendered her to the sword of her own son. The vengeance she has taken for herself must provoke vengeance on herself. Clytaemestra's purpose to kill her husband had been locked in her heart long before the tidings had been flashed across the Aegean that his coming was at hand. She will not recover from the past that moment when "duty and inclination came to the grapple" in her soul—the contest between her vanishing loyalty to her husband and her growing passion for Aegisthus. There is no recollection of the time when her moral sense refused to abandon the entrenchments which still defended her against the dire suggestion that only her husband's blood could atone for the blood of her daugh-

ter. In the years which followed the sacrifice of the
"much-wept" Iphigenia—years of solitary brooding,
relieved only by her incriminating association with
Aegisthus, she had nerved herself to an unswerving
purpose. Her lawless passion was indeed only
another form of her lust for vengeance. The night
that she was awakened by the loud huzzah of the
Watchman on her palace roof, she thrilled with the
hope that her vengeance awaited only the arrival of
the propitious hour. From the very moment that she
appears before us, she is a woman invincible in her
one resolve, swayed by no temporary infirmity of
purpose, by no "compunctious visitings of nature," a
creature of indomitable will, daemonic, the incarnation of inextinguishable hate. She hates her husband
the more because of her infidelity; but the supreme
passion of her being is to avenge the daughter in
whom all her maternal tenderness is centered. For
her other daughter the springs of a mother's love had
long run dry. Electra, the enforced witness of her
adulterous love, has been kenneled in the palace like
a dog. Agamemnon had betrayed the sacred name
of father, because, to charm the blasts of Thrace,
forsooth, he had sacrificed her Iphigenia whom she
had born in agony. The wrath of Artemis that
stayed the voyaging of the fleet—was it to hold the
counterpoise to her child's appeal for mercy? Often
had her child sung when men were gathered at her
father's hospitable board and with virgin voice had
been wont lovingly to do honor to her father's prayer
for blessing. That sweet mouth had felt the bit's
strong might to stay a cry that would have been a
curse upon her house. For ambition's sake, at the ur-
gency of the other kings bent on exacting vengeance

for faithless Helen, he had with his own hands taken the life of her "sweet flower," as if she had been a beast at the altar. On the mother's desire for vengeance for that unpardonable, unforgetable deed, lapse of time could work no impairment. When Clytaemestra's opportunity arrives with the coming of her detested husband, her part is not to undeceive him. She assumes those accents of affection that shall cajole him into crediting her wifely devotion; she must "bear welcome in her eye, and hand, and tongue"; in the presence of the Argive Elders she must school herself to the insincerity of protest that her womanly reserve must break down in the dear presence of her long absent lord. With a splendid realization of the force of common things she must tell of the long nights when the buzzing of the gnats made her a wakeful prey to fear for his safety. The fountain of her tears has run dry with weeping; her dreams have been haunted by visions of disaster to her beloved. She has yearned for him these long years, the seal of her wifely fidelity ever unbroken. And now he has come home! He is to be hailed as land descried by seamen beyond all hope, as dawn fair to look upon after storm, as gushing rill to wayfarer athirst. Were Agamemnon not so captive to a stupendous egotism, he might have noticed her effort to mark whether her treason is unknown to him, the nervous tension of her words, the half-stifled anxiety that no hint of her iron resolution may shape itself into a warning of his doom. But she winds about him coil after coil of her glittering rhetoric, in which reason holds its own as it librates with specious feeling. In Clytaemestra, emotion, will, and intellect are fused.

Tragedy sets forth the contest of opposing forces. Unnamed, but not unrecognized by Aristotle, the conflict of will lies at the very center of the art. Clytaemestra's conflict of soul—whether or not to kill her husband—has no place in Aeschylus' portraiture of the guilty Queen. She stands at the crisis of too "ancient a feud" now to recapture her ancient love. Her sanguinary resolve is determined in advance. In Aeschylus' earlier plays conflict is shown in its effects. The conflict in the *Agamemnon*, as in the other members of the trilogy, takes audible and visible form. In our play, when Clytaemestra comes to close contest with her husband's unwillingness to set his foot upon the rich tapestries through fear of the divine displeasure, she bends him to her imperious purpose—she will gain the wrath of God at his presumption as the moral confederate of her design. She has need of all her intellectual vigor lest she awaken any suspicion of her murderous purpose alike in the mind of her victim and in that of the Elders, who know her infidelity and must distrust her every act. Once the Elders had warned Agamemnon of his danger, but in terms too vague to arouse his suspicion. When Clytaemestra, luring him within the palace, had left the scene with her fateful appeal to Zeus, the Fulfiller, that he might fulfill her prayers, the Chorus might have intervened; but they are deterred by the thought that an Over-fate might yet rescue their master from the fate they apprehend as a deserved penalty for his past sin.

Clytaemestra is not only the intellectual author of the murder. She is also its physical executor. Revenge will not abandon one jot of its relish by relinquishing the weapon to the chances of her lover's

firmer hand nerved with its double cause for hate.
When the deed is done, the concentration of her
intellectuality does not desert her. There is no tran-
sition to contrition, no spasm of moral anguish, no
collapse to womanly weakness provoked by horror
of the sight of her husband gasping forth his life.
With the spurts of her husband's blood upon her
forehead, she disclaims all guilt, she urges her case
even on legal grounds. Elemental pity has no part in
the framework of a woman of such terrific violence.
Her ferocious joy is appalling.

> I smote him, twice; and with the second groan
> He sank: and when he had fallen, I gave a third
> Last stroke, to crown the sacrifice, and grace
> Pluto, preserver of the dead. Even then,
> His soul on wing for Hades, his keen breath
> Smote me with drops of slaughter, whose dark dew
> Refreshed my spirit, even as the bladed corn
> That swells to the ear, delighteth in heaven's rain.[1]

Though the Elders are conscious that their master
was not void of offense, they marvel at her inhumanity. His murderess must be a daimon, some unearthly
power that has fallen upon the house of Atreus and
upon her and her sister Helen, to have worked such
monstrous evil. Clytaemestra snatches at the
thought. She would assume an identity in whose
occupancy her proper self has been surrendered:
"Say not that I am Agamemnon's wife. I have only
taken on her semblance. I am in truth the ancient
evil genius of Atreus, of him who prepared that grim
feast." Her deed is thus to her a further act of an
avenging Nemesis; herself, a minister of the justice
of God. By her hand Agamemnon expiates at once

---

[1] *Agam.* 1384-1392, translated by Campbell.

his own sin and the sin of his father—both bound in
the fatal net of destiny. To Clytaemestra it is not
moral obliquity, but a moral principle, that impelled
her to the deed.

The voice of an accusing conscience does not
sound for her. If, toward the end, she bends, it is
not to break. No repentant horror and anguish overwhelm her as they do Lady Macbeth. For a moment
the heroine of Shakespeare remains a Clytaemestra:
she has the courage to enter the room where Duncan
lies murdered and to order the execution of the
grooms that she may ensure the prize of her ambition. But her assurance cannot maintain itself; her
conscience shatters her soul; despair plunges her into
the terrors of remorse without repentance. Clytaemestra is not to be undone by any recoil from her
insurrection against the laws of God. No desire for
"sovereign sway and masterdom" actuates her as it
did Lady Macbeth. She is the spirit of revenge
incarnate. But when that revenge is accomplished,
then she professes to be content if now she may make
a compact with the daimon that it quit the house
and ravage some other race. Now that she has her
lover, with her throne, she feels that blood has reaped
a sufficient harvest.

Time was to work some alteration in the spirit of
this masterful woman; but remorse was never to be
a tenant of her soul. In the *Agamemnon* she had
made light of dreams. In the *Libation-Bearers* she is
assailed in sleep by the wrathful spirit of her
murdered husband. Defiant once, now she knows
terror, terror without repentance. Yet, when herself
caught in the toils of Fate, she loses none of that
manly vigor which once had nerved her arm. With

the avenger close upon her, she does not falter.
"Quick! an ax!"—the ax that had laid Agamemnon
low. In the *Eumenides* her very ghost is the unsubstantial counterfeit of herself in the *Agamemnon*.
Her audacious resourcefulness does not abandon her:
alive she had sought to placate with offerings the
Erinyes of Agamemnon; now, a wraith among the
dead, she entreats the dread goddesses to avenge
her, slain by her own son, and still unavenged.
Clytaemestra is always the expression of an inner
necessity of her being.

But her ferocity, her cynical brutality, or even
her double sin, cannot utterly alienate our sympathy.
Absolute moral condemnation of the offense still
leaves room for a certain mental admiration of the
offender. Her limitless hypocrisy, her cunning in
equivocation, her double-faced prayers dazzle by
their very intellectual audacity. Man is somehow
made as to be unable to withhold his interest from
the most designing villain if only nature has endowed
him with high intellectual powers. But with Clytaemestra, it is also her very wrongs, so fiercely avenged,
that plead in her behalf. Outraged in her motherhood, she is no moral monster. Greek tragic art
would have recoiled before a Vittoria Corumbona,
as it would have recoiled before an Iago. Clytaemestra had not sinned for sheer lust of earthly
power: she had sinned because she had been struck,
where woman is most vulnerable, in her heart. There
yet lingers about her some faint scent of a nobler
nature before she fell a victim to Titanic passions.
The chalice of her womanhood, designed to hold love,
had, by the mischance of things and her own imper-
fect nature, become the receptacle of hate.

Nor must it be forgotten that she cherished
affection for the partner of her crime. In her loneliness during those long years in which her husband,
the slayer of her child, was warring far from home,
she had listened to the whisperings of a lover. In
conjunction with him she would fulfil the curse
resting on her husband's house. But the ancient
poet will not, like some modern reworkers of the
myth, destroy her love by making her realize that
Aegisthus' passion for her was a mere mask to cover
his design of taking vengeance upon her husband
because of Thyestes' curse of Atreus and his line.
Nor will the ancient poet, like Alfieri, picture her as
transported by passion for her lover. Aeschylus left
it for Bodmer to represent the guilty pair as cooing
like turtledoves, according to Heinemann. As
Aeschylus paints her in the *Agamemnon*, it was lust
for vengeance that swayed her being, rather than
criminal passion, which Pindar does not minimize as
the alternative motive prompting her murderous
deed. Clytaemestra's passion may not be refined
away. But she controls it. She makes no denial of
her love for Aegisthus, but her intrigue is not expressly mentioned until after the murder of her
husband is accomplished. Then, rallying her grounds
of assurance, she declares that "Hope does not tread
for me the halls of fear, so long as the fire upon my
hearth is kindled by Aegisthus, loyal to me as in days
gone by. For he is to me no slight shield of confidence." Her heart is wrung when he is slain: "Art
thou dead, valiant Aegisthus, my beloved?" Strange
indeed that Clytaemestra should have given herself
to such a man, a skulking coward, a poltroon, an
insulter of the dead, not "the twentieth part the

tithe" of her husband. But the ways of imperious women are all their own. It was the fate of each of Atreus' sons to be inferior to his wife, the fate of the polluter of Agamemnon's house to be inferior to him whom he supplanted.

The spiritual ancestor of Greek tragedy in its description of character was Homer. The epic poet cares more for the actor than for the action, yet his personages tend to be typical, though he has large opportunity to show them in different crises of their fortunes in war and peace. Within the few hours at his command, the tragic poet has to compass a human personality, and in that brief space of time he must place the crisis of a whole life. For tragedy is an epitome of life, of life at its maximum tension, and so disposed as to present an image of ideal sorrow. We moderns do not hold with Aristotle that the most fruitful means to secure that end is concentration on plot, with portraiture of character involved therein but subordinate thereto. We are much less concerned with what the hero does than how and why. We have now come to the pass where we would anatomize a human personality, penetrate to the remotest springs of action, illuminate the darkest recesses of the soul; nay more, we seek to discover motives of which the dramatic agents were themselves unconscious. Nearest to the modern ideal, but far removed from the perverse pathology of the impressionists, are Clytaemestra and Oedipus. But with neither did the dramatic art of the Greeks fathom the infinite complexities of human life. Not that they were altogether ignorant that life is compacted of tangled purposes; that cross-currents of purpose drive man hither and thither, that he is forever battling with himself.

But their ideal would not suffer them to dwell too insistently on a divided aspect of personality lest they might thereby fail to secure totality of clear impression. The Greeks were haunted by the fear lest the beauty of the whole be surrendered to overemphasis on the beauty of the parts. In their reluctance to stress shades of character they are simply different from the moderns, at least when the moderns are themselves and not obedient servants of their Hellenic masters. And we must rejoice at the difference, not repine that the Tragic Three did not depict their greatest tragic personalities other than in forms of massive simplicity, precise yet grand.

If the moderns have broken, once and for all, with the noble simplicity and beauty which an earlier generation saw incorporated in the Greek ideal of humanity, their modernization of the personages of the Aeschylean drama is only a reflection of the particular age in which they lived. In their striving for a more intimate presentation of the impulses and reactions of human nature, they have transported into the ancient myth, now French gallantry, sense of dignity, and passion for intrigue; now, latest of all, German sexual psychology. We may not quarrel with attempts to picture the libration of emotion which sways Clytaemestra as she veers from love for her husband to the desire to take vengeance upon him; nor when her mother-love for Orestes battles with her love for Aegisthus; we may even suffer a transformation of the ancient motive so as to discover love between Clytaemestra and Electra. But the result has too often been purchased at the price of a self-contradiction in character. The clear image of the ancient heroine has been distorted by the play of too

many conflicting lights. At the very center of the
Greek fable lies Orestes' vengeance on his mother.
But in their desire to free the drama from so monstrous a crime as matricide, the moderns have recourse to expedients of every sort. Voltaire makes
Clytaemestra fall by the blow which Orestes intends
for her paramour. Bodmer will let Orestes order a
slave to kill his mother but later drags in the motive
of Apollo's command. Siegert lets her take poison.
Alfieri and Lemercier picture Agamemnon as killed
in his sleep. Tempeltey will have Clytaemestra married to Aegisthus after she has heard a rumor of
Agamemnon's death; when he unexpectedly appears,
she has no other choice than to kill one of her two
husbands, and then goes mad. In König's drama
both Clytaemestra and Cassandra are rivals in their
passionate love for Agamemnon. Hofmannsthal tears
a passion to tatters. His Clytaemestra is a nervous
wreck, sensual (as is even Electra), frantic through
terror at her dreams—a pathological subject, proving,
at least in this case (as Heinemann well says) the
truth of Goethe's famous saying that classicism is
healthy, romanticism sickly.—There still survives an
impenitent imbecility that discovers in Greek tragedy
only typical characters. Clytaemestra in Aeschylus is
not a typical character because she does not display
all the subtlety of an intricate human machine. She is
a living human personality compacted of intellect and
passion, whose bodying forth challenges the utmost
resources of the most practised actor's art.

No special emphasis is laid on the direct and
visible conflict of will between the Queen and the
Chorus on the one hand or between the Queen and
the King on the other hand. Yet the play contains a

conflict, different in type, more insistent, more profound; not baldly dramatic, as external action is
dramatic. It is the conflict in the soul of the Elders,
a conflict that finds a voice in a series of choral songs
whose intrinsic poetical quality and lofty religious
aspiration know no equal in the whole range of
ancient tragedy.

These old men of Argos have brought with them
from their youth a precept rooted in the immemorial
ethics of their race: the doer must suffer, he that
doeth wrong shall pay the penalty. And another
belief is there, not the current mint of the time: the
gods do not punish mere prosperity because of
jealousy lest mortal man aspire to their Olympian
felicity. It is man's own evil deed, not man's prosperity, that brings upon him the chastisement of
Heaven.

Not without a deeper reason than its sheer power
of compelling beauty did the poet make the Elders
recover in memory the scene at Aulis: Iphigenia, fair
as in a picture, her saffron robe falling about her feet,
her fair mouth gagged, she, Agamemnon's child, held
high over the altar of sacrifice,—a deed of blood by
which, forsooth, the father might still hold to his
leadership in the war waged against the guilty city
that harbored Helen. As surely as there are gods in
Heaven who have regard for mortal things (though
men deny it in their impiety), so surely had Priam
and the people of Priam to fall—the doer must
suffer. And yet, such is the mystery of God's way,
Troy that must fall through Agamemnon as executor
of God's justice, fell though that executor had sinned
against God's justice. So long as God sits on his
throne, Agamemnon must suffer.

Nevertheless, for all the unrighteousness of a war waged to regain a worthless wife; for all the warning of evil mixed with good in Calchas' prophecy when the army marched forth; for all the inhumanity of the father who slew his child; for all his security beneath Ilium's walls for ten long years; for all the storm raised against his home-voyaging fleet—nevertheless, the fact stands clear: Agamemnon is here at Argos, safe, returned triumphant, the champion of a cause to which the gods have lent their aid. Can such things be and there yet be a moral government in the world? The High God in whom all power and all justice is centered has proclaimed it to be a fixed law that he that hath done shall be done by. Do the gods on their awful seats look only to the justification of external success?

It is the antagonism of semblance and reality, the problem which later was to stir the schools, that is here given dramatic setting and perplexes the souls of these faithful servants of their King. Since their moral consciousness insistently demands a reversal of his fortune, at the moment of his apparent absolute security and of his utmost exaltation, a vague foreboding of his danger robs them of all perfect joy in his success. A sense of the contradiction between his triumph and his apparent immunity from the just anger of a righteous God broods over a scene resplendent in external glory—dramatic chiaroscuro of surpassing and awful intensity. Clytaemestra's ax brought fulfillment to the ordinance proclaimed of old, the ordinance that in turn was to surrender her to the avenging arm of her own son.

CHAPTER VII

THE ORESTEA: II. THE LIBATION-BEARERS

Greek tragedy sets forth no consistent belief in the immortality of the soul. At times it is strangely silent, at times it reflects the clarified belief of the Orphic mystics, at times it presents conceptions seemingly warring with each other. No creed, formulated by the religion of the State, regulated men's faith in the hereafter; nor did that religion seek to reconcile the contradictions of contemporary beliefs. For, as a former pupil of mine, Miss Goldman, has well said: "The Greeks of the fifth century, with a total disregard of that logic which only enters religion when the systematizing theologian begins to blur the traces of its manifold and unreconciled origins, thought of the dead as at once removed to the lower world and residing in their tombs."[1]

On the one hand, the sovereign authority of Homer made men cling to the notion that the souls of the dead, the vaporous semblances of life, abode in Hades once their earthly tenement had been consumed by fire. Until the body had been burned man's spirit found no rest. Patroclus slain in battle, Elpenor killed by accident, hover between the world of life and the world of death, and implore the living to give them the peace of a fixed abode. Better than the fluttering torment of the restless soul are the

---

[1] Dr. Hetty Goldman, "The *Orestea* of Aeschylus as illustrated by Greek Vase-painting," *Harvard Studies in Classical Philology*, vol. 21 (1910), p. 119.

dolorous regions of Hades, whence it may not pass to revisit the confines of the upper air. There it dwells, untended by the ministrations of its kindred on earth, and powerless to affect the living for weal or woe.

On the other hand, coexistent with this terrifying aspect of the future state of all mankind was another conception, older indeed than Homer and all but obliterated in the epic. Of this conception the *Orestea* is our most important witness. The soul is removed to the nether world, whose streams still retain their old names—Cocytus, the river of wailing; by Acheron, the river of woes, Iphigenia will meet her father and throw her arms about him. Yet at the same time the spirit is conceived as dwelling in or near the place of burial, whether the body had been burned or buried; for incineration and inhumation were both common in the classical age. The ghostly tenant of the tomb is dimly sensible of earthly things. The dull, cold ear of death may still be stirred by beating on the enclosing earth, by invocation, lamentation, and appeal for help. Even from the grave the soul has power to work good or ill; it receives with satisfaction the offerings of love; it lives so long as pious hands minister to its needs; and, if injury has been done to its body in life, it is unappeased until it is avenged.

The souls of men foully done to death are *alastores*, spirits of vengeance, that find no peace within their tomb; they pursue their murderers; they terrify them with horrid dreams. As Erinyes, they afflict with torture of mind and body even their nearest kindred who neglect the sacred offices of vengeance. 'Kinsman' and 'avenger' meet in the same word

in Hebrew and in Arabic; nor did Greek tribal custom
keep them separate. The murderer might seek to
cripple or destroy the ghostly power of his victim by
mutilation of his corpse before burial; for as was the
body in its last state on earth, so was its semblance
in the other world. After Clytaemestra had killed
Agamemnon, she cut off his hands and feet, placed
them beneath his armpits, and then buried the
mutilated corpse in dishonor, unattended by the
dutiful mourning of his people and by the presence
of his children. At least one purpose of the dis-
memberment was to coerce the spirit of her husband
so that, in this crippled state, he might not take
vengeance upon her. It was not the intention of the
murderess thereby to expiate her crime by a sin-
offering to the gods of the nether world; for the passage in Sophocles' *Electra* (vv. 445-446) to the effect
that Clytaemestra "in expiation" wiped the blood
spots from her sword upon the head of her victim
is to be interpreted as a symbolical transference of
her guilt to the murdered man.

The superstition connected with the mutilation
of murdered persons appears in divers forms in
antiquity and is widely known in relatively modern
times. In the sixteenth century there is a record
from Breslau that the hands, feet, and head of a
murdered man were cut off. In the eighteenth century an insurrection of the oppressed slaves in the
island of Jamaica was instantly suppressed by the
decapitation of the dead bodies. In the same century
the original inhabitants of Lower California first
broke the spines of the corpses, which they then
rolled up like a ball and threw into a ditch. A like

conception appears in the old custom of driving a stake through the body of a suicide.[2]

In effect, Clytaemestra thought by the mutilation of the body of her murdered husband to prevent his ghost from taking the form of a were-wolf or vampire. Significant as is the *Libation-Bearers* for this aspect of Greek popular belief, it is still more significant for the conception that, even if the spirit of the dead did not quit the tomb, it was still charged with power. Disintegration of the body on the funeral pyre or in the grave did not impair its ghostly influence. No passage from ancient Greek literature rivals the importance, on this score, of the declaration of the Chorus to Orestes as they stand by the tomb of Agamemnon:

> My child, the ravening jaw of fire doth not quell the consciousness of the dead, but he bewrayeth thereafter what stirreth him. The slain man hath his dirge, the guilty man is revealed.

This belief is of the time of the poet, not consciously recovered by him from the heroic age.

Oracles play a large part in the supernatural machinery of Sophocles. Aeschylus sets great store by dreams. In the night before the opening of the play a wild cry of terror rang through the palace of Agamemnon. So awful a dream had visited Queen Clytaemestra that the very hair of her head stood erect through horror. In her sleep she fancied that she had given birth to a snake. She wrapped it in swaddling-clothes, as if it had been a child; she gave the hateful thing to suck; it bit her breast, so that

---

[2] See Kittredge, "Arm-Pitting among the Greeks," *American Journal of Philology*, vol. 6 (1885), pp. 151-169.

it drew in a clot of blood together with the mother's milk. With a scream she awoke.

In the castles of Mycenaean princes dwelt seers and interpreters of dreams. Clytaemestra's dream was read for her: a soul beneath the earth is wroth against them who had brought him to his death. Her iron will, or trivial distractions, might banish by day the dread visitations that beset a guilty soul. Night took its revenge.

Foreboding evil, but not from Orestes, to whom her dream also looked, the Queen resolves to placate the angry spirit of her husband, and to this end orders Electra, her maltreated daughter, and her slave-woman to bear libations to be offered at Agamemnon's tomb. Not that her conscience was smitten— she and her lover are triumphant, their success is even "as a god" in their sight. She is "still possessed of those effects" for which she murdered her husband. Unrepentant, her soul still stained with her crime, enjoying the fruit of her lawless love and lawless power, her son Orestes dispossessed of the throne of his father, the "godless woman" makes others offer the sacrifice she herself had rightly offered had she been stirred by the voice of conscience. Terror alone moves her, terror of the unplacated spirit of her murdered husband whose proper avenger still lives in the person of her son, Orestes, an exile from home.

That very day, by the dispensation of Providence, Orestes, now grown to manhood, returns to his native Argos in company with his kinsman Pylades the Silent, like himself the emissary of the Delphic God. He places a lock of his hair upon the tomb of his father: he had not been there to lament when his

father's corpse had been carried forth for burial—
now he will offer the mournful tribute of a son's
affection. He has come a willing visitant to the spot:
"O Zeus, grant me thy aid that I may avenge my
father's death!" He recognizes Electra, conspicuous
by her garb of mourning among her attendant
women—Greek captives taken by Agamemnon long
years before. She and they have come as unwilling
visitants to the same spot. Standing apart, Orestes
listens as his sister struggles to frame a fitting prayer
to accompany the libations which she, the true
mourner, has been commanded to make to the dead
by her mother who feigned the spirit of mourning.
She will not say that the offerings come from a
loving wife to a loving husband; she cannot pray that
her father's spirit return good for evil. The women,
who have the part of confidants, help her to her
intent. They do not scruple to suggest that she
make entreaty for the presence of one who shall take
life for life; a prayer from which she at first recoils
as unrighteous. At last, she converts the propi-
tiation sought by Clytaemestra into an explicit
appeal to the departed spirit of her father and to the
lords of the nether world—that Orestes may come
home, that she herself may be more pure in heart,
more innocent in hand, than she who bears the name
of mother; and that an avenger may appear. "Do
thou, O my father, send forth good with the help
of the gods, of Earth, and of Justice crowned with
victory!"

Amid their tears the Chorus pour their libations,
charged with this intent, upon the tomb. Meantime
Electra has discovered the lock of hair—it is like in
color to her own. Her heart dances with fear, she is

beside herself with hope. It must be a lock from her dear Orestes' head—he has sent it from afar!

Ah me! If only, like a messenger, it had a kindly voice, that I might no more be tossed by my distracted thoughts—but might plainly have bid me to spurn away this lock, had it been severed from a hated head; or, if it claim kin to me, have shared my grief, an adornment to this tomb and tribute to our sire.

Soon she observes indications of his actual presence.

I am in agony, my brain is in a whirl.

The next moment Orestes stands before her. Tremulous to her hope, she is rent by doubt. Then, surrendering to the evidence of yet other tokens, she clasps him in her arms:

O thou fond presence that hath for me four parts of love! For father I needst must call thee; and to thee falls the love I should bear my mother—she whom I most rightly hate—and the love I bore my sister, victim piteously sacrificed, and as brother thou ever hast been my trust and thou alone didst show respect to me.

Intent on another dramatic goal than his successor, Aeschylus only adumbrates the personality of the woman who was to appear as the protagonist heroine of Sophocles. To the older poet, Electra is a truly womanly character, compacted of a sense of religious awe, of fury against those she hates, and of exquisite tenderness for the dead and the living whom she loves.

Now that brother and sister are reunited at last, it is the part of Orestes to appeal to Zeus to behold the pitiable estate of Agamemnon's children; then to set forth the commission to avenge his father's death laid upon him by Apollo, together with the warning

of the god that if he prove recusant to his duty of
vengeance, the Furies of his father will blast his mind
and waste his body.—Orestes, the human instrument of the divine vengeance, his more passionate
sister, and the Chorus now take their stand about
the grave of Agamemnon, and pour forth responsive
strains designed to pierce the earth and rouse to fury
the entombed spirit of the dead. They call upon him
to behold his suppliant offspring; they implore him
to compassionate the intolerable misery of his house.
In the *Persians* incantation had raised Darius from
the grave; here, though the actual apparition of
Agamemnon is once invoked, it is rather his ghostly
confederation that is besought by lamentation and
entreaty.

External action follows hard upon the litany of
incantation which has supplied the psychological
motive force: the dramatist has learned the art of
gathering tragic impetus as he advances nearer to
the crisis. Orestes, instructed by the Chorus as to
his mother's dream, interprets it to the prospering of
his purpose, and immediately proceeds to devise a
plan of action on the part of the several conspirators.
Here, in its faint beginnings, is dramatic 'intrigue,'
which, springing from the interest of curiosity, has
been claimed to be the peculiar possession of the
modern drama.

Electra is to keep on the watch within the palace.
The Chorus, of necessity present on the scene, is now
to keep silent, now to speak as the occasion demands.
Orestes and Pylades, disguised as strangers from
Phocis and imitating the dialect of Parnassus, are to
seek entrance. If Orestes finds Aegisthus seated on
his father's throne, with one fell blow he is to strike

him dead, before he can come to speech. (For it is
not only because Aegisthus is physically the more
dangerous enemy that he must first be attacked: the
poet designs to make the more ignoble criminal fall
first.) But the plot, thus arranged by Orestes in a
species of interior prologue, is countered by events.
He has not weighed every possible eventuality—too
scrupulous prevision had been pedantic; so that an
element of surprise is clearly not foreign to Aeschylean technique, as some critics would have us assume.
—The two men are admitted as travelers seeking
shelter for the night. But, instead of finding Aegisthus as Orestes had anticipated, they are received by
Clytaemestra, who courteously offers them hospitable entertainment. Apparently on the spur of
the moment, certainly feigning ignorance of the
identity of his hostess, Orestes concocts the tale that
he is the bearer of evil tidings. On his way to Argos
he had fallen in with Strophius, who had requested
him to carry to Argos news of Orestes' death. Now
this Strophius might have been expected himself
to take the initiative in reporting the news of
Orestes' death; for to him, an ally, Clytaemestra,
just before the homecoming of Agamemnon, on the
pretext that she was fearful for her husband's life,
had sent her infant son. The mother hears the
report of the pretended messenger with an outburst
of grief; if feigned throughout, it is a marvelous
counterfeit of sincerity; if compacted of duplicity and
sincerity voicing itself in irony, it is the expression
of a double self—mother at heart, but murderess,
rejoicing at her release from the danger of vengeance
at the hands of him from whom alone vengeance was
due. But Clytaemestra, though thus affected, will

not withhold the promised hospitality. She directs
the strangers to the rooms reserved for guests, hides
the fact that Aegisthus is not at home, and, ever
cautious, dispatches Orestes' aged Nurse (strange
messenger indeed), to fetch Aegisthus with all speed
—man's keener judgment must sift the tale. It looks
as if Orestes were himself entrapped. But his cause
is furthered by no direct action on his part. From
the Nurse, a barbarian and a slave, who sheds tears
of sorrow that had not fallen from a mother's eyes,
the Chorus learn that the Queen is concealing her joy
beneath a mask of grief. Her mission to Aegisthus is
to take the message that he come with a bodyguard—
the Queen's mind is tense with suspicion. Intimating
that all is not as the Nurse imagines with regard to
the death of Orestes, the Chorus enter into the action
as direct participants, persuade her to alter the message and tell her hated master to come unattended
and without alarm. Aegisthus arrives, feigning sorrow at the sad news—but he will probe the matter
for himself. The Chorus do not deny that they have
heard of the report made by the strangers, but urge
him to go within to question them. Incautiously,
despite his boasted caution, he enters: the Chorus
wait in an agony of expectation—a scream of death
agony! A man-servant dashes in: "Aegisthus is
dead. Unbar the door to the women's rooms!
Where's Clytaemestra? Her life is near the razor's
edge." Only the fewest words are needed to picture
the intensity of the moment before the actual crisis.
Clytaemestra rushes in, hears from the servant the
cry "the dead are slaying the living," no cryptic
words to her whose dream had warned her to beware
the spirit of her murdered husband. "By guile we

are to perish even as we slew. Give me a battle-ax, some one, and quick! Let us know if we conquer or are conquered." Orestes enters. He wastes no words.

Thou art the very one I seek. He yonder—he has had enough.

Woe's me! Art thou dead, my valiant Aegisthus, my beloved?

Thou lovest the man? Then in the same grave thou shalt lie and never shalt thou play the traitress to him in death.

Hold, my son! Have pity, child, upon this breast, at which full oft, slumbering the while, with toothless gums thou didst suck the milk that nourished thee.

Pylades, what shall I do? Shall I for pity spare my mother?

What then becomes henceforth of Loxias' oracles, declared at Pytho, and of our covenant pledged on oath? Hold all the world thy foe rather than the gods.

I judge thee victor; then counsellest me well. (*To Clytaemestra*) Come with me. By his very side I do will to slay thee. And since, while he lived, thou heldest him a better man than my sire, sleep with him in death, since he is the man thou lovest, but hadst hate for him whom thou wast bound to love.

But it was I who nourished thee, and with thee I would grow old.

What! Slay my father, and then make thy home with me?

Fate, my child, must share the blame for this.

Then it is Fate that hath worked this thy doom likewise.

Hast thou no awe of a parent's curse, my son?

Thou gavest me birth and yet didst cast me out to misery.

Nay, surely I cast thee not out in sending thee to the house of an ally.

I was vilely sold, son though I was of a freeborn sire.

Where then is my price I got for thee?

Shame forbids that I should reproach thee with that outright.

Nay, but fail not to proclaim likewise the follies of that father of thine.

Accuse him not who ever labored whilst thou wast
sitting idle at home.

It is a cruel thing, my child, for women to be deprived
of a husband.

Aye, but it is the husband's toil that supports them the
while they sit at home.

Thou art resolved, it seems, to slay thy mother, child.

'Tis thou wilt slay thyself, not I.

Take heed, beware the sleuth-hounds that avenge a
mother.

But my father's—how shall I escape them, if I leave
this deed undone.

Still living, meseems, I sing a dirge beside my tomb in
vain.

Even so, since it is my father's fate that marks out this
doom for thee.

Ah me! This is the serpent that I bare and nourished.

Aye, true prophet in sooth was the terror of thy dream.
Thou slewest whom thou shouldst not; so suffer what
should not be.

The play has been called statuesque, its personages
carved, as it were, out of marble. But here at the
culminating point is action, charged with pathos,
concentrated, pitiable, terrible. The poet, whose
capital concern is to envisage the divine regulation
of the world, has a superb "sense of the theater" for
striking dramatic effect. The scene where son encounters mother is thrilling. Aeschylus made it
moving as well as thrilling: for emotional and thrilling
effect are far from being identical. Involuntarily
there rises before our mental vision another scene,
the scene where another mother must hear from her
son words that are daggers to her soul. But Hamlet's
mother is not Clytaemestra. In the very crisis of
her fate, Orestes' mother, now utterly sincere, is a
suppliant for the mercy she had not shown to others.
Her old intellectual resourcefulness does not abandon
her. Defeated at one point, she grasps at other argu-

ment. Uncontrite, though unfaithful, she urges the infidelities of Agamemnon. She would have the same standard for women as for men. Her *ultima ratio*, a mother's curse, when parried by her son's like urgent plea, the vengeance of his father's shade, leaves her without hope. In life she must lament her own doom.

Deliberate murder of a mother was no more common in Ancient Greece than in modern times; yet in Greek tragedy it could be represented only up to the moment of the actual killing; and even there only because it was a link in the chain of fate and so integral a portion of the myth that it might not be set aside by any freedom of the poet's art. Modern sensibilities, recognizing no such prescriptive authority of the myth or of fate to lessen the revolting horror of the deed, evade, as best they may, the dreadfulness of the catastrophe; with the result that only on the ancient stage are we confronted by a spectacle as imperative to the ancient drama as was, in the far-off times it reproduced, the obligation to take blood for blood, even a mother's blood.

Effective as is the thrust and parry of debate between mother and son, it is strange that Clytaemestra does not have recourse to an argument vital here to her defense as it was to her plea in the *Agamemnon:* "Thou wouldst slay me," she might have urged, "because I slew thy father; yet he slew my child." To that plea of justification no answer was returned by the Chorus in the earlier play; nor could an answer here be forthcoming, at least in such form that it would not relax the tension of the terse debate. Aeschylus in fact will not let human nature hold its course. He suffers Clytaemestra to weaken her own case that he may strengthen her son's case. He

would render the deed less abhorrent than if the son
had forced death upon his mother while her impassioned and unanswerable charge against his
father was still ringing in his ears.

Upon the main crisis of the play, the main crisis
likewise of the whole trilogy, there follows, as in the
Agamemnon, first the reaction of the deed upon the
dramatic personages, then the close with its own
crisis. The Chorus coördinate the present with the
past. Justice has brought punishment upon the sons
of Priam. Justice, breathing wrath upon her foes,
has lent her aid in the battle waged in Agamemnon's
house. "Raise a shout of triumph! Up ye walls, too
long have ye lain prostrate. Lo! the light has come."

On the spot where Clytaemestra stood when she
exulted over Agamemnon's corpse and pleaded her
right of vengeance, Orestes now takes his stand, the
two dead bodies at his feet. In justification of his
right of vengeance he spreads forth, for the all-seeing
Sun to behold, the blood-stained robe wherein his
mother had entangled her victim and then struck him
down. His speech writhes with the struggle to find
words adequate to brand her and her crime.

The mental strain begins to overpass his power of
endurance, his wits begin to wander; yet, with the
expiring effort of his conscious mind, he passionately
proclaims the justice of his cause, invoking the
behest of Loxias that acquits him of guilt. To the
shrine of the god, his champion, he will go in order
to be freed from his misery. For, lo! in frenzied
fancy, he beholds spectral figures—dark-robed shapes
with coiling snakes like unto Gorgons. "They are
my mother's vengeful hounds. God Apollo! They
come on in swarms, and from their eyes oozes horrid

blood." He rushes from the scene. To the Chorus
the visitation of the Furies is a fancy of the disordered brain of Orestes; and so the Queen in *Hamlet* discovers in the spectral apparition of her husband
only the idle fancy of her son.

Inferior to the *Agamemnon* in wealth of lofty
ideas, in sustained intensity of emotion; inferior to
the *Eumenides* in sweep of imagination, the *Libation-
Bearers* presents many aspects of interest peculiarly
its own. I propose to consider briefly only three of
these: (i) the command laid on Orestes to kill his
mother; (ii) the invocation of the spirit of Agamemnon; and (iii) the madness of Orestes.

i. Murder in sight of the spectators in the Greek
theater was forbidden by a sense of artistic propriety
coöperating with, or induced by, the fact of the
physical difficulties. Violent bodily agitation dis-
turbs the serenity of statuesque beauty; the actor,
by reason of his costume, was relatively immobile.
But it was not enough for Greek art thus to be safe-
guarded from the brutality of the modern stage. If
the last limits of terror were not to be overpassed and
the deed itself made visible, aesthetic and dramatic
reasons alike demanded such a representation of the
impelling motives that the intolerable horror of the
crime of matricide should be softened to terror and
pity. In the *Agamemnon* the wife did not inculpate
her husband before killing him—her unappeasable
hatred had no need to find voice; in the *Libation-
Bearers* the mother must be stabbed by her son's
words before his sword stabs her breast. Orestes'
exasperation, already fired by the appeal to his
father's spirit at the tomb, must be so rekindled that
Clytaemestra may be forced to quit the world of the

living with her offenses to the dead steeling her son's
purpose to the very end. Yet, despite the passion
of the moment when mother and son confront each
other, each the incarnation of a moral cause, a certain
softening of violent agitation marks the scene as it
draws to an end. One emotion gives place to another
—rage, irony, pity, incrimination, excuse; but at the
end Orestes has won a calmness that discloses him as
the instrument of destiny, a destiny that makes his
vengeance violate one of the holiest sanctions of
human nature.

It would be impertinent here to stress the divergence between ancient and modern tragic art. The
ancients attained effects grander and more terrible
by the very directness of profound emotion. Religious horror, fright, terror, give place in modern
times to greater excitement through libration of
hope and fear; stateliness surrenders to surprise,
simple action to intrigue, expectation to curiosity.
We must let each art stand for itself, and rejoice at
the difference; for each is an epitome of life in different ages and under different suns.

No modern dramatist would fail to picture a
struggle in the soul of Orestes, as in the soul of
Electra, before they resolve upon so repellent a deed
as matricide; and no modern dramatist would let
slip the moving opportunity to portray at large the
tumult of the son when, with bared breast, his mother
implores his mercy. But Aeschylus makes short work
of the scene. Dealing primarily with the catastrophe,
Aeschylus presents the hero with purpose unfalter-
ingly fixed at the outset. In the opening scene
Orestes appears before us resolved to avenge his
father; nor was Clytaemestra's purpose to take

vengeance on Iphigenia's father formed any the less
in advance. At the very center of interest lies, to
Aeschylus, not the struggle in Orestes' soul but the
impulsions to his resolve and the manner of its
accomplishment; in fact, had the poet not reverted
to the older style of entitling his plays after the
chorus, the *Libation-Bearers* might well have borne
the name of its proper hero.

In a lengthy speech, not altogether free from suspicion of interpolation, the young Prince himself
marshals the inducements to his purposed act. It is
well to mark the order of their presentation. First
and foremost, the charge, laid upon him by the god
of the Delphic oracle, to requite blood with blood.
With the important acting of this dread command
are at once associated the penalties of refusal, penalties proceeding from the Furies of his father: the
wrathful visitation of the infernal powers, leprosy,
frenzy, vain terrors of the night, and outlawry of
man and god—he shall have no part in the mixing-
bowl or in libations to the gods; no altar shall receive
him; no one shall harbor him; friendless and dishonored, he shall waste away to a cruel death.
In Apollo is concentrated not the power himself to
launch upon Orestes these afflictions, but the
prophetic knowledge that they will descend upon
him if he prove recreant to the claim of blood for
blood. The anathema of the mediaeval church cannot rival the congregated horrors to be visited upon
a son neglectful of the ghostly claims of a father's
vengeance. This Apollo is a priest of terror.

In second line stand other propulsions to the
deed. Orestes has been robbed of his heritage, and
lives in destitution (an idea already expressed in his

preceding prayer to Zeus); his fellow-citizens, the most renowned of mankind, conquered Troy, yet have been made subject to usurpers, women both of them—for at heart Aegisthus is but a woman. Now these latter arguments are only contributory to the religious motive. Orestes exhausts resource to set forth the difficulty of other choice. He stands under the independent compulsion of a god and he is subject to the punitive power of his father's manes— religious authority on the one hand, fear on the other hand, with the utmost stress laid on the appalling consequences of unfilial conduct. His determination to vengeance was not formed, as some critics would have it, under the primary impulse of self-seeking motives to gain his throne, to better his and his sister's estate, or even to free his country from disgrace. The religious inducement has precedence in place and weight; but even it is not to be interpreted as a mere symbol of an inner conviction on the part of Orestes that he cannot evade the call to perform a sacred duty. He is above all the minister of Apollo who, of his own prompting, proclaimed alike the necessity and the righteousness of retribution.

The physical and mental harassments to be visited on Orestes should he refuse to kill his father's murderess seem to derive from a double source. On the one hand, the threatened assaults of Agamemnon unavenged wear the aspect of religious consciousness. On the other hand, social consciousness appears to underlie Orestes' outlawry by mankind. Aeschylus' coördination of the two opens up the vast perspective of their primitive relation, one of the profoundest problems in the history of the development of human thought. Did the voice of the god of Delphi wait

upon the voice of man—that is, in Greece did religion
come to deal with bloodshed only after secular custom, not yet hardened into law, had included that
crime within its domain? Or did the Apolline cult
as such impose its prescriptions by virtue of sanctions established without pressure from without?
In the Middle Ages at least, social outlawry proclaimed by the vicar of Christ was the expression of
ecclesiastical theory that had won authority. But
such large issues we must resign to Westermarck and
other students of the development of moral ideas.

One aspect of the 'secular,' or social, punishment
that would fall on Orestes if he disobeyed the command to avenge his father's murder is so remarkable
as to deserve here at least the notice of a passing
word. If the son, who inherits from his father the
duty of vengeance as he inherits his property, fails
to acknowledge the obligation due a parent from his
offspring, then the 'unseen wrath' of Agamemnon
has the power to inflict on Orestes the very same
penalties that would have been visited on him had he
himself been guilty of bloodshed—the sin of omission
swings even in the balance with the sin of commission.
Whosoever steeps his hands in blood and therewith
brings pollution upon the land wherein he dwells, he
is to be driven forth as a thing defiled. No man shall
give him lodging, no man shall give him place at his
festive board. He is a thing accursed, upon whom
has descended the ban of social outlawry. In such
pitiable case stands poor Orestes: whether he slay his
mother or not, the punishment is the same.

ii. To the speech of Orestes detailing the impulsions to his purposed deed succeeds a scene un-
paralleled in all ancient tragedy, a scene unique alike

in its content and in its structural form. The invocation of the departed spirit of Agamemnon by his
children and by the Chorus at his tomb touches the
most intimate religious beliefs of the Greeks. It occu-
pies almost one-fifth of the entire drama. It is a
massive lyric, complex and simple alike, as is the
symmetry of the pedimental groups in a Doric
temple. As to the right of the central point in the
gable-field, figures are placed which balance each
other both in their immediate grouping and in correspondence to similar figures to the left; so with the
elaborate correspondence of the parts sung by
Orestes, Electra, and the Chorus in the *kommos*.

With the mutual recognition of brother and sister
the drama had advanced to a critical point where
the modern dramatist might have paused to depict
a struggle in the soul of Orestes before he proceeded
to the execution of his purpose, and let him contem-
plate the horrors of the deed to which he is impelled
by the inducements he had just assembled in detailed argument. But the delay might not be for long.
Resolve must be followed by action. To the critics
of the extreme French school who insist on the
necessity of an uninterrupted march of the dramatic
action toward its logical goal, the immensely extended tripartite center of the play appears as an
absolutely useless episode and designed, as one of
that school expresses himself, merely to afford the
audience occasion for aesthetic delight in harmonious
effusions and abundant imagery. The truth lies
rather on the side of Schlegel, to whom the cessation
of sensible progression in the action marks "a true
internal perfection: it is the stillness of expectation
before a tempest or an earthquake;" an interpreta-

tion which appears in a more persuasive form in Conington. To that great English scholar, the scene at the tomb of Agamemnon is not

in the poet's view a suspension of the action, but a part of the action itself. It is not merely an impassioned lyric, awakening successively the various tones of human feeling, but . . . an actual agent, conducting the inquisition for blood, assembling the succours under ground, and bringing on the destined hour, which, long fixed, has been waiting its summons.

We do not gainsay this verdict, yet at the same time it is not to be maintained that the absence of complication which marks the play is not here responsible for some portion of the prolongation of the scene. The poet, even in the period of his maturest art, has not completely succeeded in overcoming the difficulty presented by the necessity of filling an approximately given time with matter free from undue repetition of ideas. As he did not develop to any great length the course of events before the double murder, he was obligated to expand the central portion. If the expansion appears oppressive to the modern reader, it is oppressive only before he has entered into the genius of so moving a scene. No part of ancient Greek tragedy is in fact so removed from modern religious beliefs and observances, and for this reason so difficult to endue with the imaginative sympathy necessary for the perfect understanding of its varied pathos. We must compel our interest in a sacramental rite which is almost as foreign to our immediate moral prepossessions as is the exorcising of an evil spirit in the superstitious belief of Modern Greece. The scene is animated by a vital belief that the world of the quick may enter into actual communion with the world of the dead, that the departed spirit of loved ones is capable of being animated by the pious offices of living kinsmen. In the second place, modern tragic drama, lacking the elasticity of its ultimate Hellenic original, does not thus freely pass into oratorio or opera. Nor is the form of the cantata found in Bach's passion-music a fair parallel. Ancient tragedy, in many respects so much more simple than modern tragedy, is in fact also more complex. Song and dance were not mere ornamental additions; they were as essential to the nature of the ancient drama as the dialogue itself.

Orestes' intention to kill his mother and her lover was not formed in the course of the dramatic action; it was fixed at the very beginning of the play; whereas Hamlet has to hear from his father's ghost the crime that is his incitement to the slaying of his uncle. Greek tragedy tends to indicate the sequel at the start. The tenacity of Orestes' purpose was not relaxed when he stands nearer to its accomplishment. He has gained as his confederate his sister and he can count on the coöperation of her attendants, filled as they are with an even bitterer hate of the Queen and her lover. No infirmity of will stays Orestes' hand. He is not to be the fickle slave of favoring chance.

But Aeschylus will not have his hero stride at once to the execution of his purpose. He delays all physical action that he may portray emotion in its amplest form. Once Orestes' motives have been mustered in formal argument, they must seek reinforcement through lyric passion. His fury is thereby aroused, but there is no indication that his purpose had been blunted by any terror of the deed, no indication that he recoils in horror from his purpose to take the life of her to whom he owes his life. Aeschylus employs a different form of pathos, a somber pathos of which he was a master. The encounter between mother and son is relatively brief, and calm by reason of passion in part suppressed. But that scene is preceded and followed by the display of emotion unrestrained. At the grave of his father Orestes is made aware of everything that has happened in his absence. He, his sister, and the Chorus denounce Agamemnon's foul and most unnatural murder; they recall the insults heaped upon his poor body, the inhuman treatment of Electra by her mother; they picture the fame that had been Agamemnon's had he perished before the walls of Troy; for then he had reigned a king among the dead even as he had been a king among mortal men. They strive to incense his entombed spirit that a passion for revenge may enter into the soul of his son. By that appeal the dead is united with the living in a confederate impulse; the living son, the human instrument of vengeance, is enheartened to a deed demanded alike by the powers of the celestial and the infernal world. The fires of hate are relieved only by the softer light cast by the love of sister and brother.

Recreated in imagination, this scene at the grave of Agamemnon, around which stand his pitiable children, coheirs in misery, and their copartners in sympathy, is charged with life, intense with pathos, and sincere in its fidelity to human nature's deepest necessities. With song interpreting its heard and its suppressed passion, the scene would be a yet more faithful witness to the power of Aeschylean dramatic art.

III. Before the deed the missionary of vengeance discovers only arguments prompting him to kill his mother. Deterrent arguments do not exist—the awfulness of matricide, the possibility that the Furies guard a mother's no less than a father's right. Studious to effect forceful contrasts, Aeschylus postpones all express consciousness in Orestes' soul of the nature of his deed until it is an accomplished fact. The avenger is indeed made to hesitate for one brief moment when he encounters his mother; but he instantly surrenders his scruple when warned of Apollo's behest by Pylades; and his last words to Clytaemestra make known his resolution to do that which he ought not to do. Later, just before his reason totters, he realizes that his unenviable victory has brought pollution in its train; and at the end he foresees that he must stand trial on an evil charge.

No tragic poet may contest the supremacy of Aeschylus in his portrayal of the gradual encroachment of madness and in his ability to suggest the approach of powers more terrible because unseen. Orestes battles to preserve his reason. The passion that he had controlled when he confronted his mother now bursts all bounds, and as it advances to its utmost tension he is himself conscious that his mind has passed the limits which mark its capacity for endurance. The Orestes of Euripides is likewise thus conscious of the dethronement of his reason. Yet his case stands on a different plane. The later dramatist, purposing to depict in its realistic aspect the assaults of frenzy, makes his hero the subject of pathological study. Body as well as soul is diseased in consequence of his deed of blood. He is the prey of hallucinations, which his nurse Electra seeks to dispel. His consciousness of guilt is only one aspect of his diseased state; and the apparition of the gory-eyed and snaky-haired maidens is only a vision of his delirium.

It is common with Aeschylean critics to discover in the apparition of the Erinyes to Orestes a symbol of the torments of a guilty conscience. To my thinking, the overthrow of Orestes' reason and the sequent vision of the Avenging Spirits of his mother mark the acute consciousness of his unhappy state, produced by a deed of such frightful and unheard-of justice, rather than the agonies of a sin-stricken soul. Not only in the present play but also in the *Eumenides* is Orestes unvisited by the remorse that attacks man by reason of deeds for which he is condemned by the silent court of justice that sits within his breast. Orestes suffers, but he is not therefore criminal. Guilty, he is yet innocent. Has he not Apollo's word that he shall take life for life and yet stand clear of offense? In Aeschylus the Furies are conceived to exist apart from man, living creatures of flesh and blood, embodiments of a moral law. To Euripides they are the mythological veil of an eternal moral reality. To Goethe they are fully equated with a guilty conscience, an idea that is only embryonic in Aeschylus. Far less profound is here the psychology of the *Electra* of Sophocles. That play, complete in itself, might not look forward to a sequel. Orestes, in obedience to Apollo's command, slays his mother. But there is no reaction in his soul. He has no need of absolution. The Furies do not exist for him.

We condemn Clytaemestra, yet we pity her, anguished at the prospect of death at the hands of her own son. We pity and we condemn Orestes, bound to

the cruelest of dooms—to be the judge and execu-
tioner of her who gave him life. Justice wars with
justice, agony answers agony. Orestes' deed had the
sanction of the primeval law of blood for blood, confirmed by the authority of Apollo. In pious obedience
to the god's behest he had absolved his duty to revenge his father only to bring upon himself, and not
unwarned, the Avenging Spirits that champion a
mother's right. Shall human casuistry reach so far
as to pronounce upon such an issue? Or shall the
arbitrament be left to Heaven?

CHAPTER VIII

THE ORESTEA: III. EUMENIDES

The audacious genius of Aeschylus did not hesitate to bring into visible collision the divine forces
battling for the soul of Orestes, slayer of his mother.
It is the part of the final drama of the trilogy to present the conflict between Apollo and the Furies, and
thereby to return an answer to the despairing question of the Chorus at the end of the preceding play:

Oh when will it work its accomplishment, when will the
fury of calamity, lulled to rest, find an end and cease?

By the wisdom proclaimed of old the doer must
suffer. Shall not inexorable moral law link the fate of
Orestes with the doom of his blood-stained ancestors?
Or is the chain of causality to break, and is he to be
the restorer of his house? His case is an epitome of
the development of early Greek religious and ethical
consciousness with regard to the shedding of human
blood.

Clytaemestra and her lover must either escape all
vengeance, or it must be her son, and none other, who
shall be the agent of their doom. On the one hand,
Orestes has as his champion the god of Delphi, who
proclaims the righteousness of the *lex talionis*. The
son is commanded to slay his mother because she
has taken his father's life; her injuries at the hand of
her husband do not palliate her crime. It is a god
who promises his advocacy of the matricide and
threatens him with punishment should he disobey the

divine behest—the assaults of his father's Avenging
Spirits and the far-reaching horrors of tribal law.
On the other hand, Orestes, though thus divinely
sanctioned, has aroused against himself the powers
that avenge the taking of a mother's life.   Beset on
either hand by potencies greater than himself, he
becomes the battle-ground of immortals.   He who
had been the chief person of a heroic drama, now
declines to a subordinate position in a drama of
superhuman forces.   Orestes is the *corpus vile* in the
contest of moral forces that struggle for mastery.

To the Titanic imagination of Aeschylus, the
divine antagonists, both supernal and infernal, must
appear upon the scene of conflict.   The god of the
Delphic oracle must redeem his pledge not to betray
his suppliant.   The Furies, now no longer the spectral
images of Orestes' disordered brain, but living creatures of flesh and blood, must quit the darkness of the
underworld to urge the cause of a mother murdered
by her son.   Olympus and Tartarus confront each
other in their embattled champions.   Who is to pre-
vail—Apollo, by whose behest Orestes murdered his
mother?   Or the Erinyes, the incarnations of his
mother's sacred right and dying curse?   The daughter
of Zeus, the Supreme, Athena of the Divine Wisdom,
must be summoned to the scene, if one or the other
of the divine contestants, each armed with a proper
justice, is not to be broken.

The dramatist does not delay to introduce the divine combatants in person.   The aged priestess of
Apollo, before entering his inner sanctuary at
Delphi, pauses to magnify the authority and ascen-
dency of the god who guides her utterance to the
consultants of his oracle.   Skilled in the lore of the

sacred shrine, she contrasts, though covertly, two legends of Apollo's lordship. Theban tradition represented his control of the oracle as won only after conflict with Dionysus. Her own version apparently purports to follow the Delphic legend, according to which the god had succeeded peacefully to an inheritance descending to him from the primal prophetess, Earth, and her daughters, Themis and Phoebe. Other divinities, Athena, the Nymphs, Dionysus, Poseidon, and Zeus are not without honor in the hallowed place, but chiefest of all is Apollo, whose oracular art is inspired by Zeus, his father; for Apollo only proclaims the mind of the most high god. The priestly college at Delphi would scarcely have given its full warrant to the poet's license as to sacred legend or fact. Dionysus was sovereign there for three whole months in the year, and Zeus himself was scarcely concerned with the oracle. But the Pythoness did well to celebrate her lord. He has in his keeping the destiny of Orestes.

The prophetess enters the sanctuary, but turns back in horror. By the sacred navel-stone she has seen a man in suppliant posture and bearing the emblem of suppliance; and his hands and sword drip blood. Fronting him lies asleep a marvelous troop of women—nay, they are not women, they are Gorgons; no, not Gorgons but Harpies; yet they have no wings. They are black, disgusting altogether, their breathing is a snort, their eyes ooze horrid rheum, their dress befits not the shrine of a god or the habitation of man. Before, the priestess appeared as an antiquarian; here (as Miss Harrison says), she is like an archaeologist seeking to identify an unknown type.

Apprized by his prophetess of the presence of these strange visitants to his temple, Apollo appears and with him his suppliant Orestes, now altogether in his right mind. The god commands Orestes to flee to Athens, as a city of refuge, and there to clasp the sacred image of its tutelary goddess. He will be chased over land and sea by these hoary maidens with whom nor god nor man consorts, creatures loathed of man and Olympian gods. But the god will not abandon his votary; to the end he will stand his guardian; and—such is his clairvoyance—he knows that there, at Athens, his suppliant will find judges of his case, so that he may be freed from his sufferings. Hermes, the divine guide, is directed to conduct him to the city of Pallas.

Meantime the Furies, wearied by their pursuit of the matricide, sleep on; and as they sleep they are harassed by a dream, symbolized by the visible apparition of Clytaemestra. Rising from the lower world, her ghost reproaches the ministers of her vengeance with neglect of her cause: she is dishonored among the other dead; no divinity is wroth for her sake, who still bears the gashes inflicted by her still unpunished murderer. "Full oft have ye received sacrifices at my hand: wineless libations and food offered at night-time when none other of the gods is honored; yet all in vain. Up! your quarry has escaped!"

Mutterings and groanings stir their slumber at her upbraiding. One by one they awake; in wild confusion and with wild cries they rush forth. "Intolerable our sufferings, Apollo has stolen our victim from our very grasp. He, a young god, has trodden under foot us ancient divinities. He has polluted his very shrine. He has received into his temple a godless man."

Apollo confronts them and orders them to quit his sanctuary. They plead their case against him.

Thou alone art guilty of offense. Thou badest Orestes slay his mother.

I bade him avenge his father.

Thou hast received him in thy temple whose hands are wet with blood.

Aye, I commanded him to come in suppliance to my house.

Thou dishonorest us his pursuers.

Nay, it is not your province to come hither.

But this is our appointed duty. We chase matricides from their homes.

Do ye do the like to a wife who kills her husband?

Nay, for that deed is not murder of kindred.

Then ye set at naught the holy ordinances of marriage confirmed by Zeus and Hera. The goddess Cypris is dishonored by your plea. For marriage, ordained by Fate unto man and woman, guarded as it is by Justice, is a bond of greater power even than an oath. Ye have no right to pursue Orestes. The goddess Pallas will survey the case.

Never will I quit the man who has shed a mother's blood.

Never will I fail to defend my suppliant. For dreadful in Heaven and on earth is the wrath of a suppliant betrayed.

Apollo departs; the Chorus start in renewed pursuit of the fugitive. The scene is empty. Inflexible unity of time and place, the canon of classical French drama, finds no warrant in Greek tragedy. It is not observed in the *Ajax;* here, in the *Eumenides,* it is serenely disregarded. The scene shifts from Delphi to Athens. After long wanderings Orestes has reached the goal ordered by Apollo. He is disclosed embracing the statue of the goddess of the city in her holy house. The Chorus track him by the scent

of blood; they surround him and chant over their
"consecrated victim" the song that would bind him
to their spells:

> Thus o'er the victim chant we our refrain,
> Frenzy's dread carol, madness-fraught,
> The Furies' hymn, from Hades brought,
> Soul-binding, lyreless, mortal-blighting strain.[1]

Summoned from afar by Orestes' appeal for her
protection, Athena appears, marvels at the strange
sight presented by his pursuers, demands to know
their office, and receives their assent to submit their
case to her judgment. Orestes pleads his cause: there
is no pollution on his hands; the blood of a sacrificial victim and water have washed away his offense;
his father, he who had helped the goddess to lay
Ilium low, was foully slain. The goddess, however,
discovers it beyond her province to adjudge any case
of murder, especially one in which her petitioner
claims to be pure and harmless; and where also, if
the case goes against them, the Furies will vent their
venom upon her beloved land. She will choose the
best of her citizens as judges under oath and then let
the case proceed to trial. The Furies prophesy at
length the destruction of all moral order if they fail
to win.

The court convenes, with Apollo in attendance as
Orestes' advocate. The Furies deny his right to
participate in the case, a right defended by the god
on the plea that Orestes was his suppliant and had
been purified by him. He, the god, assumes full
responsibility for Orestes' deed. As prosecutors, the
Furies question the accused. He does not deny the
killing of his mother; he was induced to the deed by

---

[1] *Eum.*, 328-333, translated by Miss Swanwick.

Apollo; his father will assist him from the grave, for
she who slew her husband slew thereby his sire.

Well then, you live, while she is clear of her offense
by having suffered death.
Why then did ye not pursue her when she yet lived?
Because she was not kindred to him whom she slew.
What, am I blood-kin to my mother?
You wretch, she nourished you beneath her zone. Do
you reject a mother's blood?

Orestes, now reduced to extremity, appeals to his
champion. Apollo argues that Orestes' deed was
different from the murder of Agamemnon. Agamemnon was a scepter-bearing king, commander of the
fleet, and was basely slain; furthermore, only the
father is the real parent of the child, whereas the
mother is only the nurse of the implanted seed.
Father there may be without mother—witness
Athena sprung from the head of Olympian Zeus.

The issue now being closed, the goddess establishes, as a permanent tribunal, the present court,
the first to pass judgment on a case of bloodshed.
Upon the Hill of Ares it shall hold its solemn ses-
sions. While the judges vote, Apollo and the Furies
hurl taunts and abuse at each other. Then Athena
declares that it is her office at the last to cast her vote
in the case. Holding her ballot aloft she says that
she will cast it for Orestes, who wins, if the votes
stand equal. She means (I think) that, if the judges
are equally divided, her ballot symbolizes a majority
for the defendant; but others contend that she
actually voted and thus produced a tie vote. Her
reasons are that she is wholly on the side of the
father; mother she had none, and she will not attach
the greater importance to the killing of a woman who
has slain her husband, the master of the house.

The ballots are let fall from the voting-urns. They are evenly divided, the accused is acquitted. Orestes, bidding the court farewell, quits the scene declaring in gratitude to Pallas, as preserver of his house, that even when he has passed from life his spirit shall prosper her citizens and grant them victory in war. Stung to the heart by their defeat, the Furies threaten to pour out their wrath upon a people that has denied the justice of their cause. They will drop venom on the land; all things that grow shall be blasted, trees shall bear no leaves, children shall die or not come to birth. Athena pleads with them:

Ye are not dishonored, the ballots stood equal. Zeus gave witness through his son Apollo, whose oracle declared that Orestes was to be void of offense. I alone have knowledge where Zeus's thunderbolts are stored, yet I will use no force. If ye quit this place, ye shall find no other more delightsome land wherein to dwell. Time in its onward course shall bring still greater honor to its folk. I promise you a store of all good things. Ye shall receive the first-fruits of sacrifice: offerings for marriage and for children, the power to prosper every house, a sanctuary beneath the earth and ministrants of worship, both men and women. Dwell with me here in a land most dear to all the gods.

Moved by her pleading, the Furies cease their hymn of hate to sing a hymn of blessing on the city which Zeus and Ares have made the shrine that defends the altars of the gods of Greece. On the land no parching wind shall blow, it shall be unvisited by plague; the flocks shall increase twofold; untimely death shall be no more; youths shall win lovely maidens for their own; the strife of faction shall cease.—In solemn procession, with attendants bearing torches, now no longer Erinyes, Spirits of Wrath, but Venerable and Gracious Spirits, they are conducted to their sanctuary beneath the Hill of Ares; while their escort chant the harmony of Zeus and Fate.

The moral atmosphere of the tragic conflict between the champion of Orestes and his adversaries is not only alien, it is unintelligible, to us, so long as we consider the shedding of human blood only in the light of long established law. Aeschylus discerned the establishment of formal legal procedure in the prehistoric age. To him the myth provided the symbol for the fair beginning of the highly developed code of his native Athens; yet the myth rests on underlying conceptions of bloodshed which transport us both to the customs of a primeval age and to the rise of a religious ritual antecedent to the dawn of legal consciousness, a ritual that had no small share in moulding actual legal thought and procedure in the age of Pericles. By reason of the poet's fashioning of the story of Orestes, the *Eumenides* is one of the most authoritative documents for our understanding of ancient ways of thinking concerning bloodshed and its purification.

The question has long been insistent: What manner of 'divine' being is this Apollo who commands a son to kill his mother? Under what ancient conception of the godhead is a religion of revenge permissible? Is it the intent of Aeschylus, as it was that of Euripides, to defame the god? The nature of Orestes' deed, the character of his Olympian advocate, the justice of the Furies of his mother, are intelligible only in the light of the whole history of the growth of moral consciousness of the Greeks with regard to the sanctity of human life.

Blood-vengeance has been common the world over. It is attested among the Arabs, the Slavs, in Corsica, in Asia, in America. In the year 802 it found a place in the statutes of Thuringia; in the Laws of Jaroslaw published in 1017; it is known in the relatively recent code of Prince Danielo of Montenegro. With the Ancient Greeks the duty of blood-revenge was indissolubly associated with the belief that the soul survived after the death of the body; and on that belief rested ultimately the whole fabric of the Attic law of homicide. The murdered man possessed the power of curse. By this daemonic agency he could visit with unending evil his murderer and his surviving kinsmen should they fail to take blood for blood. In the most primitive period society at large, the State and religion, even in their embryonic forms, were not concerned at all with the punishment of a manslayer. The ghost of the slain man acted only on his murderer and on those upon whom devolved the obligation of vengeance. It was the affair of his relatives alone, and at their own hazard, whether or not they assumed this obligation. The murderer himself, whether his deed was voluntary or involuntary, suffered no pollution from the stain of blood; he was not criminal; he might enter the temples of the gods; he was not shunned by his fellow-men. He might be driven into exile by the avengers, but, once in a foreign land, he was free from fear. The kinsmen of his victim were not bound to pursue him abroad, for the wrath of the soul lost its compulsion beyond the limits of the land where the body had suffered death.

But such elementary notions could not long maintain themselves. To the developed moral sense of a later period, but far earlier than the poet's time, murder was seen to involve pollution not only of the murderer but also of all with whom he associated. The community at large was menaced by defilement engendered by bloodshed. For all taking of human life, for whatever cause, there was no purification or expiation. Whether a man had been done to death justly or unjustly his spirit cried out against his murderer. The ancient belief in the vitality of dead souls, which had been almost totally submerged in the society depicted by Homer, now reasserted itself. No longer might the murderer (as even in the Homeric age) save himself by payment of blood-money to the kinsmen of his victim. Nor might exile free him from the fear of the pursuit of unseen spiritual agents of vengeance that coursed over land and sea. And even upon the relatives of the dead man, if they proved rebellious to the sacred duty of blood-vengeance, the wrath of his spirit imposed the same penalties as were visited upon the actual murderer. Thus had life become only less terrible than death itself. The world was full of agony even to him who had innocently or justifiably shed the blood of his fellow-man.

It was Apollo, the god of social order, who brought some measure of deliverance and peace into a world thus harassed by angry ghosts. A humanitarian spirit lies at the center of the cathartic religion developed in post-Homeric times under the influence of the Delphic shrine. The Apolline cult had in course of time developed to the point where it was chiefly concerned with cases of homicide. If the ancient obligation of blood-revenge was too deeply fixed by custom to be remitted, the severities of the existing belief might be relaxed. Bloodshed was still seen to involve a sense of guilt, but pollution was not to be forever the lot of the manslayer and the folk he might infest. From him who had not wantonly taken human life, pollution might be washed away by prescribed use of holy blood or holy water. Absolution was gained by ceremonial rites of purification and expiation. Ceremonial purification ($\kappa\alpha\theta\alpha\rho\mu\acute{o}\varsigma$) aimed primarily to free the land and its sanctuaries from infection. Ceremonial expiation ($\acute{\iota}\lambda\alpha\sigma\mu\acute{o}\varsigma$) sought to appease the angry spirit of the dead.[2] Once the manslayer had fled the land where his crime had been committed, he was not to be refused purification. Through the benevolent efficacy of the god of Delphi, the souls of murdered men were thus no longer from their tomb to blast the living with their curse.

The Spirits of Vengeance that defend the cause of Clytaemestra are the product of religious imagination and, as such, possess no greater validity of real existence than that fairest of the creations of the ancient world, the Olympian gods. As the loveliest conceptions of that ancient world are clad in the beauty of the female form, so likewise the most terrible of all its deities are women. The hideousness with which the poet, of his own invention, has invested the Erinyes, was designed to mark not only their savage nature but also their very antiquity. Deliberately specialized by Aeschylus for his dramatic purpose as ministers of punishment of matricide, the Erinyes have taken on a corporeal being unknown to Homer, who clothed them with the

---

[2] The rites of purification and of expiation were commonly associated, but expiatory sacrifices were made especially to the powers of the nether world and under Delphic sanction.

awfulness of the unseen. To the epic poet they have a wide function as guardians of the moral and natural order of the world: they defend the weak who have no proper avengers against the strong; they protect the right of the firstborn; they champion the cause of the beggar, the suppliant, and the father no less than the mother. They do not wait for the death of injured folk in order to take vengeance on those who have done them injury. But in the Homeric poems, in which the traces of a daemonistic and a theriomorphic conception of spiritual beings have been largely obliterated, the Erinyes, 'the Wrathful Ones,' have lost their original nature as angry souls of men slain by violence. In depicting them as creatures of wrath, infuriated by reason of the slaying of Clytaemestra, Aeschylus unconsciously reproduced their essential primitive function, a function that has disappeared from the Homeric conception. The Furies of Clytaemestra are in fact only Clytaemestra herself, her ghostly spirit multiplied to form a group. Female mythological personifications tend to unite in larger units; as in the case of the Graces, the Muses, the Hours. In Aeschylus there are more than three Furies, a number perhaps first fixed in the classical period, but not attested until three or four centuries after the time of the dramatist.

As defenders of a primeval moral order against the usurpation of the Olympian regents of the world, represented by Apollo, the Erinyes assert for themselves an immemorial antiquity. They existed long before Zeus came to his throne, long before his sons and daughters received their several mandates over mankind. They are the children of Night, and the Fates are the sisters of their mother. Their home is the realm of darkness beneath the earth, where they are the servitors of the Lord of Death, the judge who surveys all things with his recording mind. In the nether world they bear the name Curses, for they are summoned into action only by the maledictions of the wronged. Initiative they have not, but once roused, as "the maddened watchers of mankind," they are untiring in pursuit of their victims. Implacable in their lust for vengeance, they hearken to no appeal for mercy. Fate has spun for them the lot to follow him who stains his hands with blood of kindred; him they pursue till he passes beneath the earth, even to the place where joy exists no more. Their right has been since time began, and it is inalienable. Nor will they suffer diminution of their ancient prerogatives by the upstart Olympian gods. If Orestes, their consecrated victim, is to escape their vengeance, their powers will be disabled. Banish the just fear of them, the house of justice falls; mortals will lightly turn their hand to every deed of violence, and suffering will cease to teach its lesson of wisdom to mankind. But their wrath assails no man who puts forth clean hands: he passes all his days unscathed of them.

Such are the embattled contestants, such their provinces. The vital question at issue is whether matricide, committed in obedience to ancient and sacred prescriptions of blood-vengeance and sanctioned by an Olympian god, admits of any justification whatever.

Orestes, clinging to the image of Athena, declares that the blood upon his hand is slumbering now and fading—the pollution wrought by his mother's slaying is washed away; for while yet fresh it was expelled at the hearth of Phoebus, by purification of slaughtered swine, and he has been cleansed elsewhere, by the mediation of men empowered to purify by blood of victims and by flowing streams. Through ceremonial purification he has regained the right to enter the habitations of gods, and communion with his fellow-men had afflicted with pollution none who had shown him hospitality, though he was still pursued by the vengeful hounds of his mother. Of ceremonial atonement, if it is consciously present to his mind or differentiated from ceremonial purification, he says nothing. Certainly he does not expressly claim that his many wanderings were a part of a formal purgation.

His first care in addressing Athena is to assure her that he is not a guilty man, who, as a petitioner for purgation, turns to her in his distress to receive absolution for his offense. He is a petitioner solely to receive a definite answer whether his deed was right or wrong. His inmost soul he does not lay bare at any point. Though harassed by the pursuit of the Erinyes, he exhibits no symptoms of the tortures of a guilty soul. Of remorse, of repentance, he says not a word. Nor has he sought to appease his mother's angry spirit. So confident indeed is he in the championship of Apollo that he expressly declares that, from the time he slew his mother until now, his life at stake, he does not blame his case. There is no true inner conflict. He had been polluted, he has been purified. Purification should have freed him from the powers of the spirit world. But Apollo's rites have no authority in that world, his suppliant is not rid of the Furies. Internal peace Orestes may have, but external peace has not followed upon purifica-

tion. The authority and the sanction of the Delphic
god has not released him from a moral responsibility.
The angry ghost of Clytaemestra, whose ministers
are the Avenging Spirits, has also its rightful justice.
Shall a son take a mother's life and then go free because he has been sprinkled with the blood of swine
by some god or man? Blood, human blood, is still
demanded for blood by the ancient law of natural
right. He who has slain his kindred, on whatever
plea, can never be absolved even by a ceremonial act.
The blood of a mother slain is morally indelible. The
blood that Orestes thought had been washed away
still clings to him and by its scent the vengeful
hounds of an unavenged mother have chased him
throughout the world. The sufferings of her en-
sanguined son, driven over land and seas, are only
the forecast of a more dreadful woe when his pursuers shall at last deliver their victim to the world
below. For below the earth there exists a Hell for
those who have no reverence for a mother's life.

The opposition of the contending powers in their
fateful collision is irreconcilable. There can be no
compromise. Nor does even the authority of sovereign Zeus as revealed by Apollo prejudge the case in
favor of Orestes. Delphi does not work as a *force
majeure*. The dicast keeps his eyes level in the face of
his gods. The parity of the ballots of the impartial
human jury is a twofold symbol—first, that it is
impossible that any human court should of itself
decide an issue raised by claims that outrange all
human wisdom, and, secondly, that each of the divine
powers has its proper right. Each of the antagonists
is partisan: each fails to comprehend the inherent
justice of the other's cause.

To the Furies their right is immutable. For blood-shed of kindred, blood must flow. To them Orestes' deed is not properly subject to any adjudication: it is of itself unpardonable. Judicial acquittal would spell mercy for a deed for which there is no mercy. Inexorable in their demands for vengeance, the Furies, looking only to the outward act, admit no plea of provocation, no plea of mitigation. To them all cases of murder of kin stand absolutely on the same plane. They take no cognizance of the sacredness of sanctuary. They stake their very reason for existence as moral powers upon the hazard of their claim to execute vengeance on those who have shed kindred blood. Losing their case, they foresee the disappearance of all morality, and in revenge they will abandon mankind to its native brutality. Their code, born of the primitive savagery of tribal custom, is to be upheld against men and gods. Ever-aging time in its advance has brought for them no lesson.

Apollo, for his part, regards the Furies as demons of an older age of the world when primitive man lived in mortal terror of spirits of primordial darkness. To him they exist only as malevolent champions of a ruthless and bloodthirsty violence. He will not recognize that his adversaries have been a subterranean police that quits the gloom of the nether world to chastise the crimes of the sons of men and that they thereby represent a moral principle necessary to the existence of an earlier stage of society. To Apollo the past contained no seed of progress.

When the gods of Greece inspire awe through their superhuman majesty and power and beauty, they correspond, though afar off, to our conception of the

Divine. Enstaged in visible presence as antagonists before a court of law, they cannot but surrender the serenity of their divinity. Only an over-idealized Hellenism may properly be acutely sensitive to the anthropomorphism of gods, when, in speech and action, they display their human qualities. For all that Aeschylus was the greatest religious poet of his nation, for all that he bodied forth a transcendent conception of the spiritual nature of the godhead, as a playwright he did not scruple to suffer the divine contestants at Orestes' trial to relax their majesty and calm. Only in the formal choral chants of the Furies is the splendor of the Divine undisturbed. But in the hostility of argument voiced in dialogue their speech loses the veritable accent of the godlike. Of all the deities engaged, only Athena, the president of the court, preserves throughout a gracious and untroubled calm. Yet even she, the incarnation of divine justice, prevails upon the Erinyes to vacate their claim to vengeance only by offering them worship at the hands of her citizens. Even the dread daughters of Night must have a *quid pro quo*. The Erinyes quote scripture like the Devil himself. Their armory is finely equipped with arguments to defame the new race of the gods who would sweep away their privileges. Did not Zeus himself bind in chains his own father? Did not Apollo make drunk the Fates? In the passion of debate, mythology darkens the face of religion. Apollo, the vicegerent of Zeus, the inspired voice of the ruler of Olympus, blusters like an attorney who vilifies his antagonist. The Erinyes at least display a sense of outraged dignity, but Apollo is a past master in the art of scurrilous vituperation. We seem to hear the jar, the jangle, the abuse, the irrelevant argument of an Athenian court-room—Philocleon in the *Wasps* will not have been the first to find delight in legal battles. Here the interest was the more compelling because the case of Orestes was unique—not only because matricide was an almost unknown crime, but also because the gods themselves participate in an action in which the slain mother had herself slain the father of her son.

But the mere external bearing of the acrimonious, though divine, disputants is a transparent device of dramatic craftsmanship to secure picturesque effect. To the essential problem involved in the conflict of the superhuman forces battling for and against Orestes, Aeschylus might return an answer only as playwright and under the limitations of the playwright's art. With Apollo and the Erinyes he had evoked spiritual potencies whose irreconcilable antagonism admitted no other than dramatic representation, potencies not to be appeased by mere forensic argument. Elsewhere the poet may display his attraction to speculative theology, especially as it found expression in syncretism and the tendency toward monotheism. But the case of Orestes he might not surrender to that new-born science. As a dramatist, he took the part of wisdom: he deliberately avoided coming to close grapple—and by pleadings always relevant—with the transcendent moral issue. He will not argue out the unarguable. The trial of Orestes was in fact to Aeschylus a *via media*, whereby, without undue subtlety, he might escape from entanglement in the ultimate difficulties presented by a problem of which it was not the business of the state-theater to afford a logical or even a legal solution.

In compensation for the impossibility of offering a
direct and precise answer, he presented a situation of
surpassing dramatic vigor. Transport ourselves in
imagination to the scene. The stern-faced judges on
their awful seats; the grim and horrible ministers of
vengeance; the radiant god, resplendent in his divine
beauty; the Virgin Goddess, Athens' guardian power,
and at her feet, clasping her image, poor Orestes, son
of the King of Men.—A scene spectacular, intense,
vibrant with passion, its appeal directed to the patriotic emotions of the spectators. But transcending
these artistic and subordinate purposes, it was the
poet's supreme objective ultimately to rise from the
legal battle to the untroubled region of eternal truth
and justice.

The trial-scene is indeed full of energy and life,
and, as such, it could not fail to reproduce something
of the counter pleadings that mark the contention
of antagonists at law. But both Apollo's defense of
Orestes and Athena's argument for his acquittal,
whatever their effect upon the ancient audience,
are, in large part, unsympathetic to the modern mind.

In his own defense, Orestes displays a naïve
astonishment that he should be regarded as blood-
kin to his mother. In his plea for his suppliant,
Apollo argues that Orestes' first duty was to his
father rather than to his mother, not on the ground
of the ancient belief that the life of a man was more
valuable than the life of a woman, but because
Orestes' father was a sceptered king by grace of God;
because he had been commander in the war against
Troy; and because he had been ignominiously done
to death on his return home. But his capital contention is a reinforcement and explanation of Orestes'

conception of the nature of blood-kinship. The male, asserts Apollo, is the author of the child's being, while the mother "as a stranger for a stranger" (that is, not kindred by blood) only preserves the young plant. This notion obtained in Egypt, according to Diodorus, who doubtless derived his information from the work of Hecataeus, with which Aeschylus may well have been familiar. It might therefore be argued that the dramatist here designed to startle his audience with another of his heterodoxies. Certainly the idea was current in the fifth century that he imported strange notions from the land of the Nile—witness Herodotus, who expressly (but wrongly) asserts that Aeschylus found in Egypt his warrant for making Artemis the daughter of Demeter.

Of itself, however, the conception is not so startling as to demand a foreign origin. More probably it is indigenous in Greece and a factor in contemporary discussion concerning the nature of kinship through descent. In Aeschylus' time, and among the later Greeks, patrilinear descent was the rule; but anthropologists are still contending whether 'mother-right' was not universal in the oldest social organization in Hellenic lands. Herodotus records as unique the fact that, among the Lycians, children were called after their mother. The Lycians were, however, partly Cretan, partly Carian. Among peoples of unmixed Hellenic stock indisputable instances of mother-right are infrequent in historical times. The Locrian nobility seem to have traced descent not from women but through women.

So far as Athens is concerned, the evidence making for the survival, either in memory or in fact, of a primitive matrilinear basis of society rests on the

statement of Varro (which at least proves antiquarian discussion of the subject); on certain prescriptions regarding permissible degrees of consanguinity
between husband and wife; on certain aspects of the
law concerning the descent of the property of
'heiresses'; and on the evidence of two plays of
Aeschylus.

In the *Suppliant Maidens* the heroines seem to
protest against endogamy, which prohibits marriage
except between persons of the same blood or stock.
They will not "purchase relations as their masters":[3]
that is, they will not put themselves in the position
of an Athenian woman, who, if she becomes an
'heiress,' falls under the power of her next of kin,
because he must claim her in marriage except her
father has, by will, determined the person who is to
be her husband. The daughters of Danaüs thus
apparently stand for mother-right, which usually
occurs in conjunction with exogamy, marriage outside the family or clan.

Consideration of the problem in its various
aspects is here impossible. So far as the contention
of Apollo in the *Eumenides* is concerned, it is either
an extreme instance of the effrontery of a pleader
forced to the wall, or it is sincere. But its sincerity
is not conditioned by the assumption that, in the
poet's day, a conflict actually existed in Athens between the advocates of the older and of the later
system of reckoning descent. The conflict between
the monarchial and the democratical principle, implicit in the *Suppliant Maidens*, had no counterpart
in actual Athenian politics in the time of Aeschylus.

---

[3] *Suppl.* 337, where, however, the reading ὠνοῖντο is disputed.

The god of Delphi is the champion of a twofold
cause—purification from bloodshed and father-right.
The Erinyes, as defenders of older mother-right,
deny the possibility of absolution for the slayer of a
mother. On both issues the younger gods stand
opposed to the guardians of an older order. Apollo
proclaims the sanctity of marriage. Looking only to
mother-right, the Erinyes are heedless of Clytaemestra's violation of the marriage-bond. Wronged
in her motherhood, Clytaemestra had taken vengeance, in the name of Justice, Ate, and Erinys,
upon her husband who had slain her child, the
husband who was no kin to her and linked to her by a
tie of social custom not of natural right. Those are
her gods, not the younger Zeus Teleios, Hera Teleia,
and Cypris, divinities of marriage. It is the part of
Aeschylus to place in conflict two antagonistic principles, each having its religious and social sanction;
and to let their mutual hostility center on the person
of the hero at a moving crisis when his fortunes are
dependent on the triumph of the humaner cause, the
cause of primary obligation.

At the moral logic of the daughter of Zeus, invested with authority as president of the court, we
stand fairly aghast. Because she had only a father
(having been born from the brain of Zeus), therefore
she stands on the side of the male—except that
she will know nothing of marriage; and the son's
slaying of his mother cannot hold the scale with a
wife's slaying of her husband. Nothing to the effect
that the murderess was a greater criminal than her
slayer because she was an adulteress; nothing to the
effect that Clytaemestra had so hardened her heart
that the sacred word 'mother' had never in love

passed the lips of her children. We look in vain for evidence whether to reverent souls in Ancient Greece Athena's plea carried the authentic warrant of a truly divine pronouncement. The human jury does not, cannot, in the nature of the case, decide the issue; Athena's vote, designedly given on irrelevant grounds, is a dramatic device to avoid pronouncing sentence as to the moral issue. Her vote procured mercy for Orestes, but it is cast without any explicit reference to divine compassion for her harassed suppliant.

The *Agamemnon* and the *Libation-Bearers* are each controlled by a singleness of dramatic purpose that rendered it necessary to set the fate of Orestes in the forefront of the final play. In the *Eumenides*, however, the stricter unity of dramatic progression is no longer maintained. The question for the poet was the installation of a significant action that should make the play contribute its third part to the winning of the prize, and at the same time enable him to attain his ultimate spiritual goal. To this end he shifted the axis of interest from Orestes to the Chorus, which became the true protagonist; with the result that the drama concludes with the attempt to pacify the Erinyes after their defeat before the court. As with warring nations, so with the Erinyes —their case remained as good or as bad as it had been before the encounter. Had they not received half of the votes of the jury? Athena is the divine mediator. The wrath of the Erinyes against Orestes is surrendered to a newborn love of her city. They are moved to forget their legal claim; even as Orestes and Clytaemestra are at the last forgotten. The gloom that had overshadowed the sin-stained race of Atreus is dispelled by the radiance of the glory of Athens.

The *Odyssey* knew of Athens as the scene of
Orestes' exile. Aeschylus transported to his native
city Orestes' champion and his pursuers. He defied
the tradition that the earliest trial for homicide was
held in the presence of the twelve gods, and was
concerned, not with Orestes, but with Ares, accused
by Poseidon of the murder of his son—Aeschylus
would, no less than Pindar, proclaim no evil of the
gods. He even set aside the legend that it was the
twelve gods who adjudged the deed of Orestes.

To him the case of Agamemnon's son was to be
ranged with events of surpassing importance for
mankind. Trial by a human jury was to be instituted under divine inspiration. Athens' highest
tribunal of judicature was to be established by the
goddess in whom was incarnated justice, the sovereign intellectual passion of her people. Before their
very eyes the Athenians beheld a moving spectacle
that witnessed to their ancient glory—the inauguration of the august Council of the Areopagus upon the
occasion of the first trial for intentional homicide.
They beheld a scene in which contemporary procedure at law was suggested alike in language and in
legal form. They beheld their patron-goddess holding aloft the ballot, which in their time, they regarded
as the symbol of a divine warrant, established in the
heroic past, for acquittal of an accused person whenever a jury was equally divided.

The fate of Orestes is thus subordinated to the
foundation of the Athenian court whose collective
conscience was to be the supreme voice of justice
regulated by man. The Areopagus, which had won
increased influence in consequence of the Persian war,
is thus recommended to reverence as the bulwark

of the State. But let the democracy now rest content with a triumphal assault that had restricted its competency to cases of homicide, its original province. Admonitions directed to external and internal policy are virtually addressed to the spectators. Let Athens war abroad, but let not her citizens imbrue their hands in their brothers' blood. Alliance between Argos and Athens is openly advocated. Not that Aeschylus was a narrow partisan in the strife of faction. The soldier-poet has the broader vision. He who had fought at Marathon and Salamis would have his Athens, the city of the gods, neither a despotism nor yet free from restraint, but self-ruled in ordered liberty, controlled by salutary awe and fear.

If the poet, under the pressure of a self-created dramatic necessity, put the trial-scene into the foreground, he did not fail to utilize that scene in order, at the last, to evolve a moral harmony. It needed his hardihood to transform the Erinyes, the Angry Ones, into the Eumenides, the Gracious Ones; to banish the savage Spirits of Wrath beneath the earth, whence they will rise, no longer to afflict mankind with their partial justice, but to serve as ministers of a wide and salutary guardianship of the children of men. The Erinyes were universal and unlocalized powers; though goddesses, they never possessed a shrine in Attica; nor did they there enjoy any official worship as abstract powers of vengeance. The play moves them from mythology into religion, gives them a local worship, but without untenanting its former possessors. Only at Athens and at the neighboring Phlya was there a cult of the Semnai Theai, the venerable goddesses, beneficent divinities

of earth and of benign aspect. At Athens their
sanctuary was a cave underneath the Hill of Ares,
and in their name jurors' oaths were taken before the
Areopagus. Kindred in nature to the Semnai Theai
were the Eumenides, deities who possessed a cult at
Colonus and in various parts of the Peloponnese.
With magnificent daring Aeschylus assimilated the
Erinyes, the Semnai Theai, and the Eumenides.

But the conversion of the Erinyes, formally
effected by the persuasive pleas of Athena, was not
in fact, as is supposed by some extreme champions
of an allegorical interpretation, the conversion of
pure spirits of evil into pure spirits of good. Apollo
had in fact vilified his opponents—the Devil is not
so black as he is painted. At first, and in their altercation with the god, the Erinyes restrict their office
to vengeance on shedders of kindred blood. But in
their solemn and awful choral chants they disclose
themselves as champions of a wider justice that
extends over all human things. They punish offenses
against parents, against guest and host, and even
against gods. Their care, as it is Athena's care, is to
safeguard the spirit of that reverence and holy fear
which must be enthroned in the heart for the well-
being of the State. *Sine auctoritate nulla vita*—they
anticipate St. Augustine's utterance.

If it suited the dramatic purpose of the poet to
depict the Erinyes as fearsome beings, he did not fail
to recover the gentler aspects of their nature. His
transcendent vision transmuted spirits of the wrath
of justice into spirits of a milder justice, and thus
gracious to mankind. Punishment and Grace are
one, one in the light of Divine Providence. Behold a
mystery to be apprehended only by the eye of faith!

In the Homeric version of the story of Orestes the legend is one of simple vengeance. Agamemnon's son returns to his home and puts to death his father's slayer and his father's adulterous wife. He held no commission from a god, nor did a god promise to grant him purification or to defend his cause. Aeschylus views the legend in the light of religion. In the *Agamemnon* Zeus is the symbol of Divine Providence. In the other plays of the trilogy it is the son of Zeus who is moved into the very heart of the myth. In the *Libation-Bearers* Apollo, in invisible presence, in the *Eumenides* in visible presence, inhabits the scene. Delphi has transformed, recreated the primitive legend in the light of a higher moral law and of its own mission. Confident in its moral authority Delphi pits the god of the Olympian religion against the elder powers of mythology. It makes Orestes' deed a supreme test case to decide the issue whether the old law shall be remade into a humaner law. Aeschylus inherited the story in the form it had assumed a century before his time under Apolline inspirations. In the Sicilian choral poet Stesichorus, the god of Delphi was the champion of Orestes against the Erinyes of his mother. The *Libation-Bearers* followed the lead of Stesichorus. The *Eumenides*, which shaped the story into an Athenian possession, gave the dramatist larger opportunity to display his originality.

As no other of the tragic poets of Athens, Aeschylus lives and moves in the myth. He accepts the myth of Orestes as it had been transformed under the influence of Apolline religion, and he does so with unquestioning reverence. To Sophocles that myth is only a fertile field for the study of human

character. Euripides may not reject the framework
of the fable, but he wrecks its dramatic unity by open
or covert attack on Apollo on the ground that the
god had countenanced the cause of a matricide. It
was not, as Wilamowitz maintains, the purpose of
Aeschylus to defame the character of Apollo.
Aeschylus envisages the myth at the time when it
was still keeping pace with the moral sense of the
Greek world, and at the stage when the antagonism
of the newer to the older moral order could be so
envisaged as to allow of scenic representation charged
with dramatic intensity. He does not, like the
rationalistic Euripides, survey the myth from the
vantage ground of a later age when a profounder
moral sense, outstripping the cruder conceptions of
homicide, had translated itself into formal law. But
while he lives and moves in the myth he nevertheless
outranges its narrower confines. He discovers afar
off the coming of the time when the *ius naturale*
abdicated to the *ius civile*, when purely private
vengeance was abolished, when the State by its inter-
vention took to itself the right to pass judgment on
all cases of murder and thus itself became the
avenger of slain men, and when punishment was
graduated according to the nature of the crime.

Aeschylus begins where there was no legal code
to cover a case in which the facts were undisputed.
He ends with heralding the sovereignty of ordered
law under the authentic warrant of the Olympian
gods.

Delphi controls the myth, but only to the moment when its god, victorious over his antagonists,
quits the scene leaving the final issue to be determined by the goddess of Athens. Athens com-

pletes what Delphi had begun. Athens brings to an end the age-long contest of the elder and the younger gods. And, with that end, Zeus reëmerges as the divine protagonist of the triune drama. If the priestly college at Delphi had imported Apollo into legends of the heroic past, it had wisely not failed to assert that the office of the god had been only to proclaim the mind of his father Zeus. Zeus it was to whom the quality of mercy was not strained. Had he not purified Ixion when no one would grant grace to that first taker of human life? And it is his daughter Athena, voice of the Divine Wisdom, who brings the message of reconciliation. Through her, peace comes to Orestes, peace to the warring gods. What mortal man cannot determine, that is determined by the Olympian father through his child, in whom are tabernacled loveliness, augustness, strength, and graciousness—the Virgin goddess, supreme of all the divine presences on the Athenian stage.

To the outer vision the myth is the story of a youth, scion of a blood-stained race, who has been caught, by no fault of his own, in the toils of a fatal necessity. To the vision of the soul it is the triumph of the Divine working in and through Fate. Moral tranquility must be won if there is a moral unity in the world. Out of the collision of moral principles, out of the discordance of passion, human and divine, emerges a final harmony. Fate at the last is discovered to be one with the will of God. In the slow marches of time, good is victorious over evil by the power of the Eternal Justice.

HEART OF FIRE

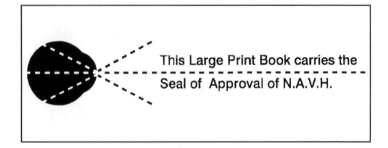

This Large Print Book carries the
Seal of Approval of N.A.V.H.

HEART OF FIRE

KAT MARTIN

THORNDIKE PRESS
A part of Gale, Cengage Learning

GALE
CENGAGE Learning™

Detroit • New York • San Francisco • New Haven, Conn • Waterville, Maine • London

GALE
CENGAGE Learning™

LIBRARY OF CONGRESS CATALOGING-IN-PUBLICATION DATA

Martin, Kat.
   Heart of fire / by Kat Martin.
     p. cm. — (Heart series) (Thorndike Press large print romance)
   ISBN-13: 978-1-4104-0763-4 (alk. paper)
   ISBN-10: 1-4104-0763-2 (alk. paper)
   1. Women journalists — Fiction. 2. London (England) — Social life and customs — 19th century — Fiction. I. Title.
PS3563.A7246H39 2008
813'.54—dc22   2008009050

Published in 2008 by arrangement with Harlequin Books S.A.

Printed in the United States of America
1 2 3 4 5 6 7 12 11 10 09 08

To children everywhere.
May they all find love, joy and peace.

ONE

London, England
January, 1844

An icy drizzle hung over the churchyard. The gravestones stood dark and unreadable in the shadows of the high rock walls of St. Michael's Church.

Gowned in layers of heavy black crepe, her face hidden beneath the veil of a wide-brimmed black bonnet, Coralee Whitmore stood next to her father and mother, the Viscount and Viscountess of Selkirk, listening to the drone of the bishop's words but not really hearing them.

In the casket beside a mound of damp earth, her sister's body lay cold and pale, retrieved only days ago from the chilly waters of the Avon River, the victim of a suicide, the authorities claimed. Laurel, they said, had jumped into the river to hide her shame.

"You're shivering." A stiff wind ruffled the

7

viscount's copper hair, the same fiery shade as Coralee's. He was a man of average height and build whose imposing presence made him seem much larger. "The bishop has finished. It is time we went home."

Corrie stared at the casket, then down at the long-stemmed white rose she carried in a black-gloved hand. Tears blurred her vision as she moved forward, her legs stiff and numb beneath her heavy black skirt, the veil on her hat fluttering in the cold February breeze. She laid the rose on top of the rosewood casket.

"I don't believe it," she whispered to the sister she would never see again. "Not for a single moment." Corrie swallowed against the painful, choking knot in her throat. "Farewell, sweet sister. I shall miss you ever so much." Turning, she walked toward her parents, the father both sisters shared and the mother who was Corrie's alone.

Laurel's mother had died in childbirth. The viscount had remarried, and Corrie had been born soon after. The girls were half sisters, raised together, always close, at least until the past few years. Then Corrie's job as society editor for *Heart to Heart,* a London ladies' gazette, had begun to absorb more and more of her time.

Laurel, who had always preferred the quiet

life of the country, had moved in with her aunt Agnes at Selkirk Hall, the family estate in Wiltshire. The girls kept in touch through letters, but in the last year even those had grown sparse.

If only I could turn back time, Corrie thought, the lump in her throat swelling, becoming even more painful. *If only I could have been there when you needed me.*

But she had been too busy with her own life, too busy attending the balls and soirées she wrote about in her column. She'd been too self-absorbed to realize Laurel was in trouble.

And now her sister was dead.

"Are you all right, Coralee?"

Standing in the Blue Salon of the Whitmores' Grosvenor Square mansion, Corrie turned at the sound of her best friend's voice. Krista Hart Draugr walked toward her across the drawing room, where the pale blue damask curtains had been draped with black crepe, as had the brocade sofa and Hepplewhite chairs.

Corrie reached beneath her heavy black veil to brush a tear from her cheek. "I'll be all right. But I miss her already and I feel so . . . responsible."

Most of the mourners, few in number

9

because of the circumstances of Laurel's death, were in the Cinnamon Room, a lavish salon done in gold and umber, with huge, sienna marble fireplaces at each end. An extravagant buffet had been set out for the guests, but Corrie had no heart for food.

"It wasn't your fault, Coralee. You had no idea your sister was in trouble." Krista was blond, fair and tall; taller, in fact, than most men, except for her husband, Leif, a blond giant of a man who towered over his wife and actually made her look small.

One of the handsomest men Corrie had ever seen, he stood across the drawing room in conversation with his brother, Thor, who was dark instead of fair, nearly equal in size and, in a fiercer way, even more handsome.

"I should have grown suspicious when her letters dwindled to nearly nothing," Corrie said. "I should have known something was wrong."

"She was twenty-three, Coralee. That is two years older than you, and she was very independent. And she wrote you from Norfolk, as I recall."

Last summer, Laurel had traveled to East Dereham in Norfolk to live with her other aunt, Gladys. Along with Allison, a cousin about Corrie's age, they were the only relatives on her mother's side that Laurel had.

Laurel had never gotten along with Corrie's mother, but her aunts, both spinsters, loved her like a daughter, and Laurel had loved them.

"She wrote to me from Norfolk, yes, but only on rare occasions. We had just resumed a serious correspondence last month, after her return to Selkirk Hall."

According to the Wiltshire County constable, when Laurel was in residence at Selkirk, she had gotten herself with child. Agnes had kept Laurel's secret until her pregnancy began to show, then sent her north to live with Gladys until the baby was born.

Corrie looked up at Krista, who stood a good six inches taller than she, a buxom young woman with lovely blue eyes, while Corrie was small-boned, with eyes a vivid shade of green. Krista was a mother now, but she still ran the gazette, a magazine for ladies that was well known for its views on social reform.

"The police believe she committed suicide," Corrie said. "They say she took the child she had carried in her womb for nine long months and jumped into the river because she couldn't bear the shame. I don't believe it. Not for a moment. My sister would never harm anyone, much less her own baby."

Krista's gaze held a trace of pity. "I know you loved her, Corrie, but even if you are right, there is nothing you can do."

Corrie ignored the feeling those words stirred. "Perhaps not."

But she wasn't completely convinced.

She had been thinking about the circumstances of her sister's death since news of the tragedy had arrived — her sister drowned, remnants of an infant's blue knit sweater clutched in her hand.

Corrie had been devastated. She loved her older sister. She couldn't imagine a world without her in it.

Dreadful things were being said about Laurel but Corrie refused to believe them. Laurel's death could not possibly have been suicide.

In time, surely the truth would be unearthed.

Two

London
Three Months Later

The offices of *Heart to Heart* weekly ladies' magazine were located in a narrow brick building just off Piccadilly. Corrie had begun working at the gazette shortly after Margaret Chapman Hart had died and her daughter, Krista, had taken over the business, running the company along with her father, Professor Sir Paxton Hart. Last year, Krista had married Leif Draugr, now the owner of a successful shipping enterprise, and nine months later had borne him a son, but Krista still worked most days at *Heart to Heart,* her pride and passion.

As Corrie entered the office in search of her friend, she spotted Bessie Briggs, the typesetter, working to get the big Stanhope press, the soul of the gazette, ready for the next edition. Bessie looked up and smiled but kept on working, paying no attention to the dismal black mourning clothes Corrie had worn for the past three months and would wear for three months more.

Corrie tapped on the open door to Krista's ground floor office.

Her friend looked up and smiled. "Since you rarely knock, I assume this must be important. Come in, Coralee."

Her stiff black skirts rustled noisily as Corrie moved to close the door behind her. "I have something I need to discuss, and since you are my very best friend . . ."

Krista eyed her with speculation. "What is it?"

Corrie sat down and smoothed a non-existent wrinkle from the front of her skirt. "I've tried to put Laurel's death behind me, but the fact is, I simply cannot. I have to find out the truth, Krista. I've never believed Laurel killed herself and her month-old child, and I am going to prove it."

Krista's features softened. "I know losing your sister has been hard on you. I know that in some way you feel responsible. But Laurel is gone and there is nothing you can do to bring her back."

"I realize that. But I failed her once when she needed me, and I will not do so again. My sister did not kill herself, which means someone else must have done it, and I intend to discover who it was."

One of Krista's blond eyebrows arched. "And how, exactly, do you plan to do that?"

"I shall start by doing some investigating right here in London. I am good at that, am I not? It is part of my job to unearth both facts and tidbits of gossip for my column."

"Yes, but that is hardly the same."

"I think it is exactly the same. I intend to go over every letter my sister wrote before she died and look for clues." Corrie glanced up, a fierce light coming into her eyes. "Then I shall leave for the country. I'm going to find out who fathered Laurel's child, and then I will know where to start looking for the answers to how and why she died."

Learning the name of the father was an important piece of the puzzle, the man her sister must have loved. Not even Aunt Agnes knew who he was. According to her, Laurel had adamantly refused to divulge his identity.

"You don't need to worry about the gazette," Corrie continued before Krista could speak. "I already have a temporary replacement in mind. Assuming you approve, I shall ask Lindsey Graham to fill in for me while I am away." Lindsey was a school chum, a former classmate at Briarhill Academy, where Krista and Corrie had met.

"Lindsay is currently penning textbook articles," Corrie said, "and extremely bored, I think. Her father is a baron and very well connected so she is able to move freely about in society. I believe she will handle my job very well."

"I imagine she could, but —"

"Actually, I considered hiring Lindsey while you and Leif were gone off to his dreadful island." Corrie smiled. "Running this place without you was a nearly impossible task. I have never been so happy in my life to see anyone return."

Leif and Krista's story was a well-guarded tale. That the big man and his brother had come from an uncharted island far north of Scotland where people still lived as Vikings was, at best, totally incredible and better left unsaid.

All that mattered was that Leif had found Krista and she had found him, and they loved each other desperately. Corrie wondered if the right man would ever come along for her.

Which returned her thoughts to her sister. In Laurel's early letters from Selkirk, she had mentioned meeting a man. She had described his many virtues and said how much she enjoyed his company. Corrie intended to review the letters, see if there might be a description, something that might help her find out his name. Who had stolen Laurel's heart, taken her virtue, then abandoned her?

Corrie wondered if the man who had fathered Laurel's child would have gone so far as to murder them.

"You can't be serious, Coralee. Tell me you do not intend to dredge up this painful affair all over again." Agnes Hatfield sat on the rose velvet settee in a small salon near the back of the Whitmores' town mansion, a room done in white and rose, an elegant, feminine salon that overlooked the garden. Three days ago, the black crepe strung round the room had been removed after three long months of mourning.

"I realize it will take some doing, Aunt Agnes, but I have given the matter considerable thought and I have no choice but to act."

Aunt Agnes, which Corrie had always called her though they were not actually blood-related, was a lady in her sixties, plump and silver-haired, and until the death of her beloved niece, always smiling. Seated next to her, Laurel's cousin, Allison Hatfield, a thin young woman with a razor-straight nose and pointed chin, very dark hair and hazel eyes, listened to Corrie with obvious trepidation. Allison's parents had died of cholera, leaving her in the care of her aging aunt.

At the viscount's invitation, both of the women had elected to remain in the city rather than return to Selkirk Hall and the awful memories the place still held for them.

"So you intend to begin some sort of investigation?" Aunt Agnes asked.

"Yes."

Allison made no comment. She was a shy, unobtrusive young woman rarely inclined to disagree with anything anyone said. Which was perhaps the reason she had agreed to leave East Dereham and accompany Laurel on her return to Selkirk Hall, pretending to be the baby's mother.

Or perhaps it was because Allison was tired of scraping by on her aging aunt Gladys's generosity, and Laurel had promised her a goodly sum and a better future in exchange for her help with the child.

"I do not believe for an instant the authorities' version of what occurred," Corrie said, "and after months of consideration, I have decided to act. I plan to take whatever steps are necessary to discover the truth of what happened to my sister. Aunt Agnes, you and Gladys helped Laurel. Now you must help me find out what happened to her and her baby."

Allison pulled a lace-trimmed handkerchief from her reticule and dabbed at her eyes. She had been as fond of Laurel and her month-old infant, Joshua Michael, as Agnes, who also dug out an embroidered square of cotton and blew her powdered nose.

The older woman took a fortifying breath. "I will help in any way I can . . . though perhaps my helping your sister is what, in the end, got her killed."

Corrie's eyes widened. "So you do not believe it was suicide, either! And if she did not take her own life, someone *must* have killed her. Laurel and the child were victims of foul play. It is the only explanation."

From her place on the rose velvet settee, Allison's soft voice whispered across the room. "There is a chance . . . I cannot say for certain . . . but it is possible that Laurel may have been meeting someone the night she disappeared. She wouldn't tell me where she was going, but she was excited. I didn't realize she had taken the baby until later, when I went into the nursery and saw his cradle was empty."

Corrie felt a rush of sadness that brought the sting of tears. She purposely leaned into the stiff bone stays of her corset, and the tiny jolt of discomfort set her back on course. "Please . . . we must try to stay focused."

Agnes blew her nose. "You are right, of course. We have all cried more than enough. And we can hardly find justice for my dear, lost angel by sitting here weeping."

Corrie's gaze fixed on dark-haired Allison. "Did you tell the authorities that Laurel might have been meeting someone the night she died?"

"It didn't seem important at the time. The constable said she had jumped into the river. The week before it happened, she had been a bit distraught, though she wouldn't tell me why. When the constable arrived with the terrible news, I thought perhaps . . . I accepted the constable's explanation for what had occurred."

Corrie made a mental note to find out what had upset her sister the week before her death. "You've had three months to consider, Allison. Do you still believe Laurel killed herself?"

She shook her head. "At the time, I was so distressed I could scarcely think straight. Laurel and baby Joshua were gone and "nothing else mattered."

"Well, it matters to me," Corrie said. "And it would matter to Laurel. Are you certain, Aunt Agnes, my sister gave no clue as to the name of the man who fathered her child?"

"None whatsoever. I'm an old woman. I paid little attention to my niece's comings and goings."

"What about men who might have paid calls at the house?"

"Oh, there were a few who stopped by now and then. Squire Morton's son Thomas paid an occasional visit. The vicar's son . . . oh, dear, what is his name? It will come to me in a moment. . . . At any rate, the boy stopped by on occasion, as well."

"Anyone else?"

"Well, yes. Castle Tremaine is nearby." In fact, it was the estate closest to Selkirk Hall. "Lord Tremaine paid his respects whenever he was in residence, occasionally accompanied by his cousin. His brother, Charles, and his sister-in-law, Rebecca, paid an occasional call, and they always stop by at Christmastime each year."

Corrie frowned as bits of information came together in her head. "Lord Tremaine, you say?"

"Well, yes. He always calls at least once when he is in the country, but he never stays overly long."

Grayson Forsythe, Earl of Tremaine. The name stirred memories of the man who had come into the Tremaine title five years ago. Corrie had never seen the earl, who seemed to keep a good deal to himself, but she had heard he was tall and incredibly handsome. The man had a wicked, extremely sordid reputation when it came to women, and in her gossip column, "Heartbeat," Corrie had alluded more than once to rumors of his many affairs.

And if memory served, the earl was often in residence at Castle Tremaine, where his brother and sister-in-law made their home.

"I can see what you are thinking," Agnes said. "I will admit the earl is attractive, but he is also a dark, rather brooding sort of fellow. I cannot imagine your sister would be interested in a man like that." She glanced away. "Laurel was always so bright and fun-loving, such a warmhearted, spirited young girl." Her eyes teared up and she used her handkerchief again.

Corrie felt a crushing weight in her chest. "Perhaps you're right," she said, determined not to let her emotions rise to the surface. "But from the gossip I have heard, the man is quite ruthless when it comes to women. I imagine if he wanted to seduce an innocent young girl, it would be easy enough for him to do."

"Perhaps." Agnes fought to bring her own emotions under control. "But I just cannot . . ." She shook her head, her silver eyebrows drawing together. "His cousin, Jason, is quite dashing. He is also in residence much of the time. I suppose if I were to guess —" She broke off again. "I am sorry, Coralee, but I simply cannot imagine any of the young men who paid calls at the house murdering our dear, sweet Laurel and her innocent little baby. That is what you are thinking, is it not?"

"It's a possibility. Perhaps the man she fell in love with did not love her in return. Perhaps he did not wish to be forced to marry her."

"And perhaps she simply went for a walk that night and was waylaid by footpads. Perhaps they tried to rob her, but when they discovered she had no money, they tossed her and the child into the river."

It was a notion Corrie had already considered. "I suppose that could have happened. Anything seems possible at this point in time, except that Laurel would kill herself and her child."

"Coralee is right," Allison said softly, from where she perched like a bird on the edge of the sofa. "Laurel loved little Joshua with every ounce of her being. She would never have done anything to hurt him. And she was so clearly determined that no one would find out the identity of the father. It does make one wonder. . . ."

Corrie nodded. "It does indeed."

Aunt Agnes eyed her warily. "I am loath to ask, but I suppose I must. Tell us, Coralee, what exactly is it you propose to do?"

She stiffened her spine. At the moment she wasn't certain. But she was going to do *something.* Of that she was completely sure.

Excited at her discovery, Corrie climbed the steps of *Heart to Heart* and opened the heavy front door. As she walked into the long, narrow printing area, she spotted Krista coming out of the back room, heading for her office. Corrie followed her and hurriedly closed the door.

"Krista — you are not going to believe what I've found!"

Her friend whirled toward her, apparently not aware until then that Coralee had entered. "So you are still digging. I know you are determined to come up with something to validate your belief that Laurel was murdered, but are you sure your sister wouldn't rather you simply accepted her death and got on with your life?"

"They say she killed her own child. Do you believe my sister would want the world to believe she did something as heinous as that?"

"The police found no sign of robbery, Corrie. There were no incriminating marks on the body."

"She had been in the water for several days when she was found. The constable said it was impossible to tell exactly what had happened, and there *was* a bruise on the side of her head."

"Yes, and if I recall, the constable believed she must have hit her skull when she fell into the river. The police believe the baby drowned and simply washed out to sea."

"And I say the police are wrong. Laurel was killed by someone who didn't want the secret of the child's birth known, or had some other nefarious motive."

Krista sighed. "Well, there have certainly been murders committed for far less reason than preventing some sort of scandal."

"Yes, and when Agnes mentioned the Earl of Tremaine, I began to think. Some years back, I'd heard gossip about him. He was whispered about at a number of affairs, and I even made mention of his scandalous reputation once or twice in my column. I decided to go back through some of our older editions. Lady Charlotte Goodnight wrote the "Heartbeat" column in the days when your mother ran the paper. I took a look at those."

For the first time, Krista appeared curious. "What did you find?"

"The articles mentioned the gossip I had heard, said the man was a complete and utter rogue where women were concerned. They called him a 'sensualist,' a master of the art of love. Apparently, Grayson Forsythe was a major in the army before he inherited the title. He spent several years in India before his older brother fell ill and he came back to assume his duties as earl."

Krista smiled. "Sounds like an interesting man."

"Yes, well, I suppose you might say that. But as I was reading about him, I remembered something else."

"And that was . . . ?"

"This morning I went down to the magistrate's office and searched for records filed under his name and there it was — the certificate of his marriage to Lady Jillian Beecher three years past."

"Now that you mention it, I remember hearing something about that. But Tremaine is a bachelor — one of the most eligible in

26

London. What happened to his wife?"

"That is the point I am trying to make. I did some more digging, spoke to some of my sources, very quietly, of course. I discovered that the earl was married less than a year when Lady Tremaine died. The countess was the daughter of a wealthy baron, an heiress worth a good deal of money. She died leaving the earl with a sizable increase in his fortune — and he was free again, able to continue his sensual pursuits."

"I don't think I ever heard the story."

"I believe the family kept the matter fairly quiet." Corrie's eyes gleamed. "And since that is the case, what you also don't know is that Lady Tremaine *drowned,* Krista — right there in the Avon River!"

THREE

A cool spring breeze floated through the open windows of the carriage as it rumbled toward the village of Castle-on-Avon, a small, picturesque market town surrounded by rolling green fields and thatch-roofed cottages. On a knoll near the edge of the village, Selkirk Hall loomed majestically over twelve hundred acres of rich grassy earth. A structure three stories high, it was built in the Georgian style, of golden Cotswold stone.

Coralee, Aunt Agnes and Allison were returning to the country in Agnes's carriage, not the viscount's fancy four-horse rig. Corrie couldn't risk her father's coachman telling him she had left the carriage before its arrival at Selkirk Hall. In fact, she meant to depart at the Hen and Raven, a nearby coaching inn, where she would hire a room for the night and continue to her destination as a different person in the morning.

It had been less than a week since Corrie had come up with her outrageous plan. Three days ago, she had presented it to Aunt Agnes and Allison.

"It will work — I know it will!"

Aunt Agnes had twisted her handkerchief in her plump hands. "I don't know, Coralee . . . it sounds extremely dangerous."

"To begin with, no one is going to know who I am," Corrie explained. "I shall pretend to be Letty Moss, the wife of Lord Tremaine's very distant cousin Cyrus. Letty is destitute in the wake of her husband's abandonment, and desperately in need of the earl's help." A story that could likely be true.

Corrie had run across the information during her research on the earl and his family. Through a friend who knew a friend who knew one of the earl's distant cousins — a man named Cyrus Moss — she had learned that Cyrus had left his much younger wife in residence in York and set off for America to make his fortune. After two years, Cyrus had not yet returned.

According to her source, Lord Tremaine had never met Letty Moss and knew little of his very distant cousin. The information gave Corrie the perfect means of getting into Castle Tremaine. Doing so, she believed, was the only way to discover if Lord Tremaine was the father of Laurel's child, and if so, whether he might be responsible for her and little Joshua's death.

"It will work, I tell you. It has to."

Aunt Agnes had fretted and argued, but in the end she had agreed to the plan. If Corrie could discover the truth of what had happened to her beloved niece, then she would go along with her scheme.

Corrie watched the landscape passing outside the carriage window — rolling hills beneath shadowy clouds, an occasional barking dog, a merchant's cart pulled by a tired-looking horse.

"I don't see how this can possibly succeed," Aunt Agnes grumbled from the opposite side of the carriage. "Surely someone from Selkirk Hall or someone in the village will recognize you."

"I haven't been to Selkirk since I was twelve years old. Mother and I both prefer London to the country. Whenever Laurel and I wished to visit, my sister always came to the city."

To distance herself even further from events at Selkirk, Corrie had decided to come out of mourning. She didn't want anyone connecting her to Laurel's death, and wearing those dreadful black garments just might put the notion in someone's head.

Corrie didn't think her sister would mind. She believed Laurel would rather the truth be discovered than that her younger sister mope about in dismal black, doing nothing to clear her name.

Agnes cast Corrie an inquiring look. "You are determined to discover the truth, but what if that truth turns out to be something you do not wish to learn?"

There was certainly a chance facts would surface that Corrie would rather not know. She would have to trust that Laurel was an innocent seduced into the affair, as Corrie believed she was.

"I'll deal with that circumstance should it arise."

"And the danger?" Agnes pressed. "If the earl is truly a murderer, what will stop him from also killing you?"

Corrie waved her aunt's worry away, though the thought had crossed her mind. "I told you, Tremaine will not know who I am. Besides, if he did murder his wife, he did it for money. And if he murdered Laurel and Joshua, he did it to keep his freedom, or perhaps to protect his family from scandal. As I am merely a destitute relative there for a visit, he would have no reason to murder me."

"And I will be there with her," Allison added softly, referring to the role she had agree to play: Corrie's maid.

"That's right. Allison will act as my liaison with you should any problem arise."

Fortunately, during the time Allison had been at Selkirk with Laurel, she had been pretending to be a widow with a newborn child. She had been dressed in mourning clothes and had never gone into the village, which meant she was safe from recognition at Castle Tremaine.

Agnes released a deep sigh. "I hope you two know what you are doing."

So did Corrie. At least she knew the Earl of Tremaine was in residence at Castle Tremaine, and had been for several weeks. Agnes had told her the man had been at the castle at the time of Laurel's death, and for several months before that. Lately he seemed to be spending even more time in the country.

Perhaps he had found a new victim on whom to ply his seductive skills.

Ignoring her companions, Corrie turned to look out the window and caught sight of the inn up ahead, the Hen and Raven. A tremor of nervous anticipation flitted through her. She was still gowned in black, her face hidden beneath a veil of black tulle, and would be until she left the inn on the morrow.

Then she would be dressed in the clothes of a gently reared young woman fallen on hard times, clothes Allison had collected from the local rag merchant: several slightly worn traveling suits, well-worn muslin day dresses, and a number of unimpressive but serviceable dinner gowns with barely frayed cuffs and soiled hems.

Though the gowns were not at all the sort she was used to wearing, in a way Corrie didn't mind.

Anything would be better than the dismal black that reminded her how she had failed her sister.

FOUR

Ignoring the creak of leather as he shifted in his saddle, Grayson Forsythe, sixth Earl of Tremaine, surveyed his estate, the lands surrounding Castle Tremaine.

All the way to the low stone wall on his left, past the dense copse of trees in the distance, to the river running along the perimeter on the right, fields of gently rolling hills, verdant with the new grass of spring, beckoned as if whispering his name. Beneath him, his big black stallion, Raja, pranced and sidestepped, eager to continue the ride they had begun early that morning. Almost as eager as Gray.

For the past ten days, the only peace he could find came from riding the hills, escaping the confines of the house, escaping his family . . . and the memories. Every year, as the dreaded day drew near, the past began to haunt him like a specter.

May 19, the day his pretty young wife, Jillian, had died.

Gray nudged the stallion down off the hill, into a ground-eating gallop. Wind tugged at the thick black hair he wore unfashionably long and tied back in a queue, and fluttered his full-sleeved, white lawn shirt.

Out here, he could examine the memories and wash them clean, know they would eventually fade, as they did every year. Back at the castle, which stood next to the river where she had died, it was nearly impossible to do.

Gray rode for the next hour, reached the far edge of his property, turned the stallion and began to walk the horse at a cooling pace back toward the house.

In time, the memories would leave him. Day-to-day problems with his tenants and his fields, Tremaine account ledgers, and the businesses he had inherited along with the title, would engage him once more, and the past would return to its place in the corner of his mind. But May 19 was almost a week away.

Gray steeled himself and urged Raja toward the ancient castle on the hill next to the river.

Corrie stared through the window of the shabby carriage she had hired at the Hen and Raven. Up ahead, at the end of a long gravel drive, Castle Tremaine perched on the top of a hill like the fortress it had once been. Inside the thick stone walls she would find Grayson Forsythe, the man who might well have murdered her sister.

"Are you certain about this, Coralee?" Allison leaned toward her, her hands clasped nervously in her lap. "Aunt Agnes could be right, you know. We might be putting ourselves into dreadful danger."

"It's Letty or Mrs. Moss. You must remember, Allison, to call me that. And they have no reason to harm us. They are going to think I am a destitute relative. And if something happens that gives us the least reason to believe we might be in danger, we shall leave in very short order."

Allison smoothed her simple printed cotton skirt, even worse for wear than Corrie's pale blue gown trimmed with ecru lace. Though the lacy overskirt had been carefully mended, it was clearly past time for the garment to be replaced. Corrie adjusted the matching blue-and-ecru lace bonnet, ignoring a soiled spot that barely showed on the lower edge of the brim.

Like the rest of the clothes in her trunks, the well-worn dresses had been altered to fit. She looked just as one would expect —

like a distant country cousin in need of a wealthy relative's aid.

With a lurch that nearly unseated them, the carriage rolled to a halt in front of the huge stone structure that was Castle Tremaine. Though the moat had been filled and planted with daffodils, the ancient building modified over the hundreds of years since its construction, the castle was impressive, with huge carved doors and two-story wings added onto each side of the high round keep that had once been the center of life there.

The Forsythe family had a respectable fortune — increased by the timely demise of Grayson Forsythe's wife.

The coachman helped Coralee and Allison from the rented carriage, tossed down their trunks, then climbed back up onto the driver's seat. "Ye want I should stay till yer settled, missus?"

Corrie shook her head. "We'll be fine. I am his lordship's cousin, you see, here for a visit." And she wanted the carriage to leave so there would be no way the earl could toss them out on their shabbily dressed derrieres.

She collected herself, gave the coachman a moment to set the carriage into motion, then heard the fading jangle of the harness as the conveyance disappeared down the long gravel drive. Ignoring the rubbery feeling in her knees, she climbed the steps to the majestic carved wooden door.

A few sharp raps and a butler, dressed immaculately in black tailcoat, black trousers and snowy white shirt, pulled open the heavy portal.

"May I help you?"

Corrie pasted on a smile. "I am here to see Lord Tremaine. You may tell him Mrs. Moss — Letty Moss, his cousin Cyrus's wife — is arrived to see him."

She wasn't sure the earl would even recognize the name, was hoping it rang only a distant bell.

"I'm afraid his lordship is not in at the moment, but his brother, Charles, is here. I shall inform him of your arrival. If you will please follow me."

The gray-haired butler, thin to the point of gaunt, led her and Allison into a drawing room that was furnished in quite a tasteful manner. It was done in a neoclassical style, with ornate white molded ceilings, a marble fireplace and graceful sofas and chairs upholstered in amber tones brightened with rich ruby accents.

Allison sat down in one of the chairs, her gloved hands clasped nervously in front of her. Corrie silently prayed the girl wouldn't completely dissolve into a fit of nerves before the first act of the drama had played out.

Seating herself on the brocade sofa, Corrie kept her smile carefully in place and waited, then rose at the swish of heavy skirts and the sound of feminine footfalls approaching down the hall. Allison rose, as well. Corrie could see she was fighting not to tremble.

A woman with golden-blond hair, parted and pulled into a cluster of glossy curls on each shoulder, swept into the drawing room. She had very blue eyes and a strikingly beautiful face. She surveyed the two women and, noticing Corrie's gown was simple and slightly frayed, but of better quality than Allison's, sharpened her gaze accordingly.

"Mrs. Moss, I presume?"

"Yes. Mrs. Cyrus Moss. My husband is Lord Tremaine's cousin."

"And this is your maid?"

"Yes . . . Miss Holbrook." Allison dropped into a curtsy, which the woman ignored. "I am here to speak to the earl on a matter of some importance."

"Lord Tremaine is not returned from his morning ride. As my husband is presently occupied, perhaps I could be of some assistance. I'm Rebecca Forsythe. If your husband is the earl's cousin, then he must be Charles's cousin, as well."

"Why, yes. It is a pleasure to meet you, Mrs. Forsythe." Corrie flicked a glance at Allison. "Perhaps my maid might wait in the kitchen so that we may speak in private."

"Of course." Rebecca called for the butler. "If you would, Mr. Flitcroft, show Miss Holbrook down to the kitchen for some refreshment. And bring tea and cakes for us."

Corrie kept her smile in place. She had been hoping to speak to the earl. Ultimately, it would be Lord Tremaine who would decide whether or not she would be allowed to stay. But she could hardly ignore this woman, who was her supposed cousin Charles's wife. Corrie would have to tell her story and hope to gain the woman's sympathy.

Allison cast her a worried look and followed the butler out of the drawing room. Corrie returned to her place on the sofa and Rebecca joined her there.

The blond woman smiled. She was incredibly beautiful, no more than five or six years older than Corrie, with a full bosom and very small waist. She was wearing a gown of aqua dimity with a full skirt heavily embroidered with roses.

"I'm afraid I've never met Cousin Cyrus,"

Rebecca said. "But I believe Charles had a distant acquaintance with his father. Where did you say you lived?"

"Cyrus and I make our home in York . . . though unfortunately, he has been away for more than two years. That is the reason I am here."

"I'm afraid I don't understand."

Corrie thought of Laurel, which helped her work up a tear. She pulled a handkerchief from her reticule and dabbed it beneath her eyes. "This is all so dreadfully embarrassing."

"Just take your time," Rebecca said encouragingly.

"I met Cyrus through friends of my parents, and in the beginning of our marriage, we were happy. Being older by nearly twenty years, he doted on me. Perhaps he loved me too much and that was the problem. You see, Cyrus had very little money, only what he inherited from his father, and that seemed to dwindle quite rapidly once we were wed. But Cyrus was determined to give me the things he believed I deserved."

Rebecca's blue gaze drifted over Corrie's worn garments. "And where is Cyrus now?"

"Well, you see, that is the crux of the matter. Cyrus wished to give me the best of everything — which is the reason, I suppose, that he left England and headed for America to make his fortune. Cyrus had plans, very big plans, and he had friends there he believed would help him."

"I do seem to recall Charles mentioning a distant cousin who left England for America in search of adventure."

Corrie nodded vigorously. "That was Cyrus. According to his letters, he arrived there safely. Then his letters stopped coming. I haven't heard from my husband in nearly two years."

"I am sorry to hear that, Mrs. Moss."

"Even worse than losing Cyrus, my funds have run out. Frankly, Mrs. Forsythe, I am quite destitute. I am here to humble myself and beg the earl to offer me shelter. If he refuses, I don't know what I am going to do." She dabbed the handkerchief again, ready to break into sobs if she thought it would help.

Rebecca began to frown. It was not a good sign. "You are not asking to take up residence *here,* are you?"

"Well, I —"

Just then voices drifted in from the stone-floored entry. One Corrie recognized as belonging to the butler, but the other was deeper, more resonant.

"I believe the earl has returned," Rebecca

42

said, rising gracefully from her place on the sofa. A faint knock sounded as she floated across the drawing room, and an instant later, the butler slid open the door.

"His lordship is returned," the gray-haired man said. "I have informed him of his visitor."

Corrie still sat on the sofa.

It was a very good thing.

The man who walked through the door was not at all what she had expected. This man, with his black hair tied back in a queue, was dressed not in a tailcoat and trousers, but mud-spattered black riding breeches, black knee-high boots and a full-sleeved white shirt. With his fathomless dark eyes, he looked more like an eighteenth-century highwayman than a wealthy English lord.

"Gray! I was hoping you would return. We have a guest, just arrived — your cousin Cyrus's wife, Letty Moss."

Those piercing eyes swung in her direction and seemed to hold her prisoner there on the sofa. "I didn't know I had a cousin Cyrus."

"I'm sure Charles has mentioned him. He is the son of your deceased third cousin, Spencer Moss. Spencer lived near York, as did Cyrus, if I recall. Mrs. Moss has come quite a distance to see you."

Tremaine didn't apologize for his rather disheveled appearance, simply turned and made a faint bow in her direction. "Mrs. Moss. Welcome to Castle Tremaine. Now, if you will excuse me, there are several pressing affairs I need to —"

"I should like a word with you, my lord." She rose from the sofa. "It is a matter of some importance and I have traveled quite far."

One of his black eyebrows arched up. It was clear he wasn't used to a woman speaking out as she had just done. For a moment he simply stared, as if taking her measure in some way.

The edge of his mouth faintly curved. "I suppose . . . since you have traveled, as you say, quite some distance, I can spare a moment." There was something in that hard-edged smile that made her stomach lift alarmingly.

Tremaine turned to his sister-in-law. "If you will excuse us, Becky . . ."

Rebecca's smile slipped. "Of course." She retreated toward the sliding doors, but didn't look happy about it. Corrie got the distinct impression the earl's sister-in-law wasn't pleased to think his impoverished distant cousin might move into the house, no matter how large it was.

The earl waited until the butler closed the drawing room doors. "You wished to speak to me. What can I do for you, Mrs. Moss?"

He didn't invite her to sit. It was clear he didn't expect the interview to take that long. Corrie steeled herself against a hint of irritation, followed by a rush of nerves. The earl was even more handsome than rumors about him had said. He was very tall and extremely broad shouldered, with a flat stomach and long, muscular legs clearly outlined by his snug black riding breeches. Looking into those penetrating dark eyes, she found it easy to imagine an innocent young woman like her sister succumbing to such sheer masculinity.

"It is difficult to know where to begin. . . ." Corrie gathered her courage and prepared to get into her role.

"Just tell me why you're here, Mrs. Moss."

Fine. So much for the long, heartrending performance she had planned to give. "Well, my lord, to put it bluntly, your cousin Cyrus — my husband — left me high and dry and ran off to adventure in America. I have waited nearly two years for his return and still have received no word of him. I have no family, no one to help me. I have spent my last farthing getting to Castle Tremaine, my lord, and I am desperate for your help."

Those dark eyes traveled over her, taking in her simple garments, the tatters that had been carefully repaired, making a thorough assessment of her bosom, which was quite full for her size and apparent even in a gown that was buttoned to the throat.

"As I said, I have never heard of Cyrus Moss. I do not doubt that he is some distant relation, since my sister-in-law has said so, but how do I know you are actually his wife? For that matter, how do I know he even has a wife?"

She had come prepared for this. According to her sources, Grayson Forsythe was a highly intelligent man. He'd been a major in the army, a man who had traveled to far distant countries. He would not be the sort to be easily duped.

Corrie reached into her reticule and pulled out two folded pieces of paper. The forged marriage certificate hadn't been cheap — or easy to come by. But she *was* in the newspaper business and she had some very good connections.

She crossed to where he stood and handed the papers to the earl, hating the fact she had to tilt her head back to look at him.

"The first document is a certificate of my marriage to Cyrus Moss three years ago, which was duly recorded in the church. The other is a letter from Cyrus, addressed to me as his wife and posted to me from the city of Philadelphia in America."

She had worked on that bit of tomfoolery herself, writing the letter with the heavy pen strokes of a man.

The earl perused the letter, reading where Cyrus professed his love and promised to return. Happily for Corrie, her sources assured her he hadn't yet set foot on English shores.

"Cyrus met your father on several occasions," she said as he finished and refolded the papers. Corrie hoped her information was correct. "I believe my husband held a high opinion of the man. Since the late earl is no longer with us, I am coming to you for help."

Tremaine frowned at the mention of his father, and she wondered if there had been some ill will between the two men. He seemed none too pleased as he handed back the documents, and Corrie held her breath.

Finally, he sighed. "If you will follow me into the study, I will write you a bank draft and you can be on your way." He turned and started walking.

Corrie fought a surge of panic. "Wait!"

Lord Tremaine turned. His attention fixed

on her face and she felt again that odd floating in her stomach.

"I said I would give you money. What
more do you want?"

Her eyes welled with tears. It wasn't that
hard to do since her plan was about to fail.
"I — I am in need of a place to stay, my
lord — but only for a while. In a few weeks'
time, I shall come into a small inheritance.
My father set up a trust, you see. When I
am two-and-twenty, I shall be eligible for a
monthly stipend that will see to my comfort.
It isn't much, but it should be enough to
keep me in simple fashion until Cyrus returns."

The earl's slashing black eyebrows drew
together. "Your father and mother are dead,
then? You have no one else who might aid
you?"

"As I said, I have no living relatives. It is
one of the reasons I married Cyrus. With
no one to look out for me, I needed his
protection. Unfortunately, his protection
didn't last all that long."

"How long were you and Cyrus together
before he left?"

"Just a little over a year."

The earl studied her for several long moments.

Corrie took a deep breath, her eyes tear-ing as she prepared to release a wailing sob she hoped would add a bit of persuasion. The earl held up his hand to forestall the outburst.

"There is no need for that. You may stay . . . at least until I can figure out what to do with you."

Her face lit up. She gave him a watery smile, brightened by an inward surge of relief. "Thank you, my lord. I shall be forever in your debt."

He merely nodded. "I'll speak to Rebecca, tell her we'll be entertaining our *cousin* for a while."

"This is very kind of you, my lord. I'm sure Cyrus would be even more grateful than I am."

Tremaine ignored the remark, turned and started for the door. As soon as he stepped out of the drawing room, Corrie sank down on the sofa, her legs no longer willing to hold her up.

She had done it! She had managed through a bit of deception to weasel her way into Castle Tremaine! As soon as she was settled, as soon as the Forsythe family had begun to let down its guard and trust her, she would begin her search.

Corrie's lips thinned. Gray Forsythe might be one of the handsomest men she had ever met, but that didn't mean he was innocent of murder. And if he had killed her sister and baby Joshua, the Earl of Tremaine was going to pay.

Gray stalked through the halls, his ill humor worse than it was before he left the house. He wasn't exactly sure how it had happened, but somehow, during her appearance in his drawing room in her mended garments, during the minutes she had looked up at him so pleadingly with her thick-lashed, jewel-green eyes, he had let down his guard and allowed a woman he had never met move into his house.

He didn't understand it. He had seen through her theatrics from the start, the false tears and wringing hands, the beseeching looks and trembly voice. But during her performance he had also caught a flash of something that intrigued him. He thought it might be desperation, for he was certain that was there, but this seemed more like determination. Whatever it was, it had interested him enough to let her stay.

Gray shook his head. For all he knew, Letty Moss was a charlatan, there to cajole him out of his money, rob him or worse.

He thought about the petite young woman with the fiery copper curls peaking out beneath the soiled brim of her bonnet, and almost smiled. He had been a soldier, a man who'd commanded troops in the British Army. If she gave him any trouble, he would simply toss her out on what held the promise of being a very attractive derriere.

The thought stirred him in a way he didn't expect. Since Jillian had died, he had slept with few women. It was his conscience, he knew, that kept him from indulging more in the pleasures of the flesh he so enjoyed, guilt that he was alive and Jillian was not. That he had not been there to protect her when she'd needed him.

He looked up to see Rebecca approaching down the hall.

"I hope you were a gentlemen about it," she said with a smile. "I realize she hoped you would let her stay here at the castle, but —"

"She's staying."

"What!"

"It won't be for long. She'll soon come into a monthly stipend that should be enough to provide for her until her husband returns."

"But . . . but we don't even know her. How can you simply let her move in?"

The smile he gave her was sardonic. "You are always chiding me about my manners.

51

It would be the height of bad taste to toss a member of our family in need of assistance out into the street."

"Yes, but I thought you would give her money, not invite her to move in."

Though Rebecca was tall for a woman, Gray looked over her shoulder toward the massive, carved wooden staircase leading up to the floors above. "There are two separate wings and seventy bedrooms in this house. Put her somewhere she won't bother you."

"But —"

He started walking. "I won't be down for supper. See that our guest has something to eat." Rebecca generally ran the household, another reason he was surprised by his actions today. On the other hand, he *was* the earl, which his family seemed mostly to forget. Perhaps it was time he made the matter clear.

Gray continued down the hall, suddenly desperate to get back outside in the sunshine, away from the thick stone walls of the house. He wondered again why he had offered the woman his protection.

Undoubtedly, it was nothing more than boredom.

Still . . .

FIVE

"I cannot believe you actually did it." Allison perched on a tapestry stool in front of the dressing table in the bedroom they had been assigned. It sat at the farthest end of the east wing of the house, a room that had not been refurbished, as had most of the other bedrooms Corrie had passed along the corridor.

The massive carved four-poster bed was a remnant of some lost century, and the Persian carpet was faded. The tassels on the dark green velvet draperies were frayed in several places, the curtains themselves so heavy they blocked the sun.

Still, it would do and quite nicely, since its distant location would also make it easier for Corrie to move about the house without being seen. She surveyed her quarters. The sheets on the bed were clean and, at her request, an adjoining room had been prepared for Allison, who was a companion,

Corrie had explained, as well as her lady's maid.

Corrie felt a shot of triumph that they had succeeded thus far.

"I don't think your dear cousin Rebecca is happy to have another relative in the house," Allison said, lifting one of Corrie's mended gowns out of the trunk and hanging it in the rosewood armoire in the corner.

"Apparently not." But it didn't really matter. Corrie was there and she meant to stay until either she had the answers to her questions or she was forced to leave.

"So what do we do now?"

She had given the matter a good deal of thought. "To begin with, since you are supposed to be a servant, I am hoping that the upper-staff will eventually accept you, and perhaps you will be able to get them to talk a bit about the scandal at Selkirk Hall. Laurel's death would be commonly known hereabouts, though Father did his best to keep the fact of the child a secret after the medical report was made. There is always gossip in a household this size. If Laurel was involved with the earl, perhaps one of them will know."

"That is a very good notion, Cor— I mean, Letty."

"And I shall seek out the people who live

in the house. I have yet to meet Charles. I was invited to supper, but I declined. I didn't wish to seem too eager. And I wanted a bit of time to compose myself, perhaps take a stroll round the house. In the meantime, why don't you go down and have some supper? I'll see you before I retire."

Allison left the bedroom, and Corrie, dressed in a more comfortable gown of printed blue muslin and leaving her bonnet behind, followed the carpet along the hall to the stairs at the end of the east wing. By now, supper was under way and she could move about without causing a stir. Still, she didn't want to appear as if she might have some ulterior motive — which of course she did.

With her nerves still strung taut from her encounter with the earl, she decided to go out to the garden. Descending a narrow staircase at the end of the hall, she pushed through a door into the cool night air. It was pleasant outside the house, and she was, she discovered as she moved along the terrace, in desperate need of a calming breath of air.

The first thing she noticed was how different it was in the country at night. The air was so clean and fresh, with not a particle of soot in the gentle breeze blowing over the landscape.

She hadn't been to the country in so many years it had never occurred to her to notice, not until tonight. Even house parties she attended had been, for the most part, held in homes at the edge of the city. Out here, the stars were so bright she could make out the constellations she had learned to name at Briarwood Academy. There was Orion, she saw, silently picking out each star, and the Big Dipper.

She wondered if Laurel had looked at the stars with Grayson Forsythe.

The thought darkened Corrie's mood. She stepped off the terrace and began to meander along one of the paths. The garden was lush, the leaves of the thick green plants flowing over the gravel walkways lit by burning torches. There were no gas lamps out here, as there were in her father's garden in the city, and somehow she liked the way the light flickered yellow and orange and cast dancing shadows against the leaves.

Corrie wandered the rambling paths, trying to collect her thoughts, plan her next move. She was rounding a corner of the path when she suddenly bumped headlong into a tall figure she hadn't seen standing in the darkness. Sucking in a breath, she scrambled to keep from falling.

A big hand shot out and caught her round the waist, pulled her upright before she took an embarrassing tumble.

"Easy."

Her stomach jerked at the sound of the deep male voice. Her gaze traveled upward, over a broad chest, up even farther to the dark, probing eyes of the earl.

"What are you doing out here?" he asked with a hint of accusation in his tone. "Why aren't you at supper?"

"Why aren't you?" she countered, wishing the man was anywhere except here. She caught herself. She wasn't a reporter doing a job; she was playing a role and she had better remember that. "I mean, I wasn't really hungry and I needed some air. It was a long ride in the carriage. I didn't think you would mind."

He studied her a moment, then turned his gaze toward the fountain bubbling a few feet farther down the path. "You enjoy being out-of-doors?"

Not really. She enjoyed dancing in lavish ballrooms, attending the opera, the theater, and dining in fine restaurants. At least she had until tonight.

"It's extremely pleasant out here. I never realized how clean the air would be."

One of his sleek black eyebrows went up.

"I spoke to Charles. He said that from what he recalled, Cyrus Moss lived on a farm."

Oh, dear Lord. "Well, yes . . . yes, of course, but . . . but there were animals, you know . . . and they smelled quite unpleasant, all those cows and sheep." What in the world was the matter with her? She sounded like a complete and utter ninny. Then again, it was probably better that way. The less intelligent she seemed, the less threatening she would appear.

Tremaine's gaze narrowed a moment, then the corners of his lips edged up — full sensuous lips that sent a funny little shiver into her stomach. "Somehow I have trouble imagining you tending a flock of sheep."

Never had a truer statement been made. She wished she'd had more information on Cyrus. It simply wasn't available, at least not quickly enough. "Well, I didn't do *that* sort of thing. Cyrus was very protective. He barely allowed me outside the house."

"I see. How long did you say you and Cyrus were together?"

What had she told him before? Sweet saints, she couldn't recall. "It was not quite a year."

For an instant his eyes seemed to sharpen, and she was terrified she had said the wrong thing.

"I suppose you miss him," the earl continued mildly, and she relaxed once more into her role.

"Why, yes, of course I . . ." She meant to continue the lie, then decided it was wiser to stay closer to the truth. She would hardly miss a man who had left her high and dry as Cyrus had done! "That isn't completely true. I know I should miss him, since he is my husband, but Cyrus was much older than I, and after the way he abandoned me, it is difficult to feel more than resentment toward him."

"I can understand your feelings." The earl's gaze assessed her, moved along her throat and over her bosom, down to the span of her waist, a slow, thorough perusal that made it suddenly hard to breathe.

"You . . . you do?" He was standing close enough that she could feel the heat of him, the power in his tall, masculine frame.

He was wearing a clean white shirt and a pair of black trousers fitted closely, as was the style, but no coat or waistcoat. His hair was clubbed back as it had been before. Corrie realized he was a man who paid little heed to convention. Combined with the rumors she had heard, it made him terribly intriguing.

She didn't think he was wearing cologne,

and yet she caught the faint, pleasant scent of sandalwood, and wondered at the source. The fragrance seemed to wrap around her, fill each of her senses, and she trembled.

"You're cold. Perhaps you should go back inside."

She swallowed. "Yes . . . yes, I believe that's a good idea." But she wasn't cold in the least. In fact, she felt overly warm. He made a faint bow, his black hair gleaming in the light of the torches, and she felt a strange pull low in her belly.

"Good night, Mrs. Moss."

She stepped backward as if to protect herself. "Good night, my lord." Then she turned and started down the path.

She was used to men's attentions. She was the daughter of a viscount, after all, and though she was a bit too outspoken, perhaps a bit willful, she knew that when she was ready for marriage, she would not lack for suitors. She enjoyed the company of men, had never been afraid of a man before, yet now, as she fled the garden, Corrie had to force herself not to run.

Gray watched the petite young woman with the fiery curls hurrying off down the garden path. In the light of the torches, she was lovely — skin as smooth as glass, luminous green eyes, and a lush mouth the color of roses. She was a beautiful woman, small but elegant, the sort to make a man think of silk sheets and even silkier thighs, though Gray suspected that perhaps she did not truly know that.

Still, she was not at all what she wanted him to believe, and that made him wary.

Gray made a rude sound in his throat. She had told him she'd lived with his cousin for more than a year, then said it was less. It was obvious she had never lived in the country, to say nothing of on a farm. Who was she? he wondered again.

For the past two years, since Jillian had died, Gray had felt restless in a way he never had before. The few women he had bedded had given him little satisfaction, just a few brief hours of sexual relief. He felt as if he had no purpose, no direction.

When he had first inherited the earldom, he'd had so much to do he'd had little time to think, had been exhausted at the end of each day. There was a great deal to learn about being an earl, and Gray had enjoyed the challenge. He had enjoyed his life, and his bachelorhood. He'd had any number of mistresses back then, and though he had tired of them easily, he always saw them well settled when the brief affair was over.

Then he'd been introduced to Jillian. She was young and beautiful, though a little too shy and a bit more reserved than perhaps he would have liked. But it was time he took a wife, time he did his duty and provided an heir, and Jillian and her family had seemed eager for the match.

Ten months later his wife was dead and he was once more alone.

Gray moved silently along the west wing hallway toward the master's suite. Since Jillian's death, he'd grown more and more restless, prowling the estate, searching for something but unable to discover what it was. With the arrival of the woman, for the first time in weeks he felt his interest piqued. Letty Moss posed a mystery and Gray meant to solve it.

He reached his suite, pulled open the heavy carved door and went into the rooms that had belonged to his father. The sitting room, with its gold velvet draperies and dark oak furniture, stirred unpleasant memories and somehow weighed Gray down. He walked on through, his mind returning to Letty Moss and what he might discover about her.

"Good evening, *sahib*." His manservant, Samir Ramaloo, walked out of the bathing chamber adjoining the bedroom. Wisps of steam from the marble tub, prepared for Gray's nightly bath, followed in his wake.

"Good evening, Samir." The small, dark-skinned man had been Gray's manservant in India during the three years he had served there in the army. Each officer kept a full retinue of servants, staff necessary for surviving the hot, arid, demanding climate.

With his impeccable service, Samir had made himself indispensable. He had also become Gray's teacher, introducing him to the customs and conventions of the exotic land, and giving him the insight to appreciate a country so different from his own. More than a servant, Samir was his friend — and the wisest man Gray had ever known.

"Your bath is ready, sire," he said now, glancing up with eyes so black they looked like bottomless pits.

Gray merely nodded and continued past him toward the marble bathing room.

"Your mind is far away," the Hindu said, knowing him well enough to sense that something was on his mind. "You think of the woman. I saw her this morning when she arrived and again tonight. She is very beautiful."

"Yes, she is." She was lovely, like a perfectly modeled porcelain doll. Likely with the same empty head. She had presented herself as a young wife married briefly, then abandoned by her husband. Gray knew women, and as skittish as this one was, he was sure she had barely known the touch of a man, and probably had never known fulfillment.

It made her story somewhat convincing, and yet he believed there was far more to her tale.

Interesting. That was Letty Moss.

Samir helped Gray disrobe, then stood aside as he stepped into the steaming water and settled his shoulders against the back of the marble tub.

"It is said the woman is your cousin."

Gray scoffed. "By marriage, and so far distant the relationship is meaningless."

"She has no husband?"

"She's married. The man left her penniless and went off to seek his fortune."

"Ah, then she is in need of a protector — and you are in need of a woman. You ignore the desires of the flesh, but they gnaw like a beast inside you. Perhaps you can give this woman what she needs and she will do the same for you."

"She has a head full of feathers," he said, trying to convince himself Samir's words held no appeal, "and she is not what she seems."

"Ah, a puzzle for you to solve. That is what makes her interesting."

"She is that. I'm not sure why she's here, but I intend to find out."

"That is good. Then you can allow yourself to pleasure the woman and enjoy her yourself. I will see what I can learn that might be of use."

Gray made no reply. He needed to keep a close eye on his so-called cousin, make sure she didn't cause any problems. Samir's watchful gaze might be helpful.

Whatever her story, Gray would soon find out the truth.

And perhaps, as Samir suggested, once he knew it, there could be other, more intimate things about Letty Moss he might find out.

Corrie's heart pounded madly as she hurried along the hall toward her bedroom. She didn't like the feeling at all. She reached her room, pulled open the door, and found Allison waiting inside.

"I thought you might need help getting out of your gown," she said.

"Thank you, Ally." Though she could certainly use the help with her buttons and corset, Corrie wasn't all that happy to find the dark-haired girl there. Not while her own mind was still swirling, replaying those unsettling moments with the earl in the garden.

"Did you find out anything useful?" Allison asked as she crossed the room.

"What . . . ? Oh, no, I just went for a walk outside." Coralee hadn't discovered a thing, except that Grayson Forsythe had a very worrisome effect on her.

She turned so that Allison could work the buttons at the back of her gown. "The earl was there. He didn't go to supper with Rebecca and his brother."

Allison's head snapped up. "You spoke to him out in the garden?"

"Why, yes."

"That is the second time you've met him. What is he like?"

Corrie bit her lip. How to describe the earl? "He is . . . the earl is a most unusual man. Besides being handsome in the extreme, there is something about him. . . . I cannot quite grasp what it is. He is very intense and has a decided air of mystery about him."

Allison helped her out of her dress and tossed it onto the bed. "Do you think he might commit murder?"

A shiver ran through her. "I am not sure. But he is a big man and clearly strong enough to accomplish such a feat if he wished. He is a man of the world, and certainly the sort to attract a woman. I'll need to investigate him further, and of course, we must find some proof that he and Laurel were involved."

Allison began to loosen the strings of her corset and Corrie drew in a welcome breath.

"You are just arrived," her companion said. "In time, you will find out the truth."

"I certainly hope so." Time was what she needed. She had to find answers about Laurel, answers about the earl.

Which meant spending more time in his company.

Corrie ignored the odd rush of heat that thought filtered into her stomach.

The morning was blustery, the breeze whipping the newly leafed branches on the trees outside the windows. Needing a moment to fortify her courage, Corrie stood outside the door to the breakfast room she had been directed to by one of the servants, a small, very thin, dark-skinned man.

Speaking with an accent unlike any she had ever heard, he'd told her his name was Samir. When she asked him where he came from, he'd said he was from the Oudh District of India, that his family was no longer living and he had come to England with Lord Tremaine.

A manservant from India. More and more the earl intrigued her. She could think of no one of her acquaintance who was anything like him.

Corrie walked into the breakfast room, a cheery place done in yellow and peach, with a table loaded with gold-rimmed porcelain and gleaming silver. Delicious smells rose from an elaborate sideboard covered with silver chafing dishes and steaming urns of coffee and tea.

"Good morning, Cousin." A handsome blond man spotted her and rose from his chair. Charles Forsythe was shorter than his brother, and as fair as his wife instead of dark like the earl. Tremaine followed suit and rose as well, but more slowly, with a casual sort of insolence that seemed to be part of his nature.

"I'm your cousin Charles," the blond man continued. "You've already met my brother, Gray, and my wife, Rebecca."

"Why, yes. It's good to meet you, Cousin Charles. Good morning, everyone." She didn't look at the earl. She didn't like the oddly disoriented feeling she experienced whenever she did.

"Do join us," Charles said. "You must be hungry. You missed supper last evening."

68

She managed a smile. "Yes, I discover I am ravenously hungry this morning."

She dared a glance at Tremaine, saw his eyes darken with something she couldn't read, and continued over to the chair Charles pulled out for her.

"You're beginning to settle in?" he asked. "Your maid has found the kitchen and acquainted herself with our servants?"

"Yes. It is very kind of you to allow me this visit."

Charles smiled. He had very white teeth and hazel eyes, and though he was not as imposing as his brother, he was a very attractive man. "I'm sure Becky will enjoy the chance for female companionship."

But when Corrie glanced at Rebecca, the tight smile she received made it clear that Cousin Becky wished Letty Moss had never arrived at Castle Tremaine.

Breakfast continued with pleasant conversation, Charles being as charming as his older brother was not. Tremaine said little, but she could feel his eyes on her, and the sensation sent nervous tremors through her core. There was something about him. . . . And yet the more she was around him, the less she could imagine her sister enjoying his company, let alone falling in love with him.

69

Laurel had always been sweet and terribly shy. A man like Gray Forsythe would have frightened her, not charmed her. But perhaps there was another side of the man that Corrie had not yet seen.

The earl had arrived earlier than the rest of his family and was nearly finished with his meal by the time a servant filled a plate for her and set it down on the table. Obviously, the man was an early riser. He finished the last of his eggs, cast her a final glance and excused himself from the group. The minute he disappeared from the breakfast room, the pressure in Corrie's chest began to ease.

She took a deep breath and released it slowly, fixed her attention on Charles and Rebecca, and joined in their light conversation.

"I'm afraid I have a prior engagement this afternoon," Rebecca said. "Perhaps tomorrow we'll have a chance to get to know each other a bit."

"That would be nice," Corrie said, not at all looking forward to the event. Still, getting to know Rebecca Forsythe might lead to information about Laurel and the earl.

As the meal continued, neither Charles nor Rebecca mentioned Letty's missing husband, Cyrus — a blessing, since Corrie knew almost nothing about him.

As soon as everyone finished, she excused herself and returned upstairs. Since Rebecca had dodged her company, Corrie intended to take advantage of the time she had to herself and walk to the village. It wasn't that far, and she was ready to begin her investigation. She hadn't been to Castle-on-Avon since she was a girl. No one would recognize her and she was anxious to discover what she might find out.

Changing into a day dress of apricot muslin, and grabbing her shawl, straw bonnet and reticule, Corrie set off for the village.

Six

A blustery wind blew the fringes of her shawl, but her full skirts and petticoats kept her legs warm. Corrie was enjoying her walk along the trail more than she had expected, noticing how green the fields were, how the wildflowers seemed to dance in the breeze. She was shading her eyes to get a better view of the copse of trees on the horizon when she saw him, a tall male figure mounted on a huge black horse.

Silhouetted against the sun, dressed in the sort of riding breeches and full-sleeved shirt he had worn yesterday, his hair tied back as before, the earl seemed out of time and place, as if he should have lived a hundred years ago.

The moment he spotted her walking along the path, he turned the stallion and began a leisurely gallop in her direction. The beautiful horse effortlessly climbed the rise to where she stood, and the earl drew the animal to a halt a few feet away.

"Mrs. Moss. I thought you would be spending the afternoon with Rebecca. Instead you are out for a stroll." He smiled, but it didn't look sincere. "You appear to be enjoying yourself."

"Why, yes I am." The words came out in an embarrassingly breathy voice and she stiffened her spine. "Your sister-in-law was busy and I was glad for a chance to get a little exercise. It's a bit windy, but the sun is warm, making it a perfect day for a walk in the countryside."

He frowned, his sleek black brows drawing together. "Where is your maid?" His voice held a hint of disapproval that sent her irritation up a notch.

"The village isn't that far, and need I remind you, my lord, I am a married woman."

His mouth barely curved. "You needn't remind me, Mrs. Moss. I have imagined you often in that manner." He said it as if he meant something else, but she couldn't quite figure out what that could be.

"I'm afraid I had better be going," she said. "I have some shopping to do and I don't wish to be late in my return."

"Perhaps I should accompany you — just to be certain you are not accosted."

"No! I mean, no thank you. I shall be fine on my own. Good afternoon, my lord."

Corrie continued walking, trying to ignore the butterflies swirling in her stomach. She couldn't figure out why the man affected her as he did, but she didn't like it. And she certainly didn't want him to go with her. She had questions to ask, and she could hardly do so with the earl tagging along.

As she continued along the trail, she dared a glance over her shoulder, saw that he was riding the opposite way, and breathed a sigh of relief. Turning her thoughts to the questions she meant to ask, she increased her pace toward the village.

The moment Letty Moss disappeared from view, Gray pulled Raja to a halt and spun the stallion in the opposite direction. Staying as far back as he could, careful to keep from being spotted, he followed the woman into the village. He saw her walk into one of the shops across from the market square and while she was inside, rode to the stable.

"I won't be long," he told one of the stable boys, handing him the horse's reins and flipping him a coin. "Take care of him till I get back."

Returning to High Street, the main street of town, he spotted Letty coming out of the shop and stepping into the one next door. As soon as she was inside, Gray made his way to the window. Inside the shop, she examined bolts of cloth, fingering the colorful swatches of silk with tender care. Then she made her way toward the clerk. He watched the two women talking, but couldn't hear what was being said.

Letty left the shop and went into the butcher's store, from which she soon exited munching on a piece of ham. Next she stopped by the hatmaker's. Letty didn't seem to be buying much, just having a look around, but then if her tale was true, she had very little money.

She appeared to be having no illicit meetings, no rendezvous with a man, nor was she doing anything that might give Gray pause.

He told himself to return to the house and leave the woman alone, but something held him back. Instead, he waited the nearly two hours Letty remained in the village, then retrieved Raja and followed her home.

He watched her walking along the path through the tall green grasses, her hips swaying as if to some silent song. His groin tightened. He couldn't believe such an innocent, unconscious movement could stir him that way. He nudged the stallion forward, eager to catch up with her.

She must have heard hoofbeats behind her, for she whirled toward the sound and her foot caught on an unseen obstacle in the grass. She went down with an unladylike yelp, falling backward over a big granite boulder. Her skirts went into the air and her frothy white petticoats flew up to her chin.

Gray found himself grinning. He couldn't remember the last time he had done that. He sobered, pulled Raja to a halt on the path, and swung down from the saddle.

"Here — let me help you."

She slapped away the hand he offered, shoved down her skirts and propped herself up on her elbows, her knees still draped over the rock. "I don't need your help. You are the reason I am in this humiliating position in the first place."

"How is it I am at fault because you tripped?" He reached down and caught her wrist, hauling her somewhat awkwardly to her feet.

She didn't bother to answer, just cast him a look that said it was true. The ribbons on her bonnet had come undone and her hat tumbled into the grass. Her glorious copper hair came loose on one side and hung down in a riot of curls against her shoulder. Gray fought an urge to tangle his fingers in the heavy mass and haul her mouth up to his for a kiss.

It was insane. He barely knew the woman, and he definitely didn't trust her. Perhaps Samir was right about denying himself for too long. He made a mental note to pay a visit to Bethany Chambers, wife of the aged Earl of Devane, whose country home, Parkside, was just beyond the next village. Gray had heard the countess had returned for the summer. Though he hadn't seen her in several months, she was a woman of strong appetites, and he knew she would welcome him into her bed.

Letty began to brush off her dress, drawing his attention to the bosom straining against her bodice. He tried not to wonder if her breasts were as full and tantalizing as they appeared, or how they might feel in his hands. Letty made no comment, just turned to begin her journey back along the path, then winced as her ankle crumpled beneath her. Gray caught her before she could fall.

She looked up at him with those jewel-green eyes. "I — I think I twisted my ankle."

"Sit down on the rock and let me take a look."

Letty sat carefully and Gray knelt in front of her. He picked up her foot, slid off her low-heeled leather boot and began to gently examine her ankle.

"What . . . what are you doing?"

"I was in the army. I want to make sure nothing's broken." Her stockings had holes, he noticed, though they had been carefully mended. At least part of her story appeared to be true. She was certainly in need of money.

"It is only twisted," she said, trying to pull the sprained limb free of his grasp. "I'm sure it is fine."

Gray didn't let go. "Hold still, will you? You're only making this harder." It wasn't the only thing getting hard. As he ran his hand over the fine bones in her feet, his groin tightened. Gray set his jaw against the unwanted arousal and continued to test each tiny bone, feeling for possible injury, trying not to think what it might be like to slide his hand upward, over the smooth silk stocking that covered a very shapely calf, all the way to the slit in her drawers, then inside to touch —

He clamped his jaw against a shot of lust and the painful throbbing of his erection. Silently he cursed. He needed a woman and badly, and though this one fired his blood, he could not have her. Not yet.

He felt her trembling and realized he still

cradled her small foot in his hands.

Gray cleared his throat. "I don't think there are any broken bones."

"I told you, I am fine."

He slid her boot back on and tied the laces, carefully helped her up from the rock. She took a step and nearly fell. "Oh, dear."

"You need to keep your weight off that ankle. You'll have to ride home with me."

He didn't give her time to argue, just scooped her up in his arms and settled her in the saddle, one leg on each side of the horse, her full skirts bunching around her knees. Raja danced and sidestepped as Gray swung up behind her, but Letty didn't seem to be afraid. At least not of the horse.

"What a beautiful animal," she said, trying to keep her balance without touching him.

Gray almost smiled. It wasn't going to happen, and since he had no choice but to see her safely home, he might as well enjoy himself. He wrapped an arm around her waist and nudged the stallion forward. Letty tried to scoot away, and nearly unseated them both.

"I would advise you to sit still, Mrs. Moss, before we both wind up on the ground."

She glanced at him over her shoulder. "What are you doing out here? I thought you were returning to the castle."

"Lucky for you, I wasn't ready to go home just yet."

She turned, tilted her head to look up at him. "You weren't following me, were you?"

"Now, why would I do that?"

Letty made no reply, but her wariness did not lessen. They rode silently along the trail until the horse started up a rise and Letty began to slide backward in the saddle. She grabbed a handful of the stallion's thick mane to hold herself in place, but it did no good, her bottom coming to a snug rest between his thighs. Even through the fabric of her skirt and petticoats, he could feel the heat of her, the roundness of her flesh, and he went hard just thinking of the soft, womanly curves beneath her gown.

"I hope I'm not making you too uncomfortable," she said.

Uncomfortable? Good God, he ached with every heartbeat. "I'm afraid that is an understatement."

She started to move, squirming to put some distance between them, making him harden even more. Gray stifled a groan. "Hold still, dammit. Just stay where you are."

Letty's head came up. "You don't have to swear. If you will recall, this is your fault in the first place."

She had accused him of that, he remembered with a hint of amusement. "Sorry, I forgot."

They didn't talk again until the castle came into view. Gray rode directly up to the front, where a groom stood, waiting to take the reins. Gray swung from the saddle, then reached up to lift Letty down, finding her waist was so small his hands wrapped completely around it.

"Thank you," she said softly. He noticed she was breathing a little too fast, and figured he must be right about her. Her experience with men was obviously limited. Cyrus was a much older man. Perhaps his desire for a woman had declined with his years.

As Samir suggested, perhaps Letty's needs would surface, and if that happened, Gray would be delighted to oblige. At least he would be once he had assured himself she was no threat to him or his family.

He looked down at the top of her head, at the fiery curls resting against her small shoulders, and fisted his hands to keep from reaching out to touch them. She might not be a woman of great intellectual capacity, but she set fire to his blood, and should she wind up in his bed, he wouldn't waste time talking.

She looked up at him as he lifted her against his chest to carry her up the front steps, and another surge of lust hit him like a fist.

Holy God. Samir was right. It was past time he took a woman. He would send a note to Bethany Chambers. Gray just hoped he would receive her reply very soon.

In her quilted satin robe, Coralee sat in the middle of the massive four-poster bed, her legs tucked up beneath her. She had babied her ankle for the past few days, and the limb seemed to have fully recovered. Perhaps she owed some thanks to Gray Forsythe, but she didn't want to think of him now.

Instead, she fixed her attention to the bundles of pale pink letters, bound with pink satin ribbon and carrying traces of Laurel's favorite perfume, that rested on the faded counterpane. Corrie had brought the letters with her from London, all that remained of the sister she had loved.

An ache throbbed in her heart as she reached for a bundle, each letter filed by the date of its arrival. She located the two stacks she had received in the past eighteen months, and untied the first one. Last year, her sister had been living at Selkirk. In August, she had journeyed to East Dereham in Norfolk to spend time with Agnes's older sister, Gladys. There was only one letter written each month during the time she'd been there.

Corrie now knew she'd been pregnant, growing heavier each day with the child she carried. Her time must have been absorbed with thoughts of the babe, and yet she'd been afraid to tell even Corrie about the infant she would bring into the world.

Corrie's eyes misted as she reread one of the letters, this one dated March 20, when Laurel had been preparing to leave Selkirk Hall.

I feel restless and uncertain. I had such dreams for the future and now they seem sullied, darkened by pain and despair. And yet I have known love. I cannot tell you how that feels. Love makes the parting worth the sadness.

Corrie remembered receiving the letter. She had penned a reply, asking her sister about the man she had fallen in love with, and why they couldn't marry if the two of them cared for each other. She had also asked the man's name.

Laurel's next letter had not come until a full month later, after her arrival in East Dereham. She had ignored Corrie's questions and instead talked about life on her aunt's farm.

Corrie had assumed her sister's infatuation had faded and that she hadn't been truly in love. Corrie's own life was so busy the subject never came up again. Instead, sparse as they were, Laurel's letters grew more and more cheerful. On September 18, she'd written:

> Though it is autumn, it is sunny today, with warm bright rays filtering through the branches of the trees outside my window. Orange and yellow leaves are beginning to fall and I can hear birds singing, the hum of crickets in the dry fall grasses. Lately, the world seems somehow brighter, and I find myself awakening each day with a sort of wonder at all God has created.

As Corrie looked back, she found it clear, from the difference in the first letters and those coming later, that something in Laurel's life had changed. Now Corrie knew that her sister was expecting a child, and it was obvious from her letters how much she looked forward to being a mother, how much she looked forward to the future.

A lump swelled in Corrie's throat to think how very short that future had turned out to be.

She finished rereading the letters but found no clue to the man Laurel had loved.

Was Gray Forsythe that man? When Corrie was around him, she found it hard to think. It was as if he had some sort of magic power, some mysterious quality she found nearly impossible to resist. Had Laurel felt it, too?

Corrie thought of the afternoon two days ago she had spent in the village. While pretending to shop, she had begun a subtle investigation into Laurel's death. She had casually mentioned the young woman from Selkirk who had drowned in the river several months back and, as always, people were eager to gossip.

"She done kilt herself," the butcher's wife said. "They say she lost her innocence to some man and couldn't stand the shame she brought down on her family." The raw-boned woman shook her head. "Don't seem right for a young girl to meet such a tragic end."

At the hatmaker's shop, the story was the same — though it was clear her father's attempt to hide the secret of Laurel's illegitimate child had failed.

"It must have come as a terrible shock to his lordship . . . findin' out his daughter weren't pure as the driven snow the way she seemed." As the heavyset woman worked on the hat she was making, she leaned over the counter. "There were a babe, I hear," she whispered. "Drowned right along with her."

Corrie felt a wave of sadness followed by a jolt of anger that the villagers should think the worst of someone as sweet as Laurel. Reminding herself why she was there, she widened her eyes, pretending shock and disbelief. "What a dreadful thing to happen. Does anyone know the father?"

The beefy woman stuck a feather into the band of blue velvet around the brim of the hat. "Heard tell it were the vicar's son, but most don't believe it. They think it was one of them fancy lords up to the castle."

Corrie's stomach knotted. "Which one?"

The hatmaker shrugged. "No one knows for certain. That dark one'll take a woman's fancy. Ain't no doubt of that."

No doubt at all, Corrie thought.

"There's the married one, but his wife keeps a pretty close watch on him." The milliner smoothed the feather, checked its position in the hatband. "The other one, young Lord Jason, they say he's stolen the virtue of half the milkmaids in the county. Like I said, nobody knows for sure, probably never will."

But Corrie intended to find out. Thanking the woman for the bit of conversation, she had walked out of the village convinced her suspicions were not unfounded.

Local gossip named one of the men in the castle as the mostly likely father of Laurel's child. Corrie would do some checking on the vicar's son, and Thomas Morton, one of Squire Morton's four boys, since Agnes had made mention of him. But it was Gray Forsythe whose wife had drowned in the same river as Laurel, Gray Forsythe who remained at the top of her suspect list.

As she sat there now, in the middle of the bed, her sister's letters scattered around her, Corrie remembered the feel of the earl's hard body, the warmth and strength of his arms as she had ridden back to the castle with him. It wasn't difficult to believe he could have seduced her shy, innocent sister.

Corrie glanced at the clock on the mantel. She had begun to gather the first pieces of the puzzle. As soon as she got the chance, she would take a look around the house, see what else she might find out.

SEVEN

At Charles's insistence, Rebecca gave Corrie a brief tour of the house. It was clearly the last thing the woman wished to do. Still, she remained distantly polite, and Corrie did the same. Any chance to glean information was a welcome opportunity.

"The castle was built in 1233," Rebecca told her as they stood in the great room in what had been the original keep. A huge fireplace dominated one wall, and heavy carved beams supported the floors above. The medieval style had been preserved through the years, and now the space served as the formal dining room.

"Of course, the house has been refurbished and added onto dozens of times. Gray's mother took great care to see it modernized. I've made a number of changes myself." There was pride in Rebecca's voice when she talked about the castle, which was magnificent, a grand medieval palace with all the modern luxuries and most elegant furnishings.

"How long has the Forsythe family lived here?" Corrie asked.

"It's been family-owned for more than two hundred years."

"So the earl lived here as a boy?"

"Yes."

"What was his family like? I mean, Gray and Charles were brothers. Were they brought up in happy circumstances?"

For a moment, Rebecca seemed uncertain how much she should say. "There were three brothers but no sisters. James was the eldest, the apple of his father's eye. Charles was the baby and he was indulged a good deal."

"And Gray?"

Rebecca shook her head, moving the golden curls on her shoulders. She was gowned in pink-and-white silk. With her creamy complexion and cornflower-blue eyes, she was a confection of loveliness, the perfect English rose. And yet Corrie sensed a core of steel inside her.

"Gray was different," she said. "He was dark where the rest of the family was fair. He was outspoken and often headstrong. He and his father . . . didn't get along."

"Is that why he joined the army?"

She shrugged her shoulders. "He was a second son. It is commonly done."

"I heard he was in India."

Rebecca nodded. They moved out of the great hall down one of the numerous corridors. "He was stationed there for three years before James fell ill. I think Gray resented having to return. He was always a bit of a wanderer. Once he became the earl, he was forced to settle down and accept his responsibilities."

Corrie followed her down the hall, past several beautifully furnished drawing rooms. "Was that the reason he married?"

"I suppose it was. It was his duty to produce an heir, and Gray wasn't the sort to shirk his duty. Jillian was beautiful and she had money and social position."

Corrie's interest stirred. "Was she in love with him?"

"I think she was mostly in love with the idea of being a countess. Jillian was still a child in many ways."

Corrie had come here for answers. She pressed for more. "Just before Cyrus left the country, he received a letter from one of his friends." Hardly true, but a way to broach the subject she needed to discuss. "The note mentioned the countess's death."

"Yes. There was a boating accident. Her

death was extremely hard on Gray."

"He must have loved her very much."

Rebecca turned toward her. "I don't know if Gray is capable of love. Certainly, he cared for her a very great deal. He blamed himself for not being there when it happened, not being able to save her."

So the earl wasn't there when his wife died. More information to file away. There would be time to examine it later.

They moved along the hallway into the long gallery, where portraits of the men in the earl's family hung, floor to ceiling, on the walls. Most of them were blond or had light brown hair and looked nothing at all like Gray, whose hair was midnight-black, his features dark and more defined, more masculine.

"Gray's mother must have been dark complexioned."

Rebecca arched a delicate eyebrow. "Clarissa Forsythe was as fair as Charles. She claimed Gray got his coloring from the women on her mother's side of the family."

Claimed. It was an interesting choice of words. Corrie studied the wall, finding not one portrait that remotely resembled Gray. Perhaps there was some doubt as to the earl's parentage. Perhaps that was the reason he and his father had not got along.

Corrie made a mental notation to include with the rest of the information she had collected.

Rebecca glanced at the clock. "I hope you've enjoyed seeing some of the house. Perhaps another time I can show you a bit more. For now you'll have to excuse me. There are several pressing matters I must attend to."

"Of course." Corrie hid her feeling of relief. Though Rebecca had been unerringly polite, it was clear the woman disliked her. Perhaps she suspected Letty Moss wasn't what she appeared, and if so, Corrie could hardly fault her. Or perhaps Rebecca simply didn't want another woman living under her roof.

Whatever the reason, they were not destined to become close friends, and considering the reason Corrie was there, perhaps it was better that way.

Left on her own, she wandered the maze of halls, memorizing which rooms were where, slowly making her way along one corridor into the next, hoping she would be able to find her way back. As she passed the library, she paused, then, drawn by the floor-to-ceiling rows of books, stepped inside.

The grand room was impressive, each oak

bookcase tightly jammed with leather-bound volumes of various sizes and shapes. It sat in one of the oldest parts of the castle, with walls of stone and wide-planked oak floors that had been worn in places over the years. And yet the wood was polished to a glossy sheen, the brass lamps on the tables gleaming. Each of the long rows of shelves had been carefully dusted, as if the books they held were of importance to the master of the house.

Corrie appreciated the value of books. Her home in London was filled with them; even her bedroom had a bookcase stuffed with volumes she treasured. She was a writer. It only made sense she was also a voracious reader.

She prowled the library, enjoying the comforting feel of the room and its familiar volumes, the slightly musty smell of old paper and ink. Laurel had also liked books. Corrie wondered if perhaps it was an interest her sister had shared with Lord Tremaine. If so, the library might hold some clue that would provide a connection between the pair. For reasons she refused to examine, a bitter taste rose in her mouth at the thought.

And the same persistent feeling that Laurel would never be attracted to a fearsome man like the earl.

She was simply too gentle, too kind, while the earl was contrary, forceful and intense.

Corrie wondered at his childhood. Gray's mother had died when he was ten, she knew, leaving him with a father who — what? Believed he was another man's son? Had Gray been mistreated? Had he joined the army to escape an unloving parent?

And what of his wife?

Rebecca had said Gray was incapable of love, and yet Jillian had seemed to have no qualms in marrying him. Was he in some way responsible for her death? Was that the reason for his guilt?

Corrie wandered the endless rows of bookshelves, picking up a volume here and there, recognizing a goodly number she had read. One section held classical Roman texts including Virgil's *Aeneid* and a volume of poetry by Lucretius, *On the Nature of Things,* printed in the original Latin. Both were books Corrie had enjoyed. She had always loved school, loved learning. Her father had ignored social custom and provided her with the best tutors money could buy.

She perused the next section, pulled a volume out of the stack and flipped it open: Homer's *Odyssey.* She had read the book years ago, an epic adventure that had spawned her desire to write. Just as before, the words on the page began to draw her in and she found herself rereading a favorite passage. She was so immersed in the tale, she didn't hear the earl's heavy footfalls, muffled by the thick Persian carpet.

"Find something interesting?" Reaching out, he plucked the book from her hand. Turning it over, he read the gold letters printed on the leather cover. "The *Odyssey*?" He started to frown. "You read Greek?"

Good heavens. "I — I . . . was just looking at the letters. They look so different than they do printed in English."

He turned away from her, shoved the book back into its place on the shelf. "You're in the library, so I presume you like to read. What sort of books do you prefer?"

She was Letty Moss, she reminded herself, a poor relation from the country. "I, umm, actually I don't read all that much. Mostly I enjoy the ladies' magazines . . . you know, *Godey's Lady's Book* and the like." She flashed a beaming smile. "They show the very latest fashions."

Gray's mouth thinned. He nodded as if he were not the least surprised. Somehow that look rankled more than anything he could have said.

"I'm sure Rebecca has something you might enjoy," he told her. "Why don't you ask her tonight at supper?"

"Yes . . . I'll do that. Thank you for the suggestion."

He stood there, waiting for her to leave, tall and dark and imposing.

"I — I do enjoy reading poetry on occasion," she said, searching for an excuse to remain in the library. "Perhaps I might find something to keep myself occupied until tonight. You don't mind if I look a bit longer, do you? It's a very pleasant room."

He studied her face. "I don't mind. I spend a good deal of time in here myself."

She summoned a sugary smile and waited for him to leave. As soon as he disappeared out the door, she set to work. No more time for dallying. She needed to see what was in the drawers of the big oak library desk, examine the writing table in the corner. As soon as she got the chance, she intended to visit Lord Tremaine's study, but that would be dangerous and certainly no daytime venture.

Corrie hurried over to the desk and began to pull open the drawers. There were all sorts of musty papers, an ink pen with a broken nib, and some old books with pages missing. She wondered why the earl had not thrown the books away then thought how hard it was for her to get rid of a beloved text. Perhaps, as she had once thought, there was a side to the earl she hadn't yet discovered.

Then again, perhaps it was Charles who had kept the books. He seemed far more sentimental.

She made her way to the writing desk. The inkwell was dry and this pen also required a new tip. Nothing had been written at the desk for some time and there was nothing to signify a connection to Laurel.

Corrie moved back to the bookshelves. Laurel loved poetry. Had she and her lover met in the castle, perhaps sat together in the library? Or had their affair remained in the dark shadows of the woods, or somewhere else lovers might tryst?

There was a top shelf full of books, a bit out of the way, that looked intriguing. It was just out of reach, so she shoved the rolling ladder over and climbed up until she could see the volumes clearly, but she didn't recognize any of them.

The Kama Sutra was the title of one of the works. She recognized a book by the French author Voltaire, the scandalous, erotic novel *Candide* she'd heard whispered about, one no decent person would read. Beside it, her eye caught on a book entitled *The Erotic Art and Frescoes of Pompeii.*

A flutter of interest ran through her. She loved to read about foreign places. Someday she hoped to travel and write stories about the people and places she visited. The book was about an ancient town in Italy, but the title implied it was far more than a travelogue. Corrie couldn't resist reaching for the volume, opening it up for a single quick glance.

The book fell open in her hand and she saw that the pages were filled with drawings. Her eyes grew wide at the first one that came into view. A wall painting from the Stabian baths, said the copy beneath the etching — a naked woman with bulbous breasts, resting on her hands and knees. A naked man knelt behind her, and the woman's head was thrown back in what appeared to be a grimace of pain.

Corrie couldn't imagine exactly what he might be doing, but her heart began to beat oddly and a drop of perspiration slid between her breasts. Hastily, she turned the page to the drawing of a mural. In it, Mercury strode naked across the picture, a huge appendage thrusting forward between his legs. Corrie just stared.

"I see you found something, after all." The

earl stood at the foot of the ladder. Corrie shrieked at the sight of the tall figure looking up at her, lost her balance and tumbled backward off the ladder. She landed squarely in the arms of the earl, the erotic book flying into the air, then falling back to earth with a soft thud, landing open in her lap.

The earl looked down at Mercury, and Corrie's face turned beet-red.

"Interesting choice," he said, and she could hear the amusement in his voice.

"Put me down!" She struggled to get free, trying to regain at least some portion of her dignity. She could feel the strength in the arms around her, the hard muscles in Tremaine's powerful chest, and her stomach contracted.

The earl set her firmly on her feet, catching the book before it tumbled to the floor. He held it open, his eyes moving over the drawing.

"I approve your selection, Mrs. Moss. I think you'll find this far more interesting than poetry, as much as I enjoy a good poem. I admit, however, I didn't think you would be quite this adventurous."

Corrie closed her eyes, her skin burning all the way to the tips of her breasts. "I — I just happened to see it. I couldn't imagine what I might find inside." She stiffened her spine. "You should be embarrassed, my lord, to keep books of this nature in your library, where any unsuspecting person might stumble upon them."

One of his black eyebrows went up. "This particular unsuspecting person had to climb to the top of a ladder to reach them. That is hardly stumbling, Mrs. Moss." The corner of his mouth curved. "Though should you wish to examine the rest of the pictures, I would not tell anyone."

"How dare you!" As insulting as the suggestion was, in truth, she would dearly love to look through the book. What had the naked man and woman been doing? she wondered. And what else might she learn?

"My apologies," said Tremaine with a trace of mockery. "I merely thought you might find it educational . . . since you are a married woman and already familiar with the intimacies shared between a man and woman."

Her face turned even redder. She remembered the book she and Krista had found in the basement of the dormitory at Briarhill Academy. It described the basics of making love, but little more. At the time, they had both been appalled by the thought of a man and a woman joined in that way.

But Krista had said that lovemaking was glorious, and considering Corrie's reaction to Gray Forsythe, the way she grew flushed and dizzy whenever he came near, she wondered if it might not be so. Whatever the truth, it was frightening, these strange feelings he stirred.

And dangerous.

"I think it is past time we ended this conversation," she said. "It is, at best, highly inappropriate to speak of such matters. If you will excuse me, my lord . . ."

Tremaine made a formal bow. "Of course. Have a good afternoon, Mrs. Moss." The amusement had returned to his voice but there was something more.

Corrie couldn't miss the hot look in his eyes, and for a moment, she couldn't glance away. Her heart was beating like rain on a roof, and her mouth felt dry.

She tried to imagine her sister with Gray, but the image would not come. Laurel would have required a gentle lover, someone who understood her shyness, her tender sensibilities. Corrie couldn't imagine Gray Forsythe in any sort of understanding role. As a lover, he would be demanding, not tender. She wasn't sure how she knew, she just did.

Turning away, careful to keep her gaze

fixed straight ahead, she walked out of the library. Though she could no longer see the earl, she could feel his gaze on her, burning with the force of a flame. The gossips called him a sensualist, a master in the art of love. It was clear from the books she had seen that he was a student of the erotic.

The man must know a dozen ways to touch a woman, a hundred ways to heighten the wild sensations that swirled through her body whenever he came near. Had her sister succumbed to the aura of masculinity that surrounded him?

Each time Corrie was with him, the notion seemed more absurd.

And yet his wife was dead and so was Laurel.

The thought sent a cold dash of reality through the fire that seemed to burn through Corrie's veins.

EIGHT

Krista sat next to Leif in the drawing room of the town house they had purchased in Berkeley Square. Upstairs, their five-month-old son, Brandon Thomas Draugr, Viscount Balfour, heir to the Earl of Hampton, lay napping in the nursery with his nanny.

"I hope we are doing the right thing."

"You have not stopped worrying about Coralee since she left. You will feel better if you do something."

"I should have *already* done something," Krista said. "I should have stopped her from going in the first place."

Leif scoffed. In the light streaming into the drawing room, his golden hair glinted and his eyes looked as blue as the sea. "Your friend is much like you, my love. Once her mind is made up, there is little chance of changing it."

Krista sighed. Leif was right. Coralee was as stubborn as Krista. Perhaps that was one of the reasons they had become such good friends.

"Apparently Allison has been able to keep in touch with Agnes Hatfield, Laurel's aunt," Krista said. "We know, for the moment at least, Coralee is safe, but she is taking a terrible risk."

Leif didn't disagree. "Perhaps your Mr. Petersen can help as he did before." Leif had insisted on hiring the investigator. Now Krista was glad.

A noise in the doorway drew her attention. "Your guest, Mr. Petersen, is arrived," the butler announced, a gray-haired man with impeccable credentials who had come to work for them shortly after she and Leif were wed.

"Send him in, Simmons." Krista rose along with Leif to greet the investigator they hadn't seen in nearly a year.

Dolph Petersen had helped Krista and her father discover the identity of a man trying to destroy the gazette. The villain had been ruthless and determined, willing to go to any lengths, including murder. With Dolph's help, they had been able to stop him. Krista hoped the investigator would be able to help them again.

Petersen appeared just then in the doorway, tall and lean, his face hard-edged yet handsome. Leif's hand settled possessively on Krista's waist, and Dolph broke into one of his rare smiles.

"It looks like the newlyweds are still in love. It's good to see you both. Congratulations on the little one. I heard it was a boy."

"Thank you." Leif's massive chest expanded with a hint of pride. He was a wonderful father, an attentive husband and a passionate lover. Krista knew how lucky she was.

Which made her think of Corrie and the trouble she faced, and why Leif had asked the investigator to come to the house.

"Why don't we sit down?" she suggested, guiding the small group farther into the drawing room. "Would you like some refreshment, Mr. Petersen? Some tea, or perhaps something stronger?"

"It's just Dolph. I think we know each other well enough by now. And I'm fine."

Krista and Leif took seats on the sofa and the investigator settled his lean frame in a chair. "So what can I do for you this time?"

Krista cast a glance at Leif, who nodded for her to begin. "You remember Miss Whitmore?" she asked. "My friend Coralee?"

"Of course."

"Well, she has become involved in a very dangerous intrigue and we are hoping you might be able to help."

Petersen leaned forward in his chair. "Go on."

Trusting the man's discretion, for the next half hour Krista and Leif explained about Laurel Whitmore's death and that of her illegitimate child. They told him the authorities had concluded it was suicide, but Corrie adamantly refused to believe her sister would do anything that would harm her baby.

"She thinks her sister was murdered," Leif said. "She is convinced the Earl of Tremaine is the man who killed her."

"Grayson Forsythe?" Petersen asked in surprise.

Leif straightened on the sofa, emphasizing his incredible height. "You know this man?"

"Yes. Aside from a rakish reputation with women, Gray Forsythe is as honorable as they come. He served in the military in India and was decorated several times before he came home. Why would Miss Whitmore believe the earl would murder her sister?"

"To begin with, the earl's estate, Castle Tremaine, sits next to Selkirk Hall. And both Laurel and the earl's wife were drowning victims. Both died in the Avon River."

Krista went on to explain that Jillian Forsythe's death had left Gray with a goodly sum of money and the chance to resume his numerous affairs. She told him Corrie knew his reputation with women and thought that he must have seduced her sister, gotten her with child, then killed her to prevent a scandal.

"Interesting. Not much is known about the circumstances of Tremaine's wife's death. The family kept the matter fairly quiet."

"Well, Coralee has managed to scheme her way into Castle Tremaine pretending to be some long lost cousin, and that is the reason Leif and I are so worried about her."

"If the earl is guilty of murder," Leif added, "Coralee could be in very grave danger."

Petersen grunted. "The lady has guts, I'll say that for her. I'll do some digging, see what I can find out. I'll also try to find out if Tremaine had a relationship with Laurel Whitmore."

"If he didn't," Leif said, "find out who did."

Petersen nodded. "I'll do my best." He stood up, and so did Krista and Leif. "I'll let you know as soon as I find anything."

Krista gave him a relieved smile. "Thank you, Mr. . . . . Dolph."

He smiled. "As I said, I'll be in touch."

Krista and Leif bade the investigator farewell and returned to the drawing room.

"I'm so glad you thought of hiring him," she said.

"Petersen is a good man. He'll do his best to find out about the earl."

Krista knew he would. She just hoped whatever he discovered wouldn't be more bad news for Coralee.

Corrie sat in her bedroom after supper. The meal had been an uncomfortable affair. Since her arrival, she had noticed a certain tension between Charles and his wife that seemed amplified when they were together for any length of time. Gray rarely appeared for the evening meal. An hour ago, she had seen him ride out of the stables, heading off toward the village.

Thinking of his reputation with women and remembering the erotic books she had found in his library, she figured he had probably gone off in search of female companionship, a notion she found oddly annoying.

A light knock sounded on the door to Allison's small, adjoining bedroom. Relieved that her friend had returned to her room, Corrie hurried over to open it.

"I've been worried about you," she said. "Where on earth have you been?"

"I was talking to Hilde Pritchard, one of the kitchen maids. The woman is a dreadful gossip — for which I am eternally grateful."

Allison sank down on the bench at the foot of the big four-poster bed, and Corrie sat beside her. "So what did you find out?"

Allison tucked a lock of dark hair up into her mobcap. She was still dressed in the simple black skirt and white blouse that had been provided for her as Corrie's maid.

"Hilde is quite friendly. She has worked here a very long time, so she knows a lot about the family. She says there was a great deal of animosity between the earl and his father. Apparently after his mother died, Gray's father treated him very badly. He was punished for the slightest infraction. Once he was caned so badly the housekeeper felt compelled to summon a physician."

Dear Lord. "Why did his father treat him so cruelly?"

"According to Hilde, the late earl didn't believe Gray was truly his son — though until the day she died, Lady Tremaine swore she had always been faithful."

Sympathy for the young boy Gray had been rose up inside Corrie. A child with a

109

father who beat him, living in a home without love. . . .

She forced herself to think of Laurel, of her pregnancy and abandonment, her senseless death. Ruthlessly, Corrie tamped any sympathy down.

"Did you ask Hilde about the earl's wife?"

Allison nodded. "It seems Rebecca had planned an outing that day. A number of guests were invited. There was to be a picnic and a boat ride down the river. At the last minute, Gray declined to go with the rest of the group. Half an hour into the journey, the craft sprang a leak and very rapidly sank. Charles was able to help Rebecca reach safety, but Jillian's garments must have caught on something beneath the surface, and she sank out of sight so fast no one was able to save her."

Corrie felt a rush of sadness for the loss of such a young life. It was followed by an unexpected pang of relief.

"So it truly was an accident."

"Apparently so."

Still, Tremaine *could* have murdered Laurel. Coralee revised the thought. She was coming to suspect the earl less and less, if for no other reason than she couldn't imagine the man in the role of Laurel's beloved.

"Perhaps the earl wasn't the one," Allison said finally, parroting Corrie's thoughts.

"Perhaps not. But there were two other men in residence at the castle much of last year. According to Aunt Agnes, both Charles and Jason Forsythe, the earl's cousin, were living here when Laurel died. If it wasn't the earl, it could have been either one of them."

"I heard Lord Jason is due to arrive on the morrow."

Corrie had heard that, too. "So it would seem. I'll have a chance to meet him, see what he is like. In the meantime, the earl has gone out for the evening. If we're lucky, he'll be gone all night — which means I'll be able to search his room."

"His room? But you just said —"

"When it comes to women, Tremaine is a rogue without conscience. I have to make certain he wasn't the man who fathered Laurel's child."

Allison eyes widened. "What if he comes back while you are in there?"

"I'll stay alert, but I don't think he will. He doesn't appear to be the sort to go long without female companionship, even should he have to pay for it." Which, as handsome as he was, she doubted very much. Corrie ignored a second stab of annoyance.

"Perhaps I should come with you," Allison suggested, but the uncertainty in her hazel eyes said she didn't really want to.

"I'll have less chance being discovered if I go by myself."

It was true, and relief shone in Allison's face. "His valet was in the kitchen when I left. He's an interesting little man. I'll try to keep him talking until you are finished."

"Good idea."

"I'll wait up for you. I won't be able to sleep until I know you are safe."

Corrie just nodded, glad to have a friend there in the castle.

With a last glance out the window to be certain no lone rider approached, she lifted the skirt of the drab gray dress she had chosen to make her less noticeable and headed out the door.

Gray rode Raja into the stable and swung down from the saddle next to a sleepy groom.

"I would 'ave waited up, milord," Dickey Michaels said in his thick Cockney accent. "I thought ye was gonna be gone fer the night."

"I thought so, too, Dickey." He handed the reins to the sandy-haired youth. "See Raja is watered, grained and rubbed down before you put him away."

"Yes, sir. I'll take real good care o' 'im." The boy led the stallion away and Gray started back to the house.

He'd been on his way to Parkside to see Bethany Chambers when he changed his mind. He needed sexual relief and badly, but somewhere along the route, he'd recalled the lady's spoiled disposition and constant demand for attention. On a hill halfway to her house, he'd pulled Raja to a halt. Need or not, the lady was just too much trouble.

On top of that, he realized, he no longer had the least desire for the lovely Lady Devane.

Dammit to hell and gone. Another female had caught his fancy and it seemed no other would do.

Gray didn't really understand it. He was a man of lusty appetites. Why this one had snagged his interest so strongly he could not say. There was something about her he couldn't quite figure out, and perhaps the mystery drew him. Whatever it was, he wanted her and he was fairly certain she wanted him.

They were both mature adults. At thirty, he wasn't too old for Letty — or whoever she turned out to be. It really no longer mattered. She posed no threat that he could discover. Whoever she was, if he had run across her in London, he would have made her his mistress. She needed money. He would set her up in a cottage somewhere near. He would treat her well, see her financially cared for and, in return, she would service his needs.

Gray almost smiled.

On the morrow, he would send a note of apology to Bethany for failing to arrive for their intended assignation. In the meantime he would begin his campaign to bring Mrs. Moss to his bed.

With that thought in mind, Gray headed toward the stairs leading up to his suite in the west wing of the castle. It was dark in the house. Only the gas wall sconces Rebecca had installed were burning, leaving just enough light to find his way. He climbed the stairs, strode down the corridor and pulled open the heavy door.

The curtains were drawn and an oil lamp burned on the bedside table, the wick turned down low. For an instant, he figured Samir must have anticipated his return in that uncanny way he seemed to have and lit the lamp for him. Gray frowned. Even Samir couldn't have read his thoughts tonight. They were too uncertain.

Stepping quietly into the sitting room, he surveyed the interior. The hair prickled at the back of his neck. The sixth sense he'd developed in the army was kicking in, telling him someone else was in the room.

At first, the space appeared to be empty. Then his gaze lit on the heavy gold velvet draperies and an unnatural bulge there. A pair of feet peeped out from underneath — small, feminine feet, he saw, encased in soft kid slippers.

The shoes were too fine to belong to a servant, yet a bit scuffed with wear. With a flash of certainty, Gray knew those small feet belonged to Letty Moss.

What was she doing here? Trying to steal his money or something else of value? Her worn garments betrayed her desperate need. He stared at the curtain, a wicked thought coming into his mind.

Dressed in his riding clothes, Gray sat down on the stool in front of the dresser and began to tug off his boots. One after the other, they hit the floor with a heavy thud. His coat came off, then his shirt, leaving him bare-chested. Rising from the stool, he started toward the window, unbuttoning the fly of his riding breeches along the way.

A faint gasp sounded through the curtain as the flap came undone and his breeches slid a little lower on his hips.

"You may come out, Mrs. Moss — unless you wish to remain there while I finish disrobing."

Slight movement rippled the curtain. With a sigh of resignation, Letty stepped out from behind the gold velvet, her chin lifting as she turned to face him. Though she stood ramrod straight, her eyes widened at the sight of his bare torso, the curly black hair on his chest. She spotted the unbuttoned fly of his breeches and her cheeks turned scarlet.

"Might I ask what you are doing in my room?" he asked calmly, though having her there was making him feel anything but calm. Letty moistened her lips, and heat pooled low in his groin.

"I, um, got lost. I was out in the garden, you see. I came up the back stairs and I — I must have turned the wrong way when I reached the second floor landing."

"Ah . . . that must be it. Your room is in about the same location at the opposite end of the house."

"Yes, it is." Her relief turned to suspicion. "How do you know the location of my room?"

He gave her a wolfish smile. "I like to personally assure myself my guests are comfortable. You *are* comfortable, are you not, Mrs. Moss?"

Her eyes narrowed. "Not at the moment."

He closed the distance between them, stopped directly in front of her. Gray caught her shoulders and felt her tremble, but she didn't back away. "I want to know what you're doing in my room, and this time I want the truth." He gently shook her. "Were you looking for money? I know you have very little. I suppose I could understand that."

Her chin firmed. "I am not a thief."

"What then?"

"I just . . ." She released a shaky breath. "I wanted to know something about you. You've allowed me into your home. I thought I might learn something of what you are like if I took a look round your suite."

His fingers dug into her shoulders. "Why would you care?"

Letty stared up at him with the greenest eyes he'd ever seen. "There are . . . a number of reasons. Some of them even I don't understand." The words rang with a sincerity that seemed to surprise them both.

Gray looked into her beautiful face, the softly winged russet eyebrows, the small indentation in her chin. He watched the rise and fall of her breasts, and a wave of lust hit him like a blow.

He wanted Letty Moss. With her lovely copper hair and small but voluptuous body, she drew him like a moth to the flame. Gray slid an arm around her waist and hauled her against him. Her eyes widened in shock the instant before his mouth crushed down over hers. For a moment, Letty stiffened, her small hands pressing against his chest as she tried to push him away, but Gray refused to let her go.

The heat of her surrounded him, the taste of her inflamed him. He drew her closer, enfolded her in his arms and kissed her until her mouth began to soften under his. Letty began to kiss him back, and a groan escaped from deep in his throat. Slanting his mouth over hers, he continued the gentle assault, inhaling her soft rose scent and hardening to the point of pain.

Coaxing her lips apart, he slid his tongue inside to taste her more fully, and Letty melted against him, her full breasts pillowing into his chest. Gray's whole body tightened and he fought the urge to open the front of her simple gown and take the creamy weight into his mouth.

Her hands ran over his bare chest, slid around his neck, and she went up on her toes to increase the contact. She was all warm, willing woman, exactly what he needed.

Gray lifted her into his arms and strode toward the door to his bedroom — and Letty began to scream.

"Quiet! What the hell are you doing? Do you want to bring the entire household down on us?"

"You put me down this instant!"

For a long moment, he just held her, his body aching with need, his shaft hard as stone. Just seconds ago, Letty had been warm and pliant. Now he could feel her stiff restraint and knew that whatever fires had burned between them had begun to flame out.

Reluctantly, he set her on her feet. "You seemed willing enough a minute ago."

She glanced away. In the dim light of the lamp, he could see the hot wash of color in her cheeks. "I — I don't know what happened. I just . . . I didn't realize it would feel so . . ." Letty shook her head and Gray frowned.

For all her passionate responses, he had always sensed her innocence. Was his bloody cousin Cyrus such a miserable lover he had never bothered with foreplay, never managed to arouse his wife in any way?

"I must go," she said. "I apologize for coming here. It was stupid and meddlesome. I hope you will forgive me."

"Listen to me, Letty. If you're frightened, you don't have to be. I won't do anything to hurt you."

"I have to go," she repeated, backing toward the door. "My maid will be waiting to help me undress." Her cheeks colored again at the mention of disrobing, and Gray felt a renewed flare of lust.

Letty spun toward the door and he didn't try to stop her. It was clear his seduction was going to take more time than he had planned.

Still, he had no doubt of the outcome.

Letty Moss was going to be his. If money was what she had come for, he would see that she had it. Whatever she needed, he would give it to her.

That and something far more enjoyable.

Gray felt the rare pull of a smile. Soon Letty Moss would be spending her nights in his bed.

Oh, dear God! Trembling at the memory of what had just occurred, Corrie stood outside the door to her bedroom, trying to catch her breath. Her heart was hammering, her composure shattered. Allison would

120

be waiting inside. She would want to know what had happened. Dear Lord, what would Ally say if she knew?

Corrie leaned her head against the wall and forced herself to take long, calming breaths. She had done as she planned and gone into the earl's private chambers, but she had found nothing of interest. At least nothing that connected Tremaine with Laurel. Careful not to disturb anything or leave something out of place, she had searched every dresser drawer, gone through two tall rosewood armoires, the earl's portable writing desk, even his clothes. She had found nothing.

Nothing except the earl himself.

Sweet saints in heaven!

How could she have allowed him to kiss her? How could she have kissed him back the way she did?

A fresh wave of heat curled through her at the remembered feel of his mouth moving hotly over hers, the hard muscles of his naked chest pressing against her breasts. She remembered the way her nipples had tightened and begun to throb, aching with a need she had never felt before. She'd wanted to touch him all over, to feel those hard muscles against her bare skin, to taste him, to —

She broke off at the horrifying thought. Sweet God, the rogue deserved every bit of his scandalous reputation. He was a devil with the skill of a sorcerer.

Unconsciously, she reached up to touch her kiss-swollen lips, which tingled and felt oddly tender. She could still taste him there. If she closed her eyes, she could recall his male scent, tinged with the fragrance of sandalwood.

He was a skillful seducer, and yet, after a sample of his scorching passion, Corrie had never held a stronger conviction that Gray Forsythe was *not* Laurel's lover, not the man her sister had fallen so deeply in love with, a man she had protected until the end of her life.

Corrie knew Laurel too well, and was beginning to know the powerful earl. The two were completely ill suited. There was no way her sister could have withstood the intensity of a man like Gray.

Still, Corrie couldn't completely exonerate him until she found the man who was Laurel's beloved.

The man who might have murdered her.

Taking a slow, deep breath, smoothing wisps of hair back into the chignon at the nape of her neck, Corrie opened the door and stepped into her bedroom.

NINE

After a long, mostly sleepless night, Corrie awakened to a rainy May morning. Anxious to escape the house and avoid the Earl of Tremaine, she skipped breakfast, dressed simply and set off for the village, despite the darkened sky.

The town, some of the stone buildings of which were as old as the castle, was quiet this early. Corrie strolled through the shops that were just opening their doors, bought a crumpet and tea in a tiny salon and a length of pretty blue silk ribbon to tie back her hair. She spoke to a number of the local women, hoping to pick up a bit of gossip, then headed for the church.

Vicar Langston had been assigned to the parish three years ago, Corrie had learned. His son, Patrick, was currently a deacon in nearby Berkshire County, but he had been living in the village at the time Laurel was murdered.

Corrie was standing in the aisle a few feet in front of the altar when the vicar approached, a fine-boned man with silver hair and kindly blue eyes.

"May I help you, young lady?"

"Well, I . . . actually, I came to say a prayer for a friend of mine. She died a few months ago. Her name was Laurel Whitmore."

The vicar shook his head. "Terrible tragedy that. My son and I often stopped by to visit Laurel and her aunt. She was such a sweet girl, a friend of my son's fiancée, Arial Collingwood."

"Your son is engaged to be married?"

"Why, yes. For more than a year. The wedding is set for next month. Miss Whitmore helped Arial make plans for the nuptials."

Corrie's chest tightened. If Laurel was a friend of the girl Patrick Langston was going to marry, she never would have gotten involved with him in any way. She simply would not have betrayed her friend.

"I've heard rumors about what happened," Corrie said carefully. "I know there was a child. I still find it difficult to believe Laurel would kill herself — and nearly impossible to imagine she would have done anything that might harm her baby."

"Yes, it came as a shock to everyone. I blame myself, somewhat. I should have sensed her distress. She was a member of my congregation, after all. Of course, I didn't know about the child . . . not until later. In fact, the truth didn't surface until after both of them were gone. The family tried to keep the information private, but it's difficult to keep a secret like that in a town this small."

"I imagine it would be." She cast a glance at the altar, where a row of flickering beeswax candles cast shadows against the stone walls. "You would think the father of the child would come forward. I don't suppose anyone knows who he is."

"I'm afraid not. Perhaps he never knew about the babe . . . at least not until it was too late. By then it didn't really matter."

Good heavens, she had never thought of that. Was it possible Laurel had never told the man she loved that she carried his child? And if so, why not?

"I am truly sorry about your friend," the vicar said. "I liked Miss Whitmore very much."

"Thank you. So did I."

Corrie left the church, her heart aching. Laurel was dead, and speaking about her with the vicar made the pain resurface again. At least Corrie could mark another suspect off her list. She didn't believe

Patrick Langston was the man who had fathered her sister's child, not when his fiancée had been Laurel's friend.

Corrie was thinking about her sister as she walked along the path through the fields, her mind miles away, when she heard a soft whimper. She paused, her gaze searching for the source of the noise. A second whimper reached her and she left the path and headed in the direction the sound had come from. Not far away, a big gray mongrel lay on his side in the tall grass, blood oozing from a gash across his ribs.

"Easy, boy." Corrie knelt beside the dog, ran her hand over his matted fur. He was a tall animal, but thin, his gray hair long and stringy, his tail curved up over his back. He was malnourished and homely, but his eyes were dark and compelling, and when he looked at her, she saw such pain and resignation it twisted her heart.

"It's all right, boy. You're going to be all right. I'm going to take care of you." *I'm not going to let you die.* She didn't know whose dog he was, probably just a stray, but she couldn't stand to see an animal suffer.

Reaching beneath her skirt, she tore off a long strip of her petticoat, then another and another. Very carefully, she bound them around the dog's ribs, gently tying each strip

126

of cloth. The injury needed to be washed and cleaned, but first she had to get the animal back to the house.

"Just stay here," she said, smoothing her hand over his fuzzy gray brow. "I'll be back as soon as I can." Picking up her skirts, she ran for the path, then raced all the way back to the house. She was breathing hard by the time she reached the stable and rushed inside in search of a groom. She found the earl instead.

"What's happened?" he asked, coming out of Raja's stall, where he had been working. "Are you all right?"

She choked out the words, trying to catch her breath. "I need a wagon of some sort. I found a dog who's been injured. He needs help and I —"

"Wait a minute — you ran until you are barely able to stay on your feet for a *dog?* What about your ankle? You could have sprained it again."

"My ankle is fine, but the dog is injured. I need to get him home so that I can take care of him."

The earl studied her face, reading her fear for the animal. His features softened. "Come," he said gently. "I'll help you bring him back."

Relief washed through her. The earl would

help her. For reasons she could not fathom, it didn't really surprise her.

Hitching one of the horses to a gig, he helped her onto the seat and they set off down the muddy road. Taking the path would be shorter, but it was narrow, not wide enough for the cart. They would have to carry the dog to where the vehicle waited on the road.

As soon as they reached the spot, about halfway to the village, they left the cart and crossed the field to the path. It took a while to locate the place where Corrie had left the dog. He was still there, still lying on his side, her makeshift bandage soaked through in several places with bright red blood.

"It's all right, sweetheart," she said, sinking down in the grass beside him. She petted his neck and talked to him softly, then glanced up at the earl, who was looking at her strangely, wondering, she supposed, why she bothered with such a homely mutt.

Tremaine turned his attention to her makeshift bandage, went down on one knee and began to gently check for broken bones, as he had done that day with her.

"I wonder what happened to him," she said.

"I don't know. We'll know more when we get him home and take a look at the wound." He rechecked the bandage. "You used your petticoat?" he said with amazement, noticing the blood on her skirt.

"I realize I don't have all that many clothes, but I really had no choice."

His lips edged up. "No choice, indeed." But he looked as if none of the women of his acquaintance would have sacrificed their garments for a dog.

Tremaine bent over and carefully lifted the animal into his arms. The dog whimpered but didn't try to fight him.

"It's all right, old fella," he said. "We'll get you back so the lady can take care of you." The earl looked down at her. "Don't get your hopes up. He's lost quite a bit of blood. He might not make it."

She squared her shoulders. "I'm not letting him die." Lately, there had been too much death around her. Laurel. Little Joshua Michael. She wasn't letting this poor animal die, as well.

The earl started walking and Corrie hurried to keep up with his long strides. He placed the dog on the blanket they had spread in the back of the gig, helped her up onto the seat, then climbed up beside her.

He hadn't mentioned the scene in his room last night, had, in fact, treated her as if nothing at all had occurred. Instead of

feeling grateful, she was annoyed the encounter had left him so little affected.

Still, he was helping her with the dog. For
now that was all that mattered.

They reached the barn, and two of the
grooms raced up to the cart. One carried
the dog into a stall and placed him carefully
on a bed of straw. Corrie sank down beside
him.

"Easy, boy." She petted the mangy gray
hair on his head as the earl unwrapped the
bandages around his ribs. One of the
grooms brought a bucket of water and a
stack of rags, and Corrie used the cloths to
cleanse the wound, rinsing away the blood
and dirt.

Her gown was ruined. She had brought
only a few with her, and Letty Moss could
certainly not afford to buy more. But when
the dog rested his paw on her hand with
what she thought was a look of gratitude,
she decided he was worth the loss of the
gown.

"The cut's pretty deep," Tremaine said,
after assessing the long gash, "but it's not as
bad as I thought. We'll bind the wound, and
if he rests and recovers his strength, he
might be all right."

Corrie looked up eagerly. "Do you think
so?"

"I'd say there's a very good chance."

She smiled in relief. "Thank you for helping him."

The earl's gaze found hers. "I was helping you, Letty, not the dog." But the gentleness he had shown made her believe that if he had been the one who found the animal, he wouldn't have simply left him there to die.

"He needs a name," she said. "What do you think we should call him?"

"You shouldn't name him until you're certain he's going to live. It'll just make it harder if he doesn't."

"In that case I shall most certainly name him." She ran her hand over his unkempt fur. "I think I'll call him Homer."

"Homer? From the *Odyssey* and the *Iliad*?"

Oh, dear, that was exactly the reason. The dog seemed to be a wanderer. After she'd found the book in the library, the name had just popped out. Corrie thought quickly. "Homer was the name of my dog back in York. Is he also a character in a book?"

Gray shook his head. "He's an ancient Greek writer. And I suppose it's as good a name as any."

"It is a wonderful name." She stroked the dog's matted fur. "Isn't it, Homer?"

The animal licked her hand as if in agreement. When she looked up at the earl, there was a tenderness in his expression she had never seen before.

"You've a soft heart, Letty Moss." He rose from his place in the straw beside her. "Let me know if you need any more help." And then he was gone.

Corrie should have felt relieved.

Instead, she found herself wishing he had stayed.

Lord Jason arrived the next day, and good grief the man was handsome. Corrie had heard the servants tittering about him, but seeing him in person made their comments as bland as mush.

In a different, less fearsome way, Jason Forsythe, youngest son of the Marquess of Drindle, was even more handsome than Gray. Though not as tall nor as solidly built, with his light brown hair and stunning blue eyes he was every woman's fantasy. His warm smiles came often, carving an amazing pair of dimples into his cheeks, and his laughter had a merry ring.

He was five-and-twenty, Allison told her, just two years older than Laurel, a discovery made through a growing friendship with the servants. As charming as he was, it was easy to imagine the two of them together.

It was easy to imagine Laurel falling in love with Lord Jason — and nearly impossible to believe the man was a murderer.

"I didn't realize what charming company I would find here at the castle," he said on their first meeting. "If I had, I might have come home sooner." He made an extravagant bow over Corrie's hand, pressing a kiss against the back. "I'm afraid I've never had the pleasure of meeting your husband, Mrs. Moss, but I must say he has exceptional taste in women."

Corrie lowered her eyes, enjoying but not the least taken in by the man's flattery, which, unlike the earl, he seemed to hand out in great measure.

"I only hope Cyrus is safe," she said, keeping to her role. "It is difficult not to worry after not having heard from him for so long."

"I imagine you must be terribly lonely," Jason said, extending an arm to escort her in to supper. "Perhaps I can help in that regard while I am here."

Corrie smiled up at him, liking him as much as everyone seemed to. "I'm certain you will."

They walked into the dining room the family used for less formal evenings, a lovely space holding a long rosewood table with

twelve matching high-back chairs upholstered in forest green. Only the main rooms
and hallways had been converted to gas
lighting and none of the bedrooms, but here
a gas-burning crystal chandelier hung above
the table, illuminating the interior with a
soft yellow glow.

Jason seated her, then took a chair across
from her. Rebecca and Charles took their
usual places, Rebecca wearing a cream-and-
gold taffeta gown that set off the golden
highlights in her hair. Corrie tried not to
think of the gown she herself was wearing, a
turquoise silk that had never been the height
of fashion. Though the gown rode low on
her shoulders, as was the current mode,
mended roses cupped her breasts and the
hem was slightly frayed.

For once, the earl had decided to join
them. Taking his place at the head of the
table, he cast Corrie a penetrating glance.
With a burst of clarity, she realized Tremaine
wasn't happy she was paying so much attention to his extremely handsome cousin.
Why that pleased her so inordinately, she
refused to consider.

But as the servants began arriving with
the first course of the meal, a delicate cream
of leek soup, Corrie gave Jason an even
brighter smile.

"Rebecca says you are just returned from the Continent. How long were you there?"

"Only the past two months. I was in Italy mostly, but I also spent time in France."

Gray took a drink of his wine. "Mrs. Moss is particularly interested in Italian history." His dark eyes burned into her. "Did you happen to visit Pompeii while you were there?"

Corrie choked on the sip of wine she had taken.

"Are you all right?" Jason reached over and took the glass from her unsteady hand, set it back down on the table.

"I — I am fine. It must have gone down the wrong way."

"You were saying . . . ?" Gray pressed, and Corrie wanted to hit him.

"I'm afraid I didn't get as far as Pompeii. Mostly I was in Rome."

Corrie cast a furious glance at Gray, then returned her attention to Lord Jason. "I should love to see Rome. The history of the Colosseum is fascinating. I read once that in its glory the arena seated more than fifty thousand people, and the opening games lasted a hundred days. I thought it was amazing they could actually fill the arena with water and stage naval battles. The ruins must be an incredible sight."

Gray was frowning. "I thought you only read ladies' magazines." His suspicious tone jarred her back to reality. She was Letty Moss, for heaven sake! Letty didn't read Roman history in the original Latin!

Corrie pasted on a smile. "Well, that is mostly true. What I meant to say is I have a friend who knows a lot about history. She particularly enjoyed reading about Rome. We discussed it on occasion."

"The Colosseum *was* fascinating," Jason said, picking up the thread of conversation — thank God. "There were all sorts of cells and tunnels under the floor where the Romans kept the animals and gladiators. You could almost imagine Julius Caesar sitting up in the gallery."

"I would love to see it someday."

While they dined on stuffed capon and drank expensive French wine, Jason described the sights of Rome, and Corrie was enthralled. She would so much love to travel. Reading about a foreign country wasn't the same as seeing it in person.

She asked about other of his visits, and he told her a bit about France.

Jason smiled at her across the table. *"Vous êtes une trés belle femme,"* he teased, his blue eyes twinkling. *You're a very beautiful woman.*

136

"Et vous, monsieur, êtes un flattereur," she couldn't resist retorting. *And you, sir, are a flatterer.*

Gray eyed her with suspicion.

"I only know the basics," she explained with a sweetly regretful smile. "How to count to fifty, how to find the ladies' retiring room or respond to a compliment. I should love to be able to speak French — it is so romantic, is it not? But alas, I've never had a knack for language."

Liar. She was fluent in both French and Italian, and lately, even spoke a bit of Old Norse that Krista's husband, Leif, had taught her. She had always had an ear for language. She yearned to travel to France and talk to the people who lived there.

"Gray is really the traveler, not me," Jason said. "He lived abroad for several years before he joined the army. You know he was stationed in India?"

She looked over at Gray, realized he was watching her. "Yes . . . Rebecca mentioned he was there."

"Perhaps he'll tell you about it sometime."

And she would dearly love to hear what he had to say. But the earl made no effort to continue the subject, just leaned back in his chair and looked down the table at her in that arrogant way of his.

Dressed entirely in black except for a showy white shirt and dove-gray waistcoat, his black hair glinting in the light of the gas chandelier, he was the most compelling man she had ever met. He wore his hair queued back, accenting the hard line of his jaw and his high carved cheekbones, and it occurred to her that Lord Jason might be more handsome in the conventional sense, but Gray was by far the more masculine.

She felt a tug of awareness and realized his gaze had moved down to the line of cleavage between her breasts, exposed above the bodice of her turquoise gown. Beneath that sensual stare, her nipples hardened into tight little buds, and as she reached for her wineglass to steady herself, the top of her corset rubbed against them. With Gray's attention fixed there, the sensation was wildly disturbing.

A corner of his mouth crept up and his eyes seemed to darken. It was as if he knew, as if he'd reached out and touched her, cupped her breasts in his big dark hands. The man was a devil. Corrie told herself it was hardly her fault that some wicked part of her responded to him.

For the rest of the meal, she kept her attention firmly fixed on his cousin. As far as she was concerned, the devil earl could go straight to hell.

TEN

The house was completely silent, the family all abed. Reading to stay awake, Corrie waited impatiently for the clock to strike two. When she finally heard the soft chime, she set aside her book and made her way toward the door.

She hadn't told Allison what she intended to do. Her friend would only worry, and she didn't want that.

Dressed in a white cotton nightgown, her blue quilted wrapper buttoned up for warmth, she lit a beeswax taper, opened the door and peered out into the hall. There was rarely anyone in this part of the house, and certainly not at this time of night. Holding the candlestick in front of her, Corrie made her way to the stairs at the end of the corridor and descended to the bottom floor.

She had carefully memorized which hallway led to the study, a room she had discovered in her wanderings, and she headed straight for it. She had never been inside, and as she stepped into the interior, she wondered if Gray had taken a hand in the heavy dark furnishings that gave the interior a forbidding air. Somehow she didn't think so.

It wasn't until she spotted a door in the study wall, pushed it open and walked into a smaller chamber, that she felt his presence. It was as if she had stepped into another world, the foreign world of India. The furniture was lighter, much of it made of cane, and the faint smell of sandalwood hung in the air. She recognized the pleasant, slightly musky fragrance she had come to associate with Gray, but until now hadn't connected to India.

A thick Indian rug, intricately patterned in burgundy and navy, covered the floor, while brass urns of odd shapes and sizes sat on the tables. She held up the candle, fascinated by the array of items Gray must have collected during his travels. In a glass-fronted bookcase, pieces of carved ivory in lacy patterns rested on the shelves, and above the case, a pair of crossed military sabers hung on the wall.

She could feel Gray Forsythe in the room as if he stood behind her, and for an instant she turned, holding up the candlestick to be sure she was still alone. Relieved to discover she was, she turned back and began her search.

As she moved through the room, she found several items of interest, though nothing that connected Gray to Laurel.

In a small brass box, she found two carefully folded letters. In the first, his mother told him she loved him and that when he grew older, when he heard unpleasant rumors of his birth, he was to open the second letter. She told him to believe every word and never to doubt it, to trust his heart to know what she told him was true.

The date on the letter said Lady Tremaine had written it just before she died. Gray would have been ten.

Corrie sank down on the edge of chair, feeling like the voyeur she was, and completely unable to resist reading the words in the second missive. In it, the countess told Gray in no uncertain terms that he was a true son of the Earl of Tremaine.

I was never unfaithful to your father. No matter what he believes, I have always loved him. It is his jealousy that drives him to behave as he does. I hope someday you can find it in your heart to forgive him for being such a fool.

Corrie read the page, her chest oddly tight. As a child, Gray had suffered for his father's unfounded jealousy. He had lost his mother and his wife. Corrie felt a pang of pity for the loneliness he must have suffered in his life. She wondered if perhaps Laurel had been drawn to that loneliness. But even as kindhearted as her sister was, Corrie could not see her with Gray.

Carefully replacing the letters in the box and setting it back on the shelf, Corrie moved into the main portion of the study and began to search there, starting with the big mahogany desk that dominated the room.

Finding nothing, she searched the bookshelves along the wall, and was ready to give up and return upstairs when her eye caught on a volume pushed back from the rest, shoved between two other books in a way that made her wonder if someone had not wanted it to be seen. Reaching up, she pulled down a volume of William Shakespeare, *Sonnets and Romantic Poetry.*

Her heart began pounding. Corrie knew the book, one of Laurel's favorite works of literature. And the faded leather cover was worn in a manner that seemed somehow familiar. Her hand trembled as she opened it and her gaze fastened on the feminine scroll on the first page.

My dearest beloved,

We have shared so many beautiful moments. An afternoon of reading this together is a memory I shall always treasure.
I give it to you in the hope you will remember me in the years to come. With my
deepest love, Laurel.

Corrie's heart wrenched. Memories of her
sister rushed in and her eyes burned with
tears. Laurel sitting in the window seat reading the book, telling Corrie that someday
she hoped to find the kind of love Shakespeare had written about in the pages.
Though the inscription did not give the
name of the man Laurel had fallen in love
with, the man she had gifted with a book
she treasured, there could be no more doubt
that it was one who lived at Castle Tremaine.

Was it Gray? Corrie tried to imagine Gray
and Laurel reading the romantic poems
printed in the book. There was simply no
way she could convince herself.

She glanced round the study, toward the
door leading into the room next door. The
things that seemed most important to Gray
he kept in his private office. If the book had
been a gift, wouldn't he have kept it there?

Then again, perhaps the gift meant little to the Earl of Tremaine. She thought of the other two men in the house. Charles spent a good deal of time in the study. He was the sort of man her sister would find attractive, but he was married. She would never give herself to a married man.

Which left handsome and charming Lord Jason. This afternoon, as Corrie had walked past, Jason had been sitting behind the desk.

Which of them did you love, sweet sister?

And was this man you loved responsible for your death and that of your child?

But no answer came.

Hating to part with the precious memento, Corrie went up on her toes and replaced it on the bookshelf. At least her wild scheme to get into the castle had not been completely insane. It was clear she was on the right track. In time she would discover which man had fathered Laurel's child. Once she knew, she would find out the truth of what had happened to her sister the night she died.

Drawing her blue quilted wrapper a little closer around her, Corrie left the study and hurried along the passage toward the east wing back stairs. She had almost reached her destination when a familiar male voice sent a prickle of alarm down her spine.

"Well, Mrs. Moss . . . I see you are out on another of your nightly forays. And just where, exactly, are you headed at this hour?"

She turned to find the earl behind her, his tall figure unmistakable in the shadowy darkness of the hallway.

"I — I was just returning upstairs." She managed to smile. "I couldn't sleep. I came down to see if I might find a glass of milk in the kitchen."

"So you were in the kitchen," Gray said with obvious disbelief.

"Why, yes. You don't mind, do you? I suppose, after you found me lurking about in your room, you probably believe I came down her to steal the family silver or something."

His eyes ran over her, sending a little curl of heat into her stomach. "Or something . . ."

There wasn't the least trace of amusement in his voice and she wondered if he was still angry over the attention she had paid his cousin at supper two nights past.

"It's extremely late. I suppose I should be going."

"On the contrary," he said, an edge creeping into his voice. "Since you are unable to sleep, and I am, as well, we may as well enjoy a little conversation . . . or something."

Her pulse began to thrum. There was a hard twist to his lips, and yet his eyes said exactly what that *something* was. She started to argue, but the earl took a firm grip on her arm and began to guide her down a corridor in the opposite direction. Propelling her into one of the drawing rooms, he firmly closed the door.

"I — I don't think this is a good idea."

"Why not? You said you couldn't sleep. I know a sure cure for insomnia."

Her nerves quivered as he walked past her, over to the hearth, where the remnants of a fire still flickered behind the grate. She thought that he must have been in the room while she was in the study, and said a silent thank-you that he had been far enough away not to hear her.

Or had he?

Crouched in front of the fire, he added a bit of coal to the low-burning flames. Part of her wanted to run while she still had the chance; another part watched in silent fascination the play of sinew flexing in his thighs, the tightening of the muscles across his broad back beneath the fabric of his white lawn shirt.

He used the bellows to heighten the blaze, then rose and walked over to where she stood next to the sofa. He stared down at

147

her, and the firelight glinting in his eyes made them look forbidding. "You seem nervous. Am I keeping you from something? Perhaps a late night rendezvous with my cousin?"

Surprise widened her eyes. "Your cousin? I told you I went to the kitchen for a glass of milk. I haven't seen your cousin for the past two days."

"No? And yet he seems to have won your favor."

She watched the earl's face for a clue as to where this conversation might be leading, and noticed the hard set of his jaw. He *was* still angry. Surely he couldn't be jealous!

"Jason is a very charming man," she said carefully. "It's only natural I would enjoy his company."

"Of course." The hard edge remained in Tremaine's voice. He reached out and caught a wisp of hair that had come lose from her braid and curled next to her cheek. The heat of his hand sent a ripple of warmth through her. "I wonder . . . has he offered to make you his mistress?"

Her whole body stiffened and she drew away from his touch. "What are you talking about? Your cousin has never behaved as anything but a gentleman."

The earl shrugged. On the surface, the gesture seemed nonchalant, and yet she couldn't miss the tension in those very wide shoulders.

"You need money," he stated casually. "Jason has plenty. You're obviously attracted to him. I should think —"

She tried to control her temper but the words just popped out. "I am not sure *thinking* is something you do all that often, my lord."

Tremaine's dark eyes narrowed dangerously.

"If you did, you would know I am not attracted to your cousin in the least."

"Is that so?"

"Quite so." She lifted her chin, chiding herself for momentarily forgetting her role. "Aside from that, I'm a married woman and not the sort to trifle with another man."

His expression changed and his tension seemed to ease. There was something different in his eyes now, something hot that he had kept hidden before. "And yet that night in my room, you returned my kisses, did you not? And with a surprising amount of passion."

Faint color rose in her cheeks. "Well, I — I was caught unawares, my lord."

"Gray," he corrected softly. "Go on,

149

Letty . . . you were caught unawares and so when I kissed you, you kissed me back like a tigress coming into her first season. And you wanted more, sweeting." His gaze came to rest on her lips. "I think you still do."

She opened her mouth to argue, but his lips came down over hers, silencing her words. It was a soul-stealing, ravishing kiss, part anger, part need. He was all virile male, all strength and domination, and his sandalwood scent wrapped around her. She told herself to think of Laurel and the book she had found, and what it might mean, but when she tried to imagine Gray with her sister, the image would not come.

Instead, she saw herself in his arms as she was now, and desire for him roared like a drug through her veins. She had never experienced passion, never understood it, but she knew it now. Another woman seemed to have entered her body, a wicked, shameless creature who burned with the same fierce desire she sensed in Gray.

"I want you," he whispered, pressing hot kisses against the side of her neck. "I want you, Letty Moss, and I intend to have you."

Corrie moved her head from side to side in denial. Gray captured her face between his palms, bent his head and kissed her, a wet, hard, hungry caress that left her body weak and her mind in a numbing fog. His tongue tangled with hers as he plundered her mouth, and her hands pressed uselessly against his chest.

"Gray . . ." she whispered, searching for the strength to stop him. "Please . . . we can't . . . we can't . . ."

"Oh, yes, Letty, we can." With those words his lips began a slow journey along the line of her jaw, leaving a damp trail of heat. She didn't realize he had managed to unbutton her quilted wrapper until he slid it off her shoulders. His mouth claimed hers as he tugged at the ribbon on her nightgown, allowing the top to slip precariously low. Hot kisses trailed down her neck and across her bare shoulder, burning her skin like a brand.

She moaned as he eased the soft cotton lower, exposing her breast, settling his mouth there, suckling the tip until it puckered into a tight little bud.

"Lovely," he whispered, licking the peak, swirling his tongue around it. "I've imagined you this way."

Corrie trembled at the fierce need swirling through her, the desire that threatened to overwhelm her. Gray loosened the ribbon at the end of her braid and drew his fingers through her hair, spreading the heavy mass around her shoulders.

"Like fire," he said, burying his face in the rippling strands. "Like silken flames."

He kissed the side of her neck and her body tightened with longing. She swayed toward him, pressed herself more fully against him, and even the hot, hard length thrusting determinedly against her could not sheath the claws of her desire.

His dark head returned to her breast, taking the fullness into his mouth, and pleasure shook her with such force she thought she would surely swoon. Her other breast throbbed for his attention, and as if he knew, his long fingers tightened over her nipple, pinching harder than she expected, sending a rush of pleasure out through her limbs.

Gray sat down on the sofa and drew her onto his lap. Corrie moaned and shifted restlessly, an ache beginning to throb between her legs. One of his hands moved along her calf, raising her nightgown, sliding along the inside of her thigh, leaving a trail of fire in the wake of his touch.

Her mind signaled a sluggish warning. *You can't do this! You've got to stop him before it's too late!*

"No!" Corrie shot up from the sofa. "I — I can't. . . . Dear Lord, what am I doing?" On legs like rubber, she jerked her nightgown up to cover her breasts, and tied the pink ribbon with trembling hands.

Gray moved toward her. "It's all right, sweeting, I'm not going to hurt you. I'm only going to make love to you."

"You'll do no such thing!" She backed away from him, her cheeks burning at the shameful liberties she had allowed him to take. And how much she had enjoyed it. "How do you do it? What evil tricks do you use?"

Amusement touched those sensuous lips. "There is nothing evil about making love. I'll teach you, Letty. Come. You don't have to be afraid."

But she was already backing toward the door. Swinging it open, she rushed out into the hall. She heard Gray swearing as he strode into the passage behind her.

"You'll need your candle." He held the taper out to her. "Without it you might fall."

But Corrie just kept running, her hair streaming behind her, her body still throbbing in places that had never throbbed before.

Dear God, she had to be more careful, had to stay away from the earl and not succumb to the fierce attraction she felt for him. She thought of Laurel, pregnant and alone. Heaven above, she didn't want to wind up the victim of a man's desire.

And yet when she thought of Gray and the wild yearning he sparked inside her, she couldn't help but wonder if the danger might not be worth it.

Corrie trembled, her body still pulsing, knowing if she wasn't careful, the devil earl was going to be her downfall.

Gray walked down the hall toward the study, his mind exhausted, while his body still hummed with remnants of unspent need. He had told Letty the truth. He had been downstairs wandering in the garden, then reading for a while because he could not sleep. It happened far too often. Sexual congress gave him temporary relief, but he hadn't been with a woman in weeks.

Gray sighed. He had burned his bridges with Bethany. He would get no relief there. And in truth, there was only one woman he wanted. The mysterious creature who lived beneath his very roof.

In the darkness, he made his way toward a lamp, lit the wick and sat down behind the desk. Drawing a piece of foolscap from the drawer, he used pen and ink to scratch out a message.

He was writing a friend in London, a man named Randolph Petersen he had known since before he went into the army. At the time, Dolph had worked for the War Office, doing work he could never discuss. Several years ago, the man had become a private investigator, a good one from what Gray had heard. Dolph was the sort who had always been good at his job — no matter what it entailed.

In the letter, Gray said he wanted to hire him to investigate a woman named Letty Moss, the supposed wife of his cousin Cyrus Moss. He gave Dolph the few sketchy details he had, told him Letty had apparently lived near York with Cyrus until he left England to make his fortune in America, that she appeared to be destitute and in need of help.

Find out what you can and get back to me as soon as possible, he finished. Then signed it, *Your friend, Gray Forsythe, Earl of Tremaine.*

He sealed the letter with a drop of wax, pressed it closed with the Tremaine seal — the emblem of a lion beneath a pair of crossed sabers — and carried it with him up to his suite. In the morning, he would have Samir hire a private dispatch to carry the note to London.

Tremaine thought about the letter as he entered his sitting room, wondering what

Dolph might find out, and half tempted to rip the message to shreds. He wanted Letty Moss. He didn't want Petersen to discover something so distasteful he would have to send her away.

Standing there in the faint glow of the lamp on the dresser, he tapped the letter, then set it on top, knowing he had no choice but to send it.

"You are disturbed," Samir said, stepping silently out of the shadows. "The woman did not give you release this night."

"No."

"She desires you. It is there when she casts her eyes upon you. What does she wish in exchange for the use of her body?"

Gray almost smiled. Samir thought every problem came with a solution. There was only the matter of discovering what it was. "I think she's afraid. She has only been with her husband, and he was a very poor lover."

"This I can see, as well. But you are skilled in the art of passion. You will teach her what she needs to learn."

"I suppose . . . in time . . ." But time always seemed to slip out of his grasp when he was with Letty Moss.

He handed Samir the letter. "See it posted tomorrow, will you? Perhaps we'll learn the truth about Mrs. Moss."

Samir bowed from the waist. "As you wish, *sahib.*" He slipped off into the darkness, leaving Gray alone.

Letty was only a woman, he thought, not much different from a dozen others he'd had. And yet there was something about her . . . something that made him think she might be more than what she seemed.

He scoffed. It was only her luscious little body that drew him, that and the fiery passion inside her he had glimpsed and ached to release. Whatever Dolph learned about Letty, Gray meant to have her. Once he had sampled her charms, she would be just another woman, one that in time he would tire of and be able to forget.

Gray thought of the life he had led, the countries he had traveled, the women he had known. Until his return to England, he had never felt this restlessness, this emptiness that continued to gnaw at him.

Or perhaps he had. Perhaps all those years he'd spent traveling, the years he had lived in India, he had felt it deep down inside. But it wasn't until after Jillian had died that he'd longer been able to ignore it.

What was it he searched for? What was it he wanted that remained so elusive, that always seemed to hover just out of his grasp? He didn't know, and perhaps it was better that he didn't.

Gray sighed. Closing his mind to his unwanted musings, he shed his clothes, blew out the lamp and climbed into his empty bed.

ELEVEN

When Allison rushed into her bedroom early the following morning, Corrie was still groggy from another night of restless sleep.

"Come on! Get up! There is a woman here to see you, a dressmaker from London! The entire household is abuzz."

Corrie opened her eyes and blinked at the sunlight streaming in through the window.

"Hurry!" Allison dragged back the covers and tugged on her hand.

"For heaven's sake, what are you doing?" Groggily, she swung her legs to the side of the feather mattress. After her encounter with the earl last night, she was exhausted. Even after she had gone to bed, it was impossible to fall asleep.

"I told you — a dressmaker is here from London, some fancy French designer. The earl must have sent for her. You need to get dressed. She is waiting — and so is the earl."

"What?"

Allison began rushing around the bedroom, collecting and laying out undergarments, choosing a soft peach muslin morning dress along with matching kid slippers.

"Apparently, the earl told Rebecca that since you are a member of the family, it is his duty to see you properly clothed. I think they argued about it. The earl just ignored her."

Corrie thought of the determined man she had run into in the hall last night. "I am not surprised. He is entirely too used to getting his way."

"Perhaps you can tell him that when you go downstairs."

"I am *not* going downstairs." After their passionate encounter, the last person on earth she wished to see was Lord Tremaine.

"If you don't come down, the housekeeper said to tell you that the earl and the dressmaker will come up to your room."

"Good grief!"

"Exactly. We had better hurry."

And so, as rapidly as possible, Corrie slipped into her undergarments, stockings and slippers, then put on the peach muslin gown. Allison brushed her sleep-tangled hair and hurriedly pulled it back on the sides, fixing it in place with a pair of tortoiseshell combs.

"I cannot believe this," Corrie grumbled. "I have a houseful of clothes in London. I scarcely need more."

"No, but the earl doesn't know that. He thinks you are Letty, remember?"

Corrie groaned.

"You had better be on your way."

Resigning herself, she took a deep breath and headed for the door. At the bottom of the stairs stood the housekeeper, Mrs. Kittrick, a large-boned, buxom woman with iron-gray hair.

"They are waiting for you in the Sky Room." A drawing room in an older part of the castle whose ceiling had been painted during the Renaissance, with cherubs floating on fluffy white clouds in an azure sky. "If you will please follow me."

She fell in behind the robust woman, who rarely made an appearance above stairs. She was always busy working, and she seemed to be extremely efficient. Corrie doubted that Rebecca would settle for anything less from the staff.

Steeling herself to face the earl, Corrie walked past the housekeeper into the drawing room. Tremaine waited next to a tall, reedy woman with a slightly wrinkled face and dark hair streaked with silver.

"I am here — at your insistence," Corrie

161

said. "But I do not need you to buy me any clothes." She forced herself to look at him, refused to think of last night, and prayed she would not blush.

"Actually, you do," he said. "If you will recall, you ruined one of your shabby dresses the day you saved that mangy dog. I doubt you brought many with you, and even if you did, they are barely fit to wear." His hard look softened. "Let me do this for you, Letty. I can well afford it. I should like to give you the dresses as a gift."

She felt like the worst sort of fraud. She was one of the best dressed young women in London. In fact, she prided herself on her wardrobe. How could she let the earl spend his money on a woman who had plenty of her own, and who had come to prove him guilty of murder?

She tried to think what Letty would do, or at least the Letty she portrayed. Reaching over, she caught hold of his hand. "Please, my lord. I have been forced to humble myself by coming here and asking for your help. I would take it as a personal favor if you would not add to my humiliation by forcing me to accept more of your generosity. I would not have you purchase the very clothes on my back."

Gray looked stunned, as if no woman he

knew would refuse such a gift. "You need the dresses, Letty."

"I'll have my own income soon. Once I do, I'll be able to buy what I need."

He was frowning. "Are you certain? Most women would gladly accept such an offer."

"I am not most women, my lord."

"No," he said in that soft, deep voice that made her insides curl. "You most assuredly are not." He turned to the dressmaker. "I will, of course, pay for your time in coming all the way out here, plus a generous bonus."

The dressmaker nodded, satisfied, it would seem. "Thank you, my lord."

Corrie watched as the woman picked up her sewing basket, waited while her assistant reloaded a trunkful of sample fabrics, and the pair left the drawing room.

"Thank you, my lord," she said.

Gray just nodded. He was looking at her in a way he hadn't before, with a hint of admiration.

For the first time, Corrie realized how badly she wanted to prove Gray Forsythe innocent of her sister's murder.

It rained the following morning, but by the time Corrie was dressed and ready to set off for the village, a bright sun shone over the rolling green fields.

Grateful for the gift of such a day, which helped dispel her lingering bad mood, she stopped by the stable to check on Homer and found him anxiously prowling the stall where he was being cared for.

" 'E needs some exercise, missus." The groom, a young man named Dickey Michaels, stood at the door of the stall. " 'Omer ain't used ta being cooped up." The lanky youth scratched the dog's ears, and it was clear the animal had made a new friend.

She smiled. "I'm on my way to the village. Do you think Homer is well enough to come along?"

Dickey opened the stall door and the dog rushed out, yapping merrily and dancing around her legs.

"Seems to be feelin' just fine. I think a walk would do 'im good."

"What if he runs away?"

Dickey just shrugged. "I suppose if 'e wants 'is freedom, ye ought to give it to 'im."

"Yes, I suppose that's true."

But Homer seemed perfectly content to roam along beside her, racing after an occasional butterfly, sniffing wildflowers in the field, digging up holes in the soft, damp earth.

Corrie ruffled his long gray fur, clean now, thanks to Dickey. "Maybe we'll get some answers this time," she said to the dog as they headed away from the house, though, of course, Homer didn't reply.

After finding Laurel's book, Corrie knew the hatmaker had been right. One of the lords at Castle Tremaine was the man Laurel had fallen in love with. The question remained, which one?

Perhaps someone in the village knew, but if so, who? And how would she get them to tell her? It occurred to her that the lovers had probably not trysted at the castle. Perhaps someone at the inn had seen them together.

She headed in that direction, making her way along the row of shops, passing several freight wagons in the street. Homer barked at a huge brown mastiff in the back of one — tied tightly, thank the Lord. Walking toward the far end of the village, Corrie spotted the Green Dragon Tavern up ahead.

"You stay here," she told Homer, wondering if he really would. Then she climbed the wooden steps, opened the door and stepped into the interior.

Off to the left of the stone-floored entry was a taproom, a low-ceilinged, smoky chamber with rough-hewn beams and worn oak floors. She walked over to one of the tavern maids hoping that for a price the woman might be willing talk.

Corrie pulled a silver coin from her reticule and held it up in front of the woman's plain, dish-shaped face. She was younger, blond and fair, with a great deal of bosom exposed above the gathered neckline of her white cotton blouse. For an instant, Corrie's mind flashed back to the other night, to the feel of the earl's hand cupping her breasts, the heat of his mouth on her skin.

Fighting not to blush, she forced the shameful memory away and turned her attention to the serving girl. "Would you like to earn this coin?"

The girl eyed her with suspicion. "Course I would."

"What's your name?"

"Greta. Greta Tweed."

"Do you know the lords who live at Castle Tremaine, Greta?"

She nodded. "The earl and his brother and young Lord Jason live there most of the time." She reached for the coin, but Corrie drew it back.

"One of them was seeing a young woman named Laurel Whitmore. She lived at Selkirk Hall. Would you have any idea which of them it was?" She held out the coin and the girl eyed it with longing.

"Were that young Lord Jason, I'll wager."

She grinned. "The man's got the stamina o' a bull. He could turn the head o' just about any woman." It was clear she was speaking from experience, and Corrie felt her face heating up again.

"But you're guessing," she pressed. "You have no way of knowing for sure."

Greta shrugged her round, freckled shoulders. "All three of 'em's 'andsome as sin. Coulda been the earl 'isself. He don't pay for his fun like the younger one. Mostly, he beds down with them what calls themselves ladies. I s'ppose the daughter of a viscount would do, but he don't seem the sort to trifle with an innocent girl that way. I'd say he'd be more inclined to a woman with experience."

Greta leaned closer. "Talk is, he's built like a stallion. They say he studied all manner of lovemakin' over there in India. Knows exactly how to pleasure a woman." She grinned. "Wouldn't mind trying a bit o' that meself."

Face flaming, wishing she could turn and run for the door, Corrie handed the girl the coin. "Is there anyone who might know for certain which man it was?"

"I mostly know what's happenin' in these parts. One of them lords was sleepin' with the girl, he kept it quiet."

"Thank you for your help, Greta." Turning away, Corrie made her way to the door, ignoring the curious stares of the men in the smoky taproom as she pushed her way out into the sunshine.

She shouldn't have come. It was hardly proper for an unescorted female to enter a tavern, but it was the sort of place money could often buy information, and she'd had to take the chance.

Was it Gray? she asked herself for the hundredth time. Had he used his devil's powers to steal Laurel's innocence? After their late-night encounter, Corrie believed he certainly had the skill.

A yap at the bottom of the steps drew her attention. Homer sat on his haunches, awaiting her return, his long pink tongue hanging out. His ears perked up when he saw her, and she smiled, glad he had decided to stay. It was good to have friends, even a furry one, in a house where so much intrigue swirled around her.

She thought of the earl and felt a pang of guilt for what she'd let happen.

Perhaps that was the thing about desire. It chose you, not the other way around.

Leaving the tavern behind, Corrie made her way along the main street of the village.

There seemed to be some sort of argument going on at Pendergast's Grocery. She was surprised to see the earl talking to a boy of ten or so. The grocer was also there, a fat man with curly gray sidewhiskers.

Curious, she walked in that direction, staying close to the buildings, where she wouldn't draw attention.

"You know stealing is a crime?" Gray said to the boy, a skinny, dirty ragamuffin whose brown hair alternately poked out or stuck to his head.

"Yessir, milord."

"Are you hungry? Is that the reason you stole the bread?"

"Doesn't make a fiddler's damn," the shopkeeper interrupted. "The boy's got to be punished. A good hard birching's the only way to learn the difference between right and wrong."

The lad's face went pale, making his dark eyes look huge in his thin face. Gray flicked a warning glance at the grocer, a muscle tight in his jaw. Corrie thought he must be remembering the beatings he had suffered when he was a boy.

"I asked why you stole the bread."

One look at the earl's hard features and Corrie felt a wave of pity for the boy.

The lad looked up at him, his expression

169

a mix between fear and defiance. "Me da died of the lung disease. Me and Ma come here from London to stay with Ma's sister, but when we got ta the house, Aunt Janie was gone. We didn't have no food. Ma was weak as a kitten. I — I didn't want 'er to die like me da."

The fat man harrumphed. "I'm going for the constable. I won't put up with thievery, no matter the lad's excuse."

"Hold on, Pendergast. There's no need to run off half-cocked." The command in Tremaine's voice made his request more of an order. The boy trembled as he looked into the earl's hard face.

"What's your name, son?"

"Georgie Hobbs, milord."

"Where's your mother now?"

"In the cottage where Aunt Janie lived. 'Bout a mile out o' town."

"You know stealing is wrong."

The boy looked down, dragged the toe of his worn leather shoe. "Yessir."

"If you do it again, I'm going to let Mr. Pendergast call the constable, and they'll lock you away. You understand?"

Georgie Hobbs nodded. "Y-yessir."

Pendergast opened his mouth to argue and the earl held up a hand. "I'm going to pay for that loaf of bread you stole, as well as some cheese and some meat. You're going to take them back to your mother. When the two of you have eaten your fill, you're to come to the castle and work off the debt you owe for the food. If you don't appear, I'll come after you. I'll personally give you that whipping Mr. Pendergast thinks you deserve. Is that clear?"

"Yessir."

"Do I have your word?"

"Aye, milord. On me honor, I swear it!"

"Get him what he needs," Tremaine said to the store owner, "and put it on my account."

"Yes, my lord." The shopkeeper looked smugly pleased at making a sale he wouldn't have made before.

Leaving the boy to complete the task, the earl turned away and started walking in Corrie's direction. Good grief, she should have left sooner. Now here he was, and she had no escape.

His head came up when he saw her. "Well, Mrs. Moss . . . I hadn't thought to see you again for a while. Aside from your forced encounter with the dressmaker, I imagined you would stay in your bedroom for at least several days, holed up like a frightened rabbit."

Irritation trickled through her. She wasn't

171

a coward and never had been. "Then you would be sorely mistaken, my lord."

One of his eyebrows went up and it occurred to her that while Coralee Whitmore wasn't a coward, Letty Moss wouldn't be nearly so brave. "I mean . . . I — I realize what happened wasn't entirely your fault."

"No?"

"Well, I *am* a married woman, after all. I should have known better than to allow matters to get so out of hand."

Tremaine made no reply, but it was clear he didn't regret what had happened at all.

Homer raced up just then, yapping and begging for attention. Grateful for the distraction, Corrie reached down and petted his head.

"I'm afraid I had better get going," she said. "I was just heading back to the castle." She glanced toward Pendergast's Grocery, and a grudging compliment escaped. "That was quite well done of you, my lord. It doesn't seem fitting to punish a child for trying to feed his mother."

"No. Though stealing isn't right, either. Don't think for a moment I won't keep my promise should the lad not stand by his word."

She never doubted it. Tremaine had been a major in the army. Discipline and honor

172

would have been part of his life. *Honor.* When had she begun to think of the devil earl as a man with any sort of honor?

"I was heading back home myself," he said. "I'll see you get there safely."

Corrie clamped down on an urge to refuse his escort, to tell him she didn't need nor want him anywhere near her. It was unsettling enough just living in the same house with him. Still, she was his guest. She had no choice but to agree.

The earl retrieved his horse, then walked beside her along the path, Homer trailing in their wake. Neither of them said much along the way, and she found the companionable silence unexpectedly pleasant.

"You seem to enjoy the village," he finally said. "You spend a good deal of time there."

She shrugged, not pleased he had noticed. "I like to get out-of-doors. And the villagers are friendly."

They left the stallion and the dog with Dickey, who waited in front of the house. Tremaine took her arm to help her climb the steep stone steps to the door, which opened before they reached it. When she walked into the entry, Gray's servant, the dark-skinned man from India, waited for their approach.

"What is it, Samir?" Tremaine asked.

"A letter for the *memsahib*. It came while she was away in the village."

Corrie looked at the little man and frowned. "How did you know I went to the . . . ? Never mind." She reached for the letter addressed to Letty Moss. "If you will excuse me, my lord?"

He made a faint bow. "Of course."

Turning, she headed upstairs to her bedroom. The only people who knew where to find her, knew she was using that name, were Aunt Agnes, Allison, Krista and Leif. She wrote to her parents, of course. She didn't want them to get suspicious, but any letters from them came to Selkirk Hall and Allison brought them to her.

Corrie looked down at the letter in her hand. It came from Krista, she saw as she closed the bedroom door and broke the wax seal. The message was brief.

Leif hired Dolph Petersen to investigate Grayson Forsythe. Mr. Petersen says the earl's wife's death was a boating accident. There was no evidence of foul play. He says the earl was with Bethany Chambers, Countess of Devane, the night Laurel died. He didn't leave her house until morning. Dolph says Tremaine was barely acquainted with Laurel. Please come home.

Your friends, Krista and Leif.

Her mind spun. *Not Gray, not Gray, not Gray.*

The words revolved in her head and with them came a rush of relief so powerful it made her head swim. She sank down on the bench at the foot of the bed just as Allison knocked on the door and walked into the room.

"What is it? What's happened?" Mobcap slightly askew over her shiny dark hair, she hurried to where Corrie sat on the bench. "Are you all right? You're looking a little flushed."

Corrie held out the letter. "It wasn't Gray . . . I mean, Lord Tremaine. He was with his mistress that night." And though the knowledge rankled, it was an incredible weight off her shoulders to know the man who attracted her so fiercely had never been Laurel's lover.

Which meant it was unlikely he was responsible for what had happened to Laurel and her baby that night.

Allison read the letter and handed it back. "You thought it was the earl, but it wasn't, so now can we go home?"

Corrie sighed. "It wasn't Gray, but the

book I found in the study proves Laurel was in love with one of the men in the house. All we have to do is find out which one."

"That's all we have to do?" Allison said sarcastically.

"Well, it has to be one of them."

"So why don't you just ask them? Maybe the man who is guilty will tell you."

Good heavens, she couldn't possibly do that. Could she? But the notion intrigued her. She couldn't ask Jason or Charles, but what about Gray? She trusted Dolph Petersen to find out the truth, which meant Gray had never been involved with Laurel. But perhaps the earl knew which of the other two men had been.

A tremor of unease ran through Corrie. If she wanted to find out what the earl knew, she would have to talk to him, spend time with him, gain at least a bit of his trust. Dear God, she could barely think when he was around. She didn't trust herself when she was with him, didn't trust the wild, wanton feelings he so easily aroused.

Still, if she approached the matter carefully, if she kept her wits and her body under control, perhaps he might tell her what she wished to know.

"You have that look in your eye," Allison said, beginning to know her too well.

"I think, dear Ally, you may have a very good notion."

"What? I was jesting, Coralee. You can't simply *ask* them!"

"No, but if I handle the matter with care, perhaps I can get the information out of the earl."

Allison pointed toward the letter in Corrie's hand. "Maybe this Mr. Petersen can figure out which of the men it was."

Corrie nodded. "Good idea. I should have thought of that myself. I knew there was a reason I brought you along."

Moving toward the bed, she knelt and dragged out her trunk, opened the lid and stashed the letter in the bottom. "I shall write to Krista tonight, tell her about the book I found, and have her ask Mr. Petersen to continue his investigation into the other two Forsythe men. In the meantime, I'm going to see what I can find out from the earl."

Allison groaned.

Fighting a smile, Corrie headed for the door. "I'll be back in a while."

"Are you sure you know what you're —"

Corrie closed the door with a quiet click, then paused in the hallway to gather her courage. She didn't want to spend more

time with Gray, but she needed information, and to get it, she had no choice.

TWELVE

Corrie found the earl out in the stable, grooming his big black horse. He didn't seem to notice her arrival, so she simply stood there watching him, trying to dredge up the courage to approach where he worked, brushing the stallion, then setting the blanket in place and his flat leather saddle on top.

Though he was a tall, broad-shouldered man, there was a certain gracefulness in his actions, an ease about his movements and no wasted effort. A lock of black hair had come loose from the black velvet ribbon at his nape. It teased one of his high cheekbones, and her stomach contracted.

She had the strangest urge to pull the ribbon free and run her hands through his glossy hair, discover if it was as silky as it looked. She wanted him to drag her into his arms and kiss her the way he had the other night.

Good grief! It was happening again, and she wasn't even near him!

"Keep looking at me that way and I'll do exactly what it is you're thinking about."

She must have jumped several inches and a guilty flush spread into her cheeks. "I — I was only thinking that it is quite . . . quite a nice day for riding."

He paused as he tightened the cinch. "Do you ride, Letty?"

"Yes, but not all that well." She'd had lessons, of course. Krista loved to ride and was a very accomplished horsewoman, but Corrie had ridden mostly in the park, as it was fashionable to do.

"You're here in the country," he said. "I think today would be a good day for you to begin developing your skill."

"Today? But I couldn't possibly —"

"You lived on a farm. Surely you own a riding habit."

"Well, I . . . yes, of course." Allison had insisted she bring one along. Since Letty was supposed to have lived on a farm, it was probably a good thing she had.

"I'll wait here while you go in and change."

Corrie hesitated at the thought of an afternoon riding with Tremaine, being alone with him, feeling those strange unwanted urges she couldn't seem to control.

On the other hand, she needed to win his trust. She couldn't do that unless she spent time with him.

It was a terrifying thought.

She drew in a breath and pasted on a smile. "As you wish, my lord." Homer yapped at her side as she hurried back to the house.

With Allison helping, she was able to return to the stables twenty minutes later dressed in a slightly frayed, dark green velvet riding habit. A pretty little sorrel mare stood docilely next to the earl's big black. Her ears perked up at Corrie's approach.

"She's lovely."

"Tulip's very gentle." Tremaine slid a hand along the mare's sleek neck, and Corrie felt as if he was touching her. "She won't give you any trouble."

"I'm sure she'll be fine." She was thinking the only one who might give her trouble was the Earl of Tremaine.

She walked over and patted the sorrel's neck, careful to keep her distance from Gray, and glanced toward the black stallion. "What about Raja? Will he be all right with Tulip?"

"She isn't in season," he said baldly, sending a wash of color into Corrie's cheeks.

"He'll behave himself."

She only prayed Gray would also behave. "Where are we going?"

"I need to make a call on one of my tenants. His wife is with child and I want to make sure they have whatever they might need."

He was worried about his tenants. It surprised her. She thought of him as the devil earl, and devils didn't care about other people.

"Ready?" he asked, and she nodded. Walking up behind her, he set his hands at her waist and lifted her up on the sidesaddle. Corrie remembered to release the breath she was holding. Even through her corset, the heat of his hands lingered well after he had walked away.

Gray swung up on the black, nudged the horse toward a path leading from the stable, and Tulip fell in beside him. Corrie hadn't ridden in months, but the lessons she'd had over the years began to come back, and she settled more easily in the sidesaddle. The leather reins felt good between her gloved fingers, and a warm sun beat down on the back of her neck.

"You've a very nice seat, Mrs. Moss," Tremaine said with a smile as they rode along. But there was a glint in his eyes that hinted the seat he was speaking of had nothing to do with riding.

Or perhaps it did.

She colored faintly and hoped Gray wouldn't notice. "Thank you," she answered with polite formality.

The horses moved easily across the rolling green fields, and once the earl was satisfied with her ability, such as it was, he increased the pace. Tulip cantered along as if she hadn't a care in the world, and Tremaine kept his stallion to the same easy stride.

They had ridden for nearly an hour when he pulled up at the top of a rise. "That's Peter and Sarah Cardigan's house, just over there at the edge of that copse of trees." He pointed in that direction and Corrie spotted a little thatch-roofed cottage with a plume of smoke rising from the chimney.

Gray urged the stallion on and Tulip again fell into step beside him. They drew up in front of the small, white-washed house, and Gray came round to help Corrie down. She steeled herself as his hands found her waist and he lifted her off the horse. Instead of setting her on the ground, he eased her down the length of his body, letting her feel his hard frame inch by inch.

Her breathing hitched. Her heart began to pound. "Put me down, Gray."

A corner of his mouth edged up as if he had won some small victory, and she realized that in calling him by his first name, he had. "As you wish."

He set her on her feet and turned away, tied the horses' reins to a post in front of the cottage, guided her over and knocked on the door.

A soft groan greeted them.

"Mrs. Cardigan?" Gray called out.

"Please . . ." whispered a woman's voice, so softly it went almost unheard. "Please . . . help me. . . ."

Gray thrust open the door and strode inside the house, and Corrie hurried in behind him. They raced through a small living area made comfortable with handmade furniture upholstered in chintz and covered by crocheted doilies, past an area that served as a kitchen, into a cozy bedroom off to one side. A woman lay amid the bedcovers, the huge girth of her belly sticking up beneath the sheet, her dark hair tumbling wildly across the pillow beneath her head.

Tremaine reached her side and took hold of her shaking hand. "Mrs. Cardigan, where is your husband? Where is Peter?"

She swallowed, moistened her dry lips. "He went — went for the midwife. I told him . . . there wasn't time, but . . . but he didn't know what else to do." She groaned in pain and started panting to catch her breath. "Please . . . help me."

The earl turned to Corrie. "We'll need hot water and towels of some kind. The stove is already burning. The well is just outside."

"What . . . what are you going to do?"

"Help Mrs. Cardigan have her baby." He turned away, stripped off his riding coat and tossed it over a chair, then reached down to lift the sheet.

Corrie's eyes widened. "But . . . but you can't possibly mean to . . ."

The earl swung back to her, his gaze hard. "Do what I told you. The woman needs our help. Get out there and bring me what I need!" The command in his voice settled her, as he had meant for it to do.

Corrie swallowed, took a deep breath and nodded. "Yes, yes, of course. Water and towels. I'll get them as quickly as I can."

The earl seemed relieved. Corrie ran out of the bedroom, into the tiny kitchen. A fire was burning in the old iron stove, but it wasn't hot enough. Tossing off her jaunty little hat and removing her jacket, she added a few pieces of wood, grabbed the water bucket off its hook and raced outside. She had never done household chores, but it didn't take long to figure out how to haul up the bucket from the bottom of the well and transfer water to the pail she had brought with her.

A sharp shriek split the air and Corrie jerked so hard she almost spilled the water. Frightened for both mother and child, she carried the heavy pail into the kitchen and dumped its contents into a pan sitting on the stove.

Towels.

She glanced around. Thank God, there was a stack of clean white linen resting on the end of the counter, preparations Mrs. Cardigan had apparently made for the coming birth of her child.

Corrie's chest tightened. She had never been anywhere near a woman giving birth, but she had heard stories of the terrible pain and suffering. The woman cried out again, her wrenching cries coming far more often, and Corrie thought of Laurel and the pain she must have suffered to bring her child into the world. Surely, she would have done anything to protect a gift that had come at so high a price.

Grabbing the stack of linens off the counter, Corrie rushed into the bedroom. "Here are the towels. The water's almost —" She broke off in horror as she realized the woman's nightgown was shoved up to

186

her waist, leaving her naked, and her legs were spread wide apart. There was blood on the sheets and on Gray's white linen shirt.

"Oh, my God!"

He didn't spare her a glance, but his voice was soft when he spoke to her. "It's all right, Letty. Sarah is doing just fine."

"But . . . but there's so much blood."

"That's just part of having a baby." He looked up, a slight frown marring his forehead. "Surely on a farm, you saw animals being birthed."

"Well, I . . ." She took a deep breath. "As I said, Cyrus was very protective. He didn't believe it was a proper thing for a lady to see."

Gray's gaze held hers for an instant, then he returned his attention to the woman on the bed.

"You're going to be all right," he said to her. "Letty and I are going to help you."

Corrie swallowed and set the towels down on the nightstand. Sarah Cardigan screamed in pain, and Corrie started shaking. Dear God, she had no idea how to help a woman birth a child!

She forced herself to calm down. Hurrying out of the bedroom, she ran back for the water, which was boiling away on the stove. She ladled some into a smaller pan and carried it back into the bedroom, then went for cold water and a cloth to sponge the poor woman's face.

By the time she returned to the bedroom, Mrs. Cardigan's skin was the color of paper and she was soaked in perspiration. Corrie sponged her forehead, then wiped down her throat and shoulders.

"Thank you . . ." Sarah said through dry lips. Corrie laid the damp cloth over them, giving her a bit of moisture. The earl glanced her way, saw what she was doing, and something softened in his face.

A piercing cry rent the air and she realized that the head of the baby had begun to shove its way out of the woman's body. Unconsciously, Corrie reached for Sarah's hand, whose icy fingers tightened into a grip of steel.

"It's all right," Corrie soothed. "The earl knows what to do."

He flashed her a glance, then returned his attention to the woman. Well, he did seem to know, she thought as he urged Sarah to push at just the right time, whispering words of encouragement in a voice so deeply male it resonated through Corrie's entire body.

"The baby's coming," he said. "Get me a knife and make sure it's clean."

"A knife?"

He glanced up. "And a piece of string."

Having no idea what the items might be used for, Corrie raced back to the kitchen and found a knife and string set out where she had found the linens. She picked up the butcher knife, tested its sharpness, washed it in some of the boiling water, and grabbed the length of string. Hurrying back to the bedroom, she set the knife down beside the linens, turned and saw Tremaine leaning over the woman.

When he stepped back, he was holding a newborn infant, his long fingers wrapped around the baby's ankles. A quick slap to the bottom and the baby let out an earsplitting scream. Corrie watched in fascination as he used the knife and string to sever the long cord that connected the child to its mother, then wrapped the infant in one of the linen towels and set the bundle in Corrie's arms.

"I — I don't know how to hold a baby," she said nervously.

Tremaine made a sound in his throat. "Every woman knows how to hold a baby. I think it's something to do with your makeup as a female." He turned to the woman on the bed. "You've a daughter, Sarah. A beautiful little girl."

Tears rolled down the woman's cheeks. "God bless you both for what you've done." She was a big woman, but pretty, her limbs firm and strong, the sort of female made for birthing babies.

While Tremaine worked to clean up the infant, Corrie changed the linens on the bed and helped the mother into a fresh nightgown. When she finished, she looked up to see Gray looking down at the infant he cradled in his arms. There was so much emotion in his face her breath caught.

Dear Lord, surely it wasn't yearning.

Wrapping the baby in a yellow woolen blanket he found folded and waiting on the dresser, he carried her over to the bed and settled her in the crook of her mother's arm.

Corrie watched Sarah and the baby, feeling an odd melting in her chest. She moved quietly toward them.

"She's so tiny." She reached out, yearning to touch the child, her heart swelling with emotion. "She's beautiful, Sarah."

"Thank you. Thank you for everything."

A lump rose in Corrie's throat, making it impossible to speak. She blinked to hold back tears. She had helped bring a new life into the world. It was amazing, exhilarating, the most incredible experience of her life. She turned toward Gray and saw the same

190

exhilaration reflected in his eyes.

Neither of them spoke, unwilling to end the moment. Then the door burst open and Peter Cardigan rushed into the room.

"Midwife's gone off to birth another babe. God Almighty, Sarah, what are we gonna —" His eyes locked on the earl and he blinked, as if he couldn't believe what he was seeing.

"You've a daughter, Peter. And with a little rest, your wife is going to be fine."

Peter Cardigan just stood there, a look of disbelief on his ruddy, dirt-smudged face. Without a word, he rushed to his wife's side and knelt next to the bed. "Sarah . . . God above, I never should have left you."

His wife managed a tired but reassuring smile. "It's all right, luv. Your daughter is here — thanks to the earl and his lady. Everything is fine."

Peter Cardigan seemed to regain his wits. He turned to Tremaine and began a round of thanks that seemed to have no end. Eventually, Corrie and the earl were able to retrieve their belongings and slip away, leaving the proud parents with the daughter they named Mary Kate.

"You knew what you were doing in there," Corrie said to the earl as they walked toward the well to wash up. "You've delivered a baby before."

He nodded, tossed his riding coat over one shoulder. "In India. There was a woman . . . a camp follower. I found her in the bushes along the road. There wasn't time to fetch the surgeon. There was no one to help her but me."

Corrie studied him with renewed respect. "Another man might have left them."

He shrugged. "Perhaps. I'm not a man who could."

She mulled that over, adding it to the list of things she was beginning to know about him. "What happened to the child and its mother? Were they all right?"

"They were the last time I saw them, just before I left India to return to England."

He was talking, opening up to her. She needed him to continue. "You seemed comfortable with the infant. Did you want a family when you were married?"

Tremaine stopped dead in his tracks. Corrie held her breath, waiting to see if he would answer. "I wanted children then. Not anymore."

"Why not?"

"I'm not cut out to be a father. I should have realized that before I married. I wouldn't know how to raise a child."

She looked up at him. "Because you never

192

really had a father of your own."

His jaw tightened.

"I've heard the stories. I know the late earl treated you very badly."

Gray scoffed as if she had just made a grand understatement. "Douglas Forsythe was a real bastard."

She should have been shocked at his language. Instead when she thought of the beatings he had suffered, the loveless home he had grown up in, she silently agreed.

"Whatever sort of man your father was, I saw you in there with Sarah and her baby, and I think you would make a wonderful father."

"Well, it isn't going to happen. I've no intention of marrying again, so you needn't concern yourself."

"But —"

"That's enough, Letty." Gray started walking, his jaw clenched as it hadn't been before. And yet he had opened himself up to her a little. In time, perhaps she could get him to talk about his brother and his cousin.

As she walked along beside him, she thought of what he had said, that he would never remarry, that he no longer wanted a family.

It shouldn't have bothered her, but it did.

Gray studied the woman beside him. Once she'd gotten over the shock of the baby's impending birth, she had given herself over to the task without reservation.

Not one of the upper-class women he knew would be willing to dirty her hands to help a simple peasant woman, but Letty seemed not to mind. In fact, she had been fascinated by the miracle of the infant's birth.

Letty had surprised him today. But then, she continued to surprise him, which, he supposed, was one of the reasons he was so attracted to her. That and her innocent responses. And of course, there was the not-so-small matter of her extremely passionate nature and luscious body. If only he could make her see how good it could be between them.

Thinking of the frustration he continued to suffer, Gray silently cursed.

Letty had said she wasn't attracted to his cousin, and after Gray had overcome his unwanted and completely unexpected jealousy, he believed her. Letty belonged to him in some way, and though she protested mightily, it was only a matter of time before she would acknowledge the pull between them and let him make love to her.

His mind returned to the questions she had asked him about his marriage. It was a forbidden topic. He didn't discuss his late wife or the grief he had suffered when she died. People who knew him knew better than to bring up the painful subject, or risk calling down his wrath on their heads.

But Letty hadn't realized the subject was taboo, and Gray had surprised himself by answering her questions. He didn't know why, but with Letty, it didn't seem as difficult as it was with someone else.

Gray pondered the notion as he walked to the well, his mood turning dark once more. After his mother had died, he had built a protective wall around his emotions. He'd done so in order to survive the terrible years with his father.

Even after his marriage, that had not changed. Jillian was his wife and Gray had cared for her greatly, was devastated by his failure to protect her as he should have.

Still, he had never allowed her to get too close, had never let down his guard where his wife was concerned. He didn't intend for that to change.

He wasn't about to let anyone, not even

sweet little Letty, find a way inside the wall that had protected him all these years.

Thirteen

Corrie studied Gray's grim features as they approached the well. "You're different than I thought you were. I can't seem to figure you out."

His head came up. The hardness left his face. "I haven't managed to figure you out yet, either."

Thank goodness for that, she thought. She could only imagine Tremaine's dark rage if he knew who she was and why she had schemed her way into his home.

"You did well in there," he said. "Most of the women I know would have fainted dead away at the sight of all that blood."

Corrie tried not to be pleased. "As you said, Sarah needed our help."

Tremaine paused beside the well, tossed his jacket aside and pulled up a bucket of water. She didn't realize his intention until he grabbed the hem of his bloodstained shirt and pulled it off over his head. Smooth dark skin covered a wide chest rippling with muscle. A crisp mat of coarse black hair arrowed down over a flat stomach ridged with muscle and disappeared into the waistband of his snug black riding breeches.

A ripple of desire washed through her, settled deep in her core. A large, very masculine bulge at the front of his breeches caught her attention, and Corrie remembered the tavern maid's words, *"Talk is he's built like a stallion."*

"You're looking at me that way again, Letty. I hope you like what you see."

Hot color washed into her cheeks. "I was *not* looking at you, and you, my lord, are extremely conceited. Besides, looking is hardly my fault when you strip off your clothes at every opportunity."

He actually grinned. Her breath caught at the changes it made in his face. He looked younger and even more handsome, and as his grin slowly faded, she wondered what it might be like if he laughed. Would those same faint lines crinkle beside his eyes? Would his laughter sound deep and husky, the way his voice often did?

"Sorry," he said with amusement. "I forgot your delicate sensibilities. Unfortunately, I didn't think to bring along a clean shirt." He dumped water onto the stained white linen to rinse out the blood, washed his face and chest, then put the wet shirt back on.

"Does this satisfy your modesty?" he asked, though of course the wet shirt clung to every ridge and sinew, and was so transparent she could see his flat copper nipples.

Heat curled low in her belly and she had to glance away. She washed her face and hands as best she could, then dried them on the handkerchief he handed her.

Afraid to look at him, she studied the horizon, where gently rolling hills met the bright blue sky. "It's time to head back to the castle."

She could feel his eyes on her. "I suppose you're right."

Taking her hand, he led her back to the horses, lifted her up on Tulip, then swung onto the black. After her unsuccessful effort to replace her hat, he plucked it from her hand, stuffed it into his saddlebags, and they set off for home. As far as Coralee was concerned, it had been a very long afternoon.

Gray nudged Raja into an easy gallop, and Tulip took up the pace. The blissful afternoon he had envisioned had come to a fruitless end. He had imagined, after a brief stop to check on his tenants, sharing lunch and a flask of wine with Letty, making love to her until his wild craving for her had at last been satisfied.

Gray sighed as they rode along. If a man's plans could be destroyed in a heartbeat, certainly finding a pregnant woman in the throes of labor had done so better than anything he could have imagined.

And yet, as he spotted the secluded copse of trees up ahead where he had planned to accomplish his seduction, it occurred to him that perhaps his plans could be salvaged.

Just thinking about making love to Letty made him hard. Gray turned the stallion, and Letty followed him into the grove. Pulling Raja to a halt, he swung down from the saddle.

"Why are we stopping?"

Gray just kept striding toward her. "You haven't ridden much. You looked as if you could use a rest."

"I am fine. I don't need a rest."

"There's some meat and cheese in my saddlebags. You haven't eaten since we left."

"I told you I am fine."

Ignoring her protests, he wrapped his hands around her waist, lifted her down from the sidesaddle and straight into his arms.

"Letty . . ." Bending his head, he settled his mouth very softly over hers. Her lips were as sweet as heaven, and the scent of her filled his senses. His tongue traced the corners of her mouth, coaxing her to open for him, and the taste of her made him even harder.

He could feel her resistance, her uncertainty in the slight pressure of her hands against his chest. Gray ignored her subtle protest, kissing her until she made a soft little sighing sound in her throat, rose up on her toes and kissed him back.

Inwardly he groaned. The heat of her, the feel of her feminine curves pressed against him, sent a jolt of fire through his blood. He pulled her into the vee of his legs, letting her feel how hard he was, how much he wanted her, ached to be inside her.

"Gray . . ." she whispered as he kissed her neck, nipped the lobe of an ear.

"I need you, Letty." He kissed her again, more deeply this time, and her body seemed to melt into his.

Need poured through him, the powerful urge to make her his. "Let me take care of you," he whispered. "I'll find you a nice place to live. . . ." He cupped her breasts, gently kneaded them. "A house not too far from the castle . . ."

Another searing kiss had her swaying against him.

"I'll see you have whatever you require," he said softly, "whatever you want."

His words finally seemed to reach her. But instead of looking up at him as if he were her savior, Letty jerked away as if he had slapped her.

"You aren't suggesting . . . you're not thinking I should — should become your *mistress?*"

Gray caught both her hands, hating the look of betrayal on her face. "Your husband is gone. You have no idea when, or if, he'll ever return. You need a man to protect you. Would it really be so bad if I were that man?"

Her cheeks flamed. "I — I am not interested in any sort of arrangement. In a few weeks time, I shall . . . shall come into my inheritance and be gone from here for good." She glanced away and he could see that he had hurt her. It was the last thing he'd meant to do.

"I was a fool to allow you to take liberties," she finished. "I am sorry if I gave you a false impression."

He caught the glint of tears in her eyes the instant before she turned and walked away.

"Letty!"

She ignored him, caught her horse's reins and led the mare over to a stump to regain her seat.

Dammit to hell and gone. Gray caught up with her and turned her to face him, desperate to make her understand. "You want me, Letty. You can't deny it. Let me make love to you. I can show you pleasure unlike anything you've dreamed."

She took a step back, as if to shield herself from him. "I'm sorry, my lord, I can't."

Gray lifted her chin with his fingers. "Are you certain?" Bending his head, he kissed her very softly on the lips. "We'll be good together, Letty. I promise you."

She stared at him for several long moments and his hopes soared.

Then she shook her head. "I told you . . . I can't."

Clamping down hard on his disappointment, Gray said nothing more. He fought an urge to call her back, try once more to make her agree.

Instead, he lifted her onto her sidesaddle, his mood even darker than before. His shaft pulsed with unspent need, and every time he looked at Letty, the sharp edge of lust cut into him. He would get no satisfaction today, he knew. Yet Letty's flat refusal to become his mistress made it imperative he succeed in seducing her soon.

He would woo her and take her, he vowed, give her the pleasure he had promised.

Once she was his, she would not refuse him again.

Gray clenched his teeth. Letty Moss had gotten under his skin and he would not be rid of her until he had possessed her. Once he had tasted her shy passion, once he had satisfied his craving for her, he would be free of whatever mysterious hold she had over him.

He flicked her a glance, caught the gleam of her fiery hair, and his loins swelled painfully. He wanted Letty Moss and he intended to have her.

Today was only a skirmish in what he intended to be a very short campaign.

Homer was yapping at the end of his tether, fiercely wagging his tail, when Corrie and the earl rode into the courtyard. Gray swung from his horse, walked over and lifted Corrie down. She turned away from him as soon as her feet touched the ground.

She hadn't been prepared for the earl's indecent proposal, or her wild yearning to agree. It was ridiculous. She wasn't Letty Moss, gently reared, impoverished, abandoned wife. She was Coralee Whitmore, the daughter of a viscount, and she wouldn't cast her virtue aside for a scoundrel like the Earl of Tremaine no matter how appealing he was.

She hadn't forgotten the womanizing rogue she had written about in her column, nor his recent affair with Lady Devane. The man was a scandalous knave who wanted nothing more from her than the use of her body. It was insane to feel this ridiculous longing for him.

Hurrying toward the dog, she untied the rope round his neck and ruffled his long gray fur. "Did you miss me, boy?" She scratched his head, careful not to look at Gray. Homer yapped one last time, then raced off in search of a rabbit or whatever he might find in the field.

" 'E'll be back," Dickey said. " 'E's happy 'ere. 'E's found 'imself a 'ome. Don't think 'e ever really 'ad one before."

"Perhaps not." A memory of her conversation with Gray returned and Corrie wondered if perhaps the reason he didn't want a family was because he had never really had one. He had lost his mother as a boy, been raised by a father who didn't love him, then married and lost his wife.

Perhaps he feared that if he remarried, he

might lose something precious again. The thought softened her anger toward him, and she turned at the sound of his deep voice.

"Thank you for your help this afternoon. I didn't invite you along to help birth a babe, but I'm glad you were there."

Reluctant pleasure filled her. "I did little. You handled everything that mattered."

"It would have been a lot harder without you." He caught her hand. "I had planned a quiet outing. It didn't turn out that way, but perhaps I could make it up to you on the morrow."

She quickly shook her head. "You know how I feel, Gray."

"Even if I promise not to touch you?"

She was torn. If she hoped to discover the name of the man who had been Laurel's lover, she needed to spend time with the earl. And yet his indecent proposition still stung. She wasn't ready to beard the lion again quite so soon, and she couldn't resist a little sting of her own.

Corrie gave him a too-bright smile. "I appreciate the thought, my lord, but your cousin Jason has offered to show me round the conservatory. He seems to have quite an interest in flowers."

A muscle tightened in Tremaine's hard jaw. "The only flower Jason has an interest in is the one beneath your skirts."

Her false smile faded, replaced by a flash of anger that colored her cheeks. "Is that so? Then it would seem the two of you have at least one thing in common." The man was incorrigible! He said whatever he pleased with no concern for decorum.

Still, it was his very unconventionality that made him so appealing.

Turning away from him, she started toward the house.

"We aren't finished, Letty."

She glanced back, once more, pasting the false smile on her face. "Oh, but we are, my lord."

Behind her, she heard the earl's soft curse.

FOURTEEN

Corrie sat across from Charles, next to Jason in the breakfast room. As he entered, Gray cast her a dark, forbidding glance and took his place at the head of the table.

Rebecca floated airily into the room and the men rose politely. Charles seated his wife next to him.

"Thank you, darling."

Charles filled a plate of sausage and eggs from the sideboard, then set the plate in front of his wife. She cast a brief glance at Gray, her mouth curving into one of her feline smiles.

"I'll expect everyone for luncheon," she said. "The Countess of Devane will be arriving sometime late this morning."

Corrie's stomach knotted. Lady Devane was the woman Gray had been with the night of Laurel's murder. The countess was Gray's mistress! Corrie's gaze shot to his face and she saw that he was frowning.

"The countess is a friend of Becky's," Charles explained. "Her country estate, Parkside, is less than an hour's ride away."

Coralee knew who she was, though they had never been introduced. Lady Devane was quite well known in society.

Gray's jaw looked tight. "I'm afraid I have plans for the afternoon." He flicked a glance at Corrie. "Mrs. Cardigan had a baby yesterday. I thought I would take her and her husband a basket of food, see how their newborn is faring."

Though his concern pleased her, Corrie said nothing. The earl's mistress was coming to luncheon. Dear God, she would have to smile and converse and try not to wonder at the things the two of them had done together.

"Surely your visit can wait until tomorrow," Rebecca said. "I've planned a very nice meal to be served on the terrace. You don't wish to insult the countess, do you?"

"Come on, have pity, Gray," Jason teased. "You know the only reason she's coming is to see you."

"Jason, behave yourself," Rebecca chided. "The countess is a married woman."

Jason grinned, digging dimples into his cheeks. "A married woman with a husband as old as Methuselah."

Rebecca tried for a look of reproach, but Corrie thought that secretly she seemed pleased Jason had made the relationship clear. Corrie wasn't a fool. Even if Krista's letter had not revealed the information, she would have known from the conversation that the countess was Gray's mistress.

The earl leveled his hard gaze on Rebecca. "I suppose I can stay until after luncheon . . . as I'm sure you and the countess planned."

Rebecca merely smiled.

Corrie felt sick to her stomach. She swallowed a bite of eggs, but it seemed to stick in her throat. The meal passed in a blur, little of which she recalled, and as soon as she could politely excuse herself, she left the breakfast room.

She headed straight for the garden, desperate for a breath of fresh, untainted air. It was a cloudy, late spring morning, but the crocuses had bloomed, the trees were leafing out above the walkways. She was standing next to the fountain, taking deep, calming breaths, when she heard familiar footfalls approaching behind her.

She kept her back to Gray. "Please go away."

"At least let me explain."

It was insane to feel jealous. She knew the

sort of man he was, knew he was a complete and utter rogue who hadn't the least desire for anything from her but the use of her body. Yet thinking of Gray with another woman made her insides swirl with nausea.

"She's your mistress, Gray." She turned and looked up at him. "What is there to explain?"

"She isn't my mistress — not anymore." He released a slow breath. "After Jillian died, I couldn't bring myself to . . . I wasn't interested in physical gratification." He glanced away, as if picturing that dark time. "Bethany and Rebecca were friends. The countess came to the house quite often and eventually she made her interest clear. I wanted to forget the past. Bethany provided a way for me to do that. But our relationship was based on physical need, nothing more. We were never so much as friends."

Corrie was surprised by the turbulence she saw in his dark eyes, as if he cared what she thought, as if he was worried that he had hurt her.

"Most of the time, Bethany lives in London," he added. "Since her return to Parkside more than a month ago, I haven't seen her. I don't intend to."

Corrie lifted her chin. "Your relationship with the countess is none of my business."

"Perhaps not. I just . . . wanted you to know that Bethany means nothing to me. She never has."

Corrie looked into his handsome face and saw that he was truly concerned. But why should he care?

"Thank you for telling me."

He nodded. "Bethany has worse claws than Rebecca. I won't leave you alone with her."

So he had noticed his sister-in-law's behavior, the treatment that bordered on rudeness. "I suppose I should be grateful, but I don't think I am."

His mouth curved faintly. "I was hoping you would be. I could show you ways to repay me that —"

She pressed a hand over his lips, felt the warmth of his breath against her fingertips.

He straightened away from her, made her a formal bow. "I shall see you at luncheon, Mrs. Moss."

She watched him walk away, thinking how he must have suffered after his wife died, that he must have loved her at least in his own way. Corrie thought how lonely he often seemed, and wished she didn't feel such a fierce urge to comfort him. The man was a notorious rogue. He needed her body, not her heart.

And yet lately when he looked at her, she saw a need in him she hadn't recognized before. It called to her, made her want to hold him, erase the pain he had suffered through the years. It made her want to give him the one thing he had never had.

Love.

The realization burst over her, sank into her, made her gasp for breath. Dear God, she couldn't love Gray! Would not allow herself to love him. The man would ruin her without a backward glance. He would never love her in return — she wasn't sure he even knew how. If she fell in love with the Earl of Tremaine, he would break her heart into a thousand little pieces.

Corrie took a deep, strengthening breath. She wasn't in love with Gray, and from now on she wouldn't take any chances. She wouldn't allow him to get too close, to use those yearning looks and persuasive glances.

She would be careful to guard her heart.

Gray watched Letty in the drawing room. Bethany had just arrived, driving up in her husband's coach and four, wearing an elaborate gown of pale blue silk and ivory lace, the bodice cut a little too low for an afternoon luncheon. With her mahogany curls, finely arched brows and expanse of creamy bosom displayed by the gown, she looked every inch the countess.

Standing next to her, Letty wore a dress of yellow gauze and lace he had seen before, slightly outdated, the cuffs a bit frayed. She was shorter, more petite than the countess, a little unsure how to behave under the circumstances, and to his way of thinking, far more desirable than Bethany ever would be.

Letty looked fresh and lovely and innocent, and he wanted her more than he ever had before.

"So you are married to Gray's cousin." The countess raised her chin so she could look down her fine, straight nose at Letty.

"That is correct. My husband is traveling at present. I thought it a good time for a visit."

Bethany smiled with cunning. "Yes, well, Gray has a reputation for picking up strays."

He inwardly cursed. The claws were out, but Letty pretended not to notice.

"Unfortunately, I shan't be able to visit much longer." She smiled as if it were she who was doing him the favor by paying him a call. "I shall be off to London soon."

Gray almost smiled in turn. She was holding her own, he was only a little surprised to see. She might not have much of an education, might not be as well read or as versed in the social graces as some of the women he had known, but she was no fool.

Bethany's blue eyes ran over the shabby yellow gown. "Perhaps once you are in London, you will have a chance to shop. It must be difficult to maintain a fashionable wardrobe when one lives so far from the city."

Faint color rose in Letty's cheeks, but she merely smiled. "Yes, it is."

She didn't trade barbs, and that very fact seemed to elevate her above them in some way.

"So what do you think, Gray?" It was Rebecca, hoping to draw him into the conversation.

Unfortunately, his attention had been so fixed on Letty, he had missed what the countess had said. He moved into the group, nearer Letty's side, caught a whiff of her soft rose perfume.

"I'm sorry, my mind must have wandered. What was it you were saying, Lady Devane?"

"I said I've been thinking of having a costume ball. Arthur is still in the city and it gets rather lonely out here by oneself."

"You have at leave fifty servants, Countess. You are scarcely alone."

Bethany's smile slipped a little. "Yes, well, I still think a ball is a marvelous idea."

"As do I," Rebecca agreed. "I shall come as Marie Antoinette."

"And I as Diana the huntress." Bethany cast him a seductive smile that made clear whom she was hunting, and Gray inwardly cursed. How he had ever found the woman the least appealing he didn't understand.

Just then a footman announcing luncheon appeared at the door of the drawing room, and Gray said a silent prayer of thanks.

"Shall we go in?" he suggested, managing to smile, offering his arm to the countess, the lady of highest rank in the room.

She gave him a man-eating smile in return and rested her gloved hand on the sleeve of his coat. "Yes, let's. I discover I am starving."

And it was more than clear to Gray which appetite she wished to sate. When he glanced at Letty, there was an unusual spark in her brilliant green eyes. He hoped it was jealousy, and thought that perhaps having the countess to lunch wasn't such a bad idea, after all.

Gray almost smiled.

He glanced up just as Samir appeared silently at the door of the drawing room. Gray excused himself and walked over to where the small man stood waiting.

"What is it?"

"I am sorry to disturb you, *sahib,* but a message for you has just arrived."

Gray took the wax-sealed letter from Samir's leathery hand. "Thank you, my friend."

He broke the seal and read the note.

In the matter of your investigation of Mrs. Letty Moss, I am sorry to disappoint, my lord, but I am not at liberty to accept the position, as it would be a conflict of interest. Respectfully, your friend,

Dolph Petersen.

There was a post script.

I wouldn't concern myself overly about Mrs. Moss.

Gray read the note, then read it again. Dolph was in some way connected with Letty? Or had he been hired by another person to investigate the lady? And why the subtle message that she was no threat?

Tremaine was more curious than ever, and at the same time vastly relieved. He trusted Dolph Petersen. If Dolph said not to be concerned about Letty, then he wouldn't be. He would simply continue with his planned seduction.

Sliding the note into the pocket of his tailcoat, he returned to the others. He just hoped that while he was gone, Rebecca and Bethany hadn't sunk their sharp claws too deeply into sweet little Letty Moss.

She had to get away. As she sat across from Gray and the countess, luncheon had seemed interminable. Every time the woman cast him one of her come-hither glances, every time she wet her ruby lips and smiled at him as if he were a succulent piece of meat, Corrie had wanted to rip out the catty female's gleaming dark hair.

The woman was a she-devil, the perfect match for the roguish devil earl.

As soon as the meal was over, Corrie excused herself and slipped away, went upstairs and changed into her riding habit. Yesterday she had discovered the joy of riding as she never had in the city. She felt confident with Tulip, able to relax and enjoy herself. Yesterday, she had ridden with Gray. Today she intended to rid herself of his haunting image.

Out at the stable, she asked Dickey Michaels to saddle Tulip, then waited while he went to see it done. He brought the horse round, saddled and ready, then frowned when he looked up at the sky.

"I don't know, missus. Looks like a storm's comin' in. Might be best if ye waited till mornin'."

"I'm going now, Dickey."

He nodded. "Whatever ye say. Won't take a minute to saddle meself an 'orse. I'll be ready in a jiff."

"Wait, Dickey — I appreciate your offer, truly I do, but I don't need you to come along. I'll be fine by myself."

The youth's sandy eyebrows drew together. " 'Is lordship will skin me I let ye go alone."

"I'm afraid I'm not giving you a choice. You may tell him that if he gives you any trouble. I'll be back in a couple of hours."

Homer yapped just then and wagged his tail, wanting to go along. "Not this time, boy." She turned to the groom. "Hold on to him, Dickey, until I'm out of sight."

She needed to be alone. Even Homer was more company than she wanted at the moment.

Urging Tulip into a trot, she rode out of the stable yard, heading off in the direction she had taken yesterday with Gray, figuring she would be able to find her way back to the castle. The wind had kicked up and the sky looked a little dark, but the storm still seemed some distance away.

She wouldn't stay out long, she told herself. Just long enough to clear her head and bring her turbulent emotions under control. Not for the first time since she had arrived at the castle, she wished she could go home.

Corrie sighed as she rode along the trail. In London she would be free of Gray and the uncertain feelings he stirred, free to return to the life she had lived before. London and her work at *Heart to Heart* had never seemed more appealing, but she just wasn't ready to give up yet. She had pledged to Laurel to find out the truth. Corrie had made some progress but it wasn't enough. She had to continue — and she would.

All she needed was some time away from the castle, away from Rebecca's pinched expression and the countess's smirks, away from Gray and the unwanted feelings he stirred.

And so when the wind picked up, she merely shrugged. When Tulip shied at a rabbit and she nearly lost her seat, she didn't care. Instead, she urged the mare into a gallop, feeling free for the first time in days.

She wasn't ready to return, not yet.

Not until she'd had time to gird herself to face the devil earl.

FIFTEEN

Gray searched for Letty in the castle. He looked for her in the garden. By the time he thought of Homer and considered she might have gone out to the stable to see the scruffy mutt, nearly an hour had passed.

"Have you seen Mrs. Moss?" he asked Dickey Michaels, who was busily sweeping the earthen floor in one of the stalls.

"That I 'ave, milord. The missus rode out on Tulip a while ago."

"By herself?"

He nodded. "Tried to get 'er to let me go with her, but she wouldn't 'ave it. Wouldn't even let 'Omer go along."

Gray bit back a curse. It wasn't Dickey's fault, it was his. He should have known she'd be upset after the dismal luncheon with his ex-mistress that she had been forced to endure. He just hadn't expected her to go off on her own like this.

"Which way did she ride out?"

"Same way the two of ye went yesterday. I told 'er a storm looked t' be comin' in. Said she'd be back in a couple of hours."

Gray glanced at the flat dark clouds swelling on the horizon. "Saddle Raja. I'll bring her back." And wring her pretty little neck for putting herself in danger.

Damn stubborn female.

He thought of his offer to make her his mistress. Letty had been insulted, though it was a very sensible solution to her troubles. *Too damn proud for her own good. Too damn naive.*

He looked up at the sky as Dickey brought the stallion over and handed him the reins. "If she comes back, tell her I went looking for her. Tell her I intend to have a talk with her when I return."

One of Dickey's sandy eyebrows went up. "Aye, milord."

Why was it everyone was afraid of him, except Letty Moss?

Gray set his jaw and headed off in the direction of the Cardigan cottage, hoping he would catch up with her as she made her way back home.

Instead, an hour passed and then another.

The wind began to howl. Grass and leaves blew into the air, and the first drops of rain began to fall. He stopped at the Cardigans' long enough to discover that the baby was doing well and Letty hadn't been there, then returned to his search.

If she had stayed on the main path, she would have missed the turn to the cottage. The trail would have taken her toward the old hunting lodge, a structure that had been built just a few years after the castle.

He started in that direction, wondering if he might have missed her and she was already safely back home. But Gray's sixth sense was kicking in, telling him that hadn't happened. It was easy to get lost out here, especially in a storm. The landscape looked different, the tree branches distorted by the wind, the trails hidden by billowing grasses.

It was starting to rain in earnest, the wind shrieking through the trees, dragging the tie from his hair. It whipped the heavy black strands into his face with stinging force, mimicking the ferocity of the storm, and his worry kicked up another notch.

Letty was only a passable rider. What if she had taken a spill? What if Tulip had stepped in a hole and gone down? What if Letty was injured and lying out in the storm somewhere?

His pulse accelerated. Worry made his insides tighten into a knot. He shouted her name again and again, but the wind blew the sound away.

He wished he had thought to bring Homer. The dog loved Letty and might have been able to find her.

A dark shape moved among the trees ahead. It was Tulip, Gray saw, and his chest squeezed. The mare was riderless, her saddle gone, her reins trailing on the ground as she steadily made her way back toward the castle. Tulip knew the way home — but sweet God, what had happened to Letty?

He rode toward the sorrel, caught her reins. She didn't appear to be injured, didn't look to have taken a fall, but why had the saddle come off?

"Where is she?" Gray asked, patting the horse's wet coat. "Where's our girl?"

The sorrel nickered as if she wanted to tell him. Leading Tulip, Gray started in the direction she had come from, looking for any sign of Letty up ahead. A low stone wall loomed in the distance, just off the main path. When the mare's ears perked up and she nickered again, Gray kicked Raja into a gallop and rode for the wall.

His heart constricted when he spotted Letty, pale as death, lying on the opposite side. Quickly dismounting, he raced toward her, fear crawling down the back of his neck.

Let her be all right. Please, let her be all right.

Thoughts of the day Jillian had died came back to him, and the bitter taste of bile rose in his mouth. Kneeling in the wet grass, he reached for Letty's pale hand. It felt as cold as death.

"Letty . . . Letty, can you hear me?" For an instant, he thought she was dead, and a wave of nausea hit him. He checked her pulse with a shaking hand. It was there, strong and steady, and the knot in his stomach began to uncurl. She was breathing evenly, and the painful constriction in his chest began to ease.

He checked for broken bones, found none, and just as he finished, her eyelids started to flutter.

"Letty! Letty, it's Gray!"

"Gray . . . ?"

He reached down and captured her hand. "I'm right here, sweeting. Are you injured? Tell me where it hurts."

She swallowed, tried to raise her head.

"Easy . . . Just tell me where you're hurt." Lightning flashed in the distance, warning him of the storm's approach, and the roll of thunder followed.

"The wind was . . . blowing," she said. "We were galloping along and I felt . . . so

226

free. The wall was there and I thought we could make it. If the cinch hadn't broken —"

"Dammit, Letty, tell me where you're hurt!"

Her luminous green eyes came to rest on his face. "My head hurts a little. I must have hit it when I fell. Aside from that, I think I'm all right."

A wave of relief rolled through him, so strong a tremor followed. He released a slow breath. "Good. That's good." Another flash of lightning was followed by a reverberating crack of thunder. The storm was closing in, coming dangerously close. They had to get to shelter.

He glanced toward the horizon, saw the silhouette of the old hunting lodge in another bright flash of lightning.

"We've got to get out of this storm. I'm going to lift you up. Stop me if I hurt you." Reaching down, he hoisted her gently into his arms. "All right?"

She nodded, rested her head against his chest. He settled her on the saddle, then swung up behind her.

"Just lean against me. I know a place we'll be safe."

She didn't protest when he turned Raja toward the hunting lodge and set off in that direction, Tulip trotting behind them. It didn't take long to reach the rustic structure. Gray swung down, eased Letty into his arms and strode for the building that had been his place of refuge when he was a boy, and still often was.

The heavy wooden door was never locked. He lifted the latch, eased the door open with his boot, carried Letty inside, then shoved the heavy wood closed against the rain.

"How are you feeling?"

"Better. I don't think I broke anything."

He'd been sick with worry. His fear congealed into anger at her carelessness, and a muscle twitched in his jaw. "It's a wonder you didn't break your pretty little neck riding off that way. I swear I ought to thrash you for scaring me the way you did."

She colored slightly, but made no reply.

Gray settled her carefully on the brown leather sofa in front of the hearth. "I'll see to the horses and bring in some wood for a fire."

Letty still said nothing, and he couldn't tell if she was grateful he had found her or wished that he hadn't.

Sheltering the animals in the lean-to beside the lodge, he fed them some of the oats he kept there, then returned to the house carrying an armload of wood. It didn't take long to build a roaring blaze, and the heat of it began to drive the chill from the room.

The lodge wasn't all that big, only a single chamber, low-ceilinged with a roof fashioned of heavy timbers. A kitchen with an iron stove and an old oak table sat off to one side. The main room was furnished with a leather sofa and overstuffed chairs in front of the big stone fireplace, and a four-poster bed in the corner.

He built a fire in the iron stove for additional warmth, set water on to boil for a pot of tea, then returned to where Letty rested, soaked and bedraggled, on the sofa.

"We need to get out of these wet clothes."

She was shivering even as she shook her head. "I can't. I don't have anything else to put on."

He strode to the linen cupboard and dragged out a pair of woolen blankets. "These will have to do." He tossed her one and it landed next to her on the sofa.

Moving toward the fire, he began to strip off his coat, waistcoat and shirt. Letty just sat there, careful not to look at him.

"I am fine just as I am," she said. "Eventually my clothes will dry."

"And by that time, you'll have the devil's own ague."

Her chin shot up. "And if I do take them off, I'll have the devil *himself* to deal with."

His lips quirked. He didn't have to ask who that was.

Still, her health was more important than her modesty. "Sorry, sweetheart, this is one argument you're not going to win. I'll help you take off those wet clothes or I'll take them off for you. Which is it going to be?"

"You wouldn't dare!"

He began to pull off his boots. "You know I would. I don't think you have the slightest doubt."

Her eyes snapped with anger. Why was it there were times Letty seemed almost like two different women, one sweet and docile, the other full of fire?

She muttered something. Surely it wasn't a curse.

"You really are a devil," she said. She looked away while he finished undressing, picked up one of the blankets, wrapped it around his waist and tucked it in so it wouldn't fall off.

"Your turn," he said.

Letty got up slowly and Gray helped her carefully to her feet. "How are you feeling? Are you dizzy?"

"I was fine until you demanded I take off my clothes."

He bit back a smile. He had smiled only rarely since Jillian had died, but Letty managed to make it happen more and more.

"Just stand still and I'll do the work." He reached for the buttons on the bodice of her dark green riding habit, but she slapped his hands away.

"I can do it myself."

He stepped back, letting her salvage her pride, and waited as she unfastened the buttons with trembling fingers. He helped her out of the bodice, leaving her in her chemise, and draped the top over a hook next to the fire. She unfastened the tabs on the skirt and swayed precariously as she tried to step out of it.

"Easy." Gray caught her arm to steady her, and she didn't object, though it was clear from the stiffness of her spine that she would rather he kept his hands to himself.

Her petticoats went next. Soaked completely through, they sagged into a pile of soggy white cotton at her feet. He helped her step out of them, leaving her in her wet, clinging, nearly transparent undergarments.

He was trying his damnedest to behave himself — after all, the lady had suffered a fall — but his male instincts were springing to life, along with his male anatomy. Her chemise barely hid the sweet curve of her bottom, and Gray's loins began to fill.

Clearing his throat, he pulled the damp strings on her corset, loosened them, then took a step away. He thought he could trust himself. She'd been injured, if only slightly. But as he studied the feminine curve of her spine, the tantalizing swell of her hips, he began to doubt his strength of will. God, he ached for her. His erection pulsed with every heartbeat.

A bolt of lightning lit the room and the wind rattled the shutters.

"Would you please hand me the blanket?"

"What?"

"I need the blanket. Would you hand it to me, please?"

"Sorry." He unfurled the second blanket and held it up in front of him. "You need to take off the rest. I promise I won't look."

"I don't trust you."

"I don't trust myself, but I'll do my best."

He thought he heard her laugh.

"I want your word as a gentleman," she said.

"All right, you have my word as a gentleman."

He raised the blanket. Letty kept her back to him and he could hear the rustle of fabric. He lowered the cover enough to see over the top, and watched with growing lust as she stepped out of her corset and tossed it aside, then stood in front of the fire half-naked. She moved a little and he caught a glimpse of her naked breasts, which were even lovelier than he recalled, plump and rose-tipped, the color of day-old cream. A memory of the taste of them sent a fresh surge of blood to his groin.

Her drawers followed — not mended, he saw, but made of finest lawn trimmed with expensive lace. If she prized them so highly, he would buy her a dozen pairs, though once she belonged to him, he would forbid her to wear anything at all beneath her skirts. Her pink satin garters came off, and she bent over to roll down her stockings.

The sight of her sweet behind poised so temptingly in the air made his mouth water and his erection jerk. He prided himself on his control, but it seemed to elude him where Letty was concerned. Then she turned, and he couldn't take his eyes off the glossy auburn curls glinting between her pale thighs.

Letty's shriek of outrage hurt his ears.

"You gave me your word!"

He held the blanket up in front of his eyes, reluctantly blocking his view. "I gave you my word as a gentleman — which I never have been. You should have asked me to give you my word as a soldier. I would have been honor-bound by that."

"You are a . . ." she sputtered, "you are a __"

He walked toward her, wrapped her snugly in the blanket and also in his arms. "You are the most desirable woman I've ever met. So beautiful and sweet. God, I've never wanted anyone the way I want you."

And then he kissed her. Bound up in the blanket, she struggled to get free, but he just kept kissing her. Soft, teasing kisses, sweetly passionate, became hot, deep, hungry ones that made his erection go rock hard. The moment she stopped struggling, the moment her lips began to soften under his, Gray gentled the kiss, and Letty kissed him back.

He eased his hold and her arms went around his neck. He felt her fingers sliding into his wet hair.

"Letty . . ." He hadn't lied to her. He wasn't a gentleman and he never would be. He took what he wanted, and he wanted Letty Moss. In return, he would take care of her in the manner she deserved. It was the perfect arrangement for both of them.

Gray lowered the edge of the blanket and began to kiss his way toward Letty's ripe breasts, determined to accomplish the goal he had set for himself. His seduction would end her protests and she would be his.

Why that seemed so important he refused to consider. He only knew he meant to give her the pleasure he had promised, make her ache for him as he ached for her.

Gray set himself to the task.

The blanket slipped to her waist and Corrie melted into the warm arms around her. Firm lips melded with hers, and a warm, solid body took away the last of her chill. Her headache was gone, her mind filled instead with numbing pleasure.

She knew it was wrong, knew she would have to stop him, but nothing had ever felt so good, so right as this moment with Gray. He nuzzled the side of her neck. She tilted her head back to give him better access, and his thick black hair, free of its ribbon, teased her skin. She thought of the way he had looked when she had been lying there in the rain. With his legs braced apart and his unbound hair swirling round his shoulders, he was the highwayman she had always imagined him to be.

Gray deepened the kiss and the muscles across his chest pressed into her breasts. They tingled and her nipples went hard. A soft ache pulsed between her legs. Liquid heat sank low in her belly and desire swirled through her, as tempting as the snake in the garden.

She was nearly twenty-two years old. In all the parties she had attended, and all the men who had paid her court, she had never met a man like Gray. None of their kisses had stirred her; not one of them could move her as he did.

She thought of the man he was, remembered the dog and how he'd helped her care for him, the boy he had rescued in the village. She thought of the baby he had delivered, the care he had shown mother and child. She remembered the pain he had lived through, the losses he had suffered.

The blanket slipped a few more inches and she felt the heat of his mouth on her breast, the strong pull of his teeth, and a rush of pleasure tore through her. The wanton creature she had been before rose up inside her, daring her to take what she wanted. To experience what no other man could give her.

It was true, she realized. If she denied herself now, she might never know the sort of pleasure Gray offered. She didn't intend to marry for years — there were too many things she wanted to do. Even after she wed, she might not feel the passion for her husband that Gray made her feel.

His hands slid into her wet hair, pulling out the pins. Then he was running his fingers through the heavy strands, spreading them around her shoulders.

"I love your hair," he whispered against her ear. "I love every sweet curve of your beautiful body."

His words seduced her along with his hands. He skimmed them over her naked flesh, teased and caressed her, made her skin tingle at his slightest touch. His mouth claimed hers in another ravishing kiss, his tongue delving in, coaxing hers to respond.

She arched backward, bringing her body into full contact with his, and realized both blankets had fallen to the floor. The two of them were completely naked. She could feel Gray's arousal, the hard male length that so intrigued her, and eased back a little to see what it looked like.

Her eyes widened at the heavy appendage thrusting toward her, reminding her of the image of Mercury she had seen in his erotic book. "Oh, my heavens!"

His mouth curved. "It's all right. We'll just take our time."

It was now or never. If she didn't stop him this instant it would be too late. She looked up at him, saw the hot desire burning in his eyes, and there was something more, a yearning so powerful it seemed to reach inside her. She felt mesmerized by it, captured and unable to resist.

"I need you, Letty," he whispered, drawing her into his arms and kissing her again. "I need you so damn much."

The longing was there in his voice, the loneliness. Her mind whirled, fought to discover what this feeling was that gripped her, held her in its thrall.

And then there it was, so crystal clear she couldn't believe she had been able to deny it before.

Dear God, she was in love with him!

Not a little in love, as she had feared, but desperately, wildly in love.

It was too late to protect her heart, too late to save herself, and because she could not, the only choice she had was for her to save *him.*

She looked up at him and tears stung her eyes. "I need you, too, Gray."

Something moved across his features, dark and turbulent. Gray stared down at her with an intensity she had never seen before. His kiss was hard and deep, no longer seductive. It was the savage kiss of a man claiming his mate, and Corrie responded with eager abandon.

Wet, sensual kisses left her dizzy. Hot, passionate caresses sent liquid heat into her core. He touched her, teased her sensitive skin. His fingers sifted through the curls at the juncture of her legs and breached her as no man ever had.

Wild desire burned through her. This was what she needed, what she had been waiting for all of her life.

"Make love to me, Gray."

She heard his deep groan, tinged with male satisfaction.

Then he was lifting her into his arms, carrying her over to the bed in the corner. Gray followed her down on the soft feather mattress, kissing her even more deeply than before. Corrie burned for him, ached for more of the searing pleasure his hard body promised.

And yet she was no longer the naive young woman that she had been in London.

"I'm afraid, Gray. What if there is a child?"

He brushed her tumbled damp hair back from her temple. "There are ways to prevent it. A French letter, other ways. I won't let it happen. Even if it did, I would take care of you."

God help her, she believed him. Perhaps she truly was a fool.

Whatever happened, it no longer mattered. She loved him and she wanted him. Corrie kissed him with all of the newly found love she felt for him, and let him work his magic.

Gray tried to remember the skills he had learned in India, the dozens of tricks that could give a woman pleasure, but his mind was clouded by his need for Letty. He had waited too long, wanted her too badly. He kissed her deeply, stroked her until she was wet and ready, writhing beneath him and begging him to take her. Parting her legs with his knee, he came up over her, found the entrance to her passage and began to ease himself toward his goal.

She was tight. Amazingly so, but then it had been two years since she had been with her husband. Gray kissed her slowly, thoroughly, and she kissed him back, thrusting her small tongue into his mouth and driving him insane. He prided himself on his control, on his skill at lovemaking, but all he could think of was Letty and how badly he needed to be inside her. He could feel the tightness of her feminine sheath and desire overwhelmed him.

"Gray," she whispered, sliding her fingers into his damp hair, dragging his mouth down to hers for another burning kiss.

Gray's tight control slipped, then dis-appeared completely. With a single hard thrust, he drove himself home, impaling himself full length in her sweet little body. When Letty cried out, it took a moment for his lust-filled brain to realize he had hurt her, that the thin barrier he had felt and ignored was her maidenhead.

That Mrs. Letty Moss was a virgin.

"What the hell?" Fury shot through him. He lifted himself away enough to gaze into her tear-damp eyes. "You're no married woman! Who the hell are you, Letty? Or is that even your name?"

She swallowed, reached up to touch his face with a trembling hand. For a moment she seemed uncertain, as if there was some-thing she wanted to say. Then she shud-dered and shook her head. "We . . . we never made love. Cyrus was old. I should have told you."

Gray reached down and wiped away the tears on her cheeks. It made sense. He had recognized her innocence from the start. And suddenly he was glad his cousin was such an old fool.

"If I had known, I would have taken bet-ter care." He bent and very softly kissed her. "I'm sorry I hurt you."

She gave him a gentle smile. "It's all right.

It doesn't hurt now. I just feel . . . full of you."

Relief mingled with an odd feeling of protectiveness. "You're the most amazing woman, Letty Moss." And she was his, a virgin wife. The perfect mistress.

Gray kissed her gently, taking his time, working to arouse her again. Perspiration popped out on his forehead and the muscles across his shoulders ached with his effort at control. He wanted to please her, to give her satisfaction.

"Please, Gray," she whispered, arching beneath him, urging him to give her what she needed, and the instant she said the words he started to move.

A single deep thrust and Letty came up off the bed in a shattering climax. He could scarcely believe it. He felt a rush of triumph that he had been the man to bring her to fulfillment, but he didn't stop, just drove into her until she peaked again, her nails digging into his shoulders, stealing the last shred of his control.

Deep, powerful strokes fired his blood; the heavy thrust and drag of his shaft sent him over the edge. His body shook with the onset of his climax and the effort it took to pull himself out of her welcoming heat before he spilled his seed.

He had promised to protect her and he meant to keep his word. He kept French letters in the top drawer of his dresser. Next time he would be sure to bring them along.

Gray smiled as settled himself next to Letty in the bed and drew her snugly against his side. He couldn't remember the last time he had felt so completely relaxed, so utterly replete. The restlessness was gone, at least for the moment. Contentment filled him in a way he couldn't explain.

He pressed a kiss to her temple. "Everything is going to work out, sweetheart. I promise you."

Gray closed his eyes, enjoying the soft feel of the woman in his arms. It was getting dark and the storm still raged outside the lodge. Letty drifted into an exhausted sleep and though he wanted to rouse her, make love to her again, he thought of her innocence and let her be.

He must have drifted off himself. When he awakened, he was amazed to discover he had slept straight through until dawn.

It was the first peaceful night's sleep he'd had since Jillian had died.

Sixteen

"Where is she, Charles? Where the bloody hell is my daughter!" Justin Whitmore, Viscount Selkirk, stood in the foyer of Castle Tremaine in his damp greatcoat and high beaver hat.

As Charles walked toward him, he noticed Justin's distress, and his smile of welcome slipped away. "What the devil are you talking about? Surely you aren't speaking of Laurel. Her death came as a terrible blow to us all, but —"

"I am talking about Coralee! She is here in your home, posing as some long lost cousin of the earl's. I demand to see her, Charles. Now!"

Charles Forsythe looked stunned. For the first time, Justin realized how utterly and completely his daughter had pulled off her charade.

It didn't matter. She was an unmarried young woman. She had no business traipsing around the countryside in some wild attempt to redeem her sister's lost honor.

Charles cleared his throat. "I presume you are speaking of the young lady who calls herself Letty Moss."

"Yes, though we only just discovered her ruse. Her mother and I had been growing more and more worried about her. Her letters were spare, at best, and told us nothing of her well-being. Coralee was never one for the country, and yet she has stayed here some weeks. We decided to see how she fared, and instead discovered she is not in residence at Selkirk Hall and never has been."

"I see. Well, I had no idea, of course." His blond eyebrows drew together over his hazel eyes. "What motive, exactly, did your daughter have for such an elaborate hoax?"

"I am not quite certain of that myself."

Charles motioned for the butler to take the viscount's coat and hat, which in his haste to see Coralee, he still had on.

"Perhaps the matter would be better discussed in private" Charles suggested.

"Yes, I'm certain it would be."

"If you will please follow me." He walked into the drawing room and Justin followed. As the men settled themselves, the butler closed the door.

"I must say, your daughter is quite an accomplished actress," Charles said. "Coralee was only a child when last we saw her. You can hardly fault us for not realizing who she was."

"The fault was not yours, Charles. In fact, you have my most sincere apologies for the trouble she has caused. And you may believe when I speak to her I shall have a good deal to say in that regard. Now if you would ask her to come in here . . ."

Charles's gaze became shuttered. "I'm afraid, at the moment, there is a bit of a problem with that."

Justin's senses went on alert. "What do you mean?"

"Your daughter went out riding just before the storm hit. Gray was worried, so he went after her. I'm sure he must have found her, since he didn't come back home. They must have taken shelter someplace to wait out the storm."

"What if he didn't find her? What if she is out there injured — or worse?" Thank God he had insisted Constance wait for him at Selkirk Hall. If she knew her daughter had been out all night, she would be worried sick.

"My brother was a major in the army. If he hadn't found her, he would have come back for help. The storm raged for hours and only broke this morning. The best thing to do is give them time to get home. If they don't return in the next several hours, we'll form a search party and go after them."

It chafed Justin to wait. His daughter might be lying out there, injured or even worse. But waiting was a better alternative than riding off haphazardly with no idea where to look.

"You really believe your brother found her?"

"I'm sure of it. Gray was in the army, I repeat. He's an extremely capable man."

Justin thought of the handsome earl he had met in London on several occasions. And Grayson Forsythe's wicked reputation. An unpleasant thought occurred. "If they spent the night together, you realize what it will mean."

Charles's blond head came up. "Good God — he'll have to marry her."

Justin gritted his teeth. He'd had one daughter ruined, a scandal he and his family would suffer for years to come. He wouldn't tolerate another. If the rogue had spent the night with her, he would marry Coralee.

Justin thought of his daughter's independence, of her unruly, stubborn nature.

Dammit to hell, in this she would not defy him.

She would marry the earl — whether she wished it or not!

Corrie rode on Raja in front of Gray, while Tulip trailed along behind them. After their wild lovemaking, both of them had slept through the night. Gray had awakened early and gone out to check on the horses. With the cinch broken, the sidesaddle was useless. He planned to send Dickey Michaels back to pick it up.

Seated in front of Gray as they rode back to the house, Corrie wondered what he thought about last night. It occurred to her that a man with his reputation might cast her aside, now that she had gifted him with her virtue. If he did, he wasn't the man she had come to believe he was, and she would be better off without him.

The thought made her insides tighten. She was in love with Gray. She didn't want to lose him. But then, what would he do when he discovered that she wasn't the woman he believed, that she had come to the house to prove him guilty of her sister's murder?

All the way back to the castle, the worrisome thought swirled in her head. Neither of them spoke as they climbed the hill from the stable and went into the house through the door at the rear of the castle.

Samir was waiting when they stepped into the hall.

"There is trouble, *sahib.* I am sorry I failed you."

"What are you talking about, Samir?"

"The woman . . . I should have tried harder to learn the truth."

"Do not talk in riddles, my friend. Tell me —"

"Gray! Thank God you are returned." Charles strode toward them. "And safely, I see."

Corrie could feel a flush creeping into her cheeks and hoped Gray's brother would not see it. She was safe, but no longer the innocent young woman she had been before she had ridden out yesterday afternoon.

"Letty's cinch broke and she took a spill. She's lucky she wasn't severely injured."

Charles cast her a glance she couldn't read. "Yes, well, I am glad she is all right. However, there is a matter that requires your attention, and also . . . Letty's. If you will both come with me . . ."

"I'm not fit company for anyone," Corrie said, wanting nothing so much as to escape upstairs to her room. "I need to change out of these clothes and into something more presentable. If you will excuse me, Charles. . . ." She started past the two men, but Charles caught her arm.

"I'm afraid this can't wait."

Gray cast her an uneasy glance and Corrie felt a prickly shiver of alarm. Wordlessly, they followed Charles down the hall to the Emerald Room, an extravagant salon done in bright colors and gilded furniture. It was a room Rebecca preferred and Corrie rarely entered.

She stepped into the drawing room, saw her father and very nearly swooned. Gray must have noticed. His hand shot to her waist to steady her.

"Are you all right? Perhaps you were injured, after all, and only now showing the symptoms."

"Truly, I — I am fine."

"Good morning, Coralee." Her father walked toward her, his features set as grimly as she had ever seen them.

"Good morning . . . Father."

Gray's eyes swung from her to the viscount. "Lord Selkirk?" He looked back at Corrie. "What the devil is going on?"

Corrie swallowed, feeling faint once more.

"That is a very good question, my lord," her father said. "Would you care to explain, Coralee?"

Gray's penetrating dark eyes fixed on her face. "Coralee? That is your name?"

"I was going to tell you, Gray, I swear. I wanted to tell you last night. I just . . . couldn't. Not yet."

"Coralee is my daughter," the viscount began. "She would have been a child when last you met. She is quite grown up now, as you can see. As a matter of fact, from her bedraggled appearance, there is every chance you have discovered that for yourself."

Corrie gasped. "Father, please —"

"You are not Letty Moss," Gray said darkly. "You are Coralee Whitmore, the viscount's daughter."

"Yes . . ." The word came out on the faintest breath of air. Her heart was pounding, each beat a dull throb inside her chest. Dear God, what was Gray thinking? And how could she possibly explain?

"Why did you come here?" he asked. "Why were you pretending to be someone else?"

"I was . . ." She nervously wet her lips. "I was trying to find out who murdered my sister."

Charles cut in just then. "That is absurd. Laurel killed herself. She drowned right there in the river."

251

Corrie turned in his direction. "I don't believe my sister would do such a thing. I think she was murdered."

Charles's face went pale.

Gray's dark gaze pierced her. "Tell me you didn't come here because you think her death had something to do with one of us."

She swallowed. "I thought . . . thought it was you." She closed her eyes to block out the rage that darkened his face. "I found out about your wife, that she drowned just like Laurel. I came here to prove you had killed her."

"Bloody hell."

"I discovered it wasn't you. I found out you were with the countess that night, so I knew you weren't guilty."

Gray's jaw looked like granite. "Your sister had a child out of wedlock. It was common knowledge in the village. She killed herself when her lover refused to marry her. I'm sorry for your loss, *Miss Whitmore,* but that doesn't make up for what you've done."

Turning, the earl started to walk away, but the sharp edge in her father's voice brought him to a halt.

"Nor does it change the circumstances of what must now occur."

Gray turned, his eyes hard and glittering.

"Coralee is an unmarried young woman

252

from one of London's finest families, a family that has suffered far too much scandal already. It will soon be well known that the two of you spent last night together. You are bound by your honor, my lord, to marry my daughter."

Corrie gasped. It took all of her courage not to cringe at the fierce look on Gray's face.

"You expect me to marry her? After the lies she has told? After the way she deceived us all?"

Corrie felt the sharp sting of tears. For the first time she realized how harsh the penalty was going to be for her deceit. "I'm sorry, Gray, truly I am. I meant to tell you the truth, but I just . . . I made a vow to Laurel to find out what happened. I could not break my promise."

He looked down at her and something moved across his features. She thought it was disappointment. "You're nothing like her, are you? You aren't sweet and kind, gentle and loving. You're deceitful and conniving, a vicious little tart willing to stop at nothing to get what she wants."

Corrie blanched.

"That's enough," said the viscount. "You will not speak to my daughter that way."

The earl ignored him. "I remember you

now. You're the little harpy who wrote about me in your newspaper column. Let me see . . . what was it you called me? 'A conscienceless seducer of women.' Yes, I believe that was it." He raked her with cold, dark eyes, a silent reminder of the intimacies they had shared last night. "I suppose in your case, you were right."

He started walking again, stopped at the hard note in her father's voice. "Then you admit you took advantage of my daughter."

He turned. "I seduced Letty Moss, the lovely, destitute young wife of my very distant cousin. I don't know this woman at all."

A strangled sound caught in Corrie's throat as she watched Gray walk away. She wanted to call him back, tell him she and Letty were different parts of the same person, but she knew he wouldn't believe her.

It was over between them.

Corrie felt as if a knife had been thrust into her heart.

Gray stalked out of the house and headed for the stable. God, what a fool he was. He should have known the sweet, innocent young woman he had made love to last night didn't actually exist. She was simply too good to be true. Naive, gentle Letty was a figment of his imagination.

"Stop where you are, Tremaine."

At the sound of the viscount's voice, he halted on the stone walkway and turned to face him. He had always respected the man. It wasn't his fault his daughter was a cunning little baggage with the conscience of a whore.

"I realize my daughter duped you. I hope you will try to understand how devastated Coralee was by the news of her sister's death. Until recently, the two of them were extremely close. Coralee refused to believe Laurel's drowning was suicide. According to her aunt, she was convinced you were the man who had seduced her sister and then killed her, and she came here to prove it."

Gray ignored the grudging respect he felt that she would risk herself that way.

"Apparently, she proved just the opposite," the viscount continued. "If she hadn't believed you were innocent, there is nothing on this earth that could have moved her to give herself to you, as apparently she has."

Gray remained silent. A feeling of loss swept through him that Letty didn't exist, that the night he'd spent with her in his arms was nothing more than a fantasy.

"There's been far too much scandal in my family to let this matter go unresolved," the viscount continued. "I'll expect you to do the right thing by my daughter, Tremaine. If you refuse, I shall have to call you out."

Christ. A duel with Selkirk was the last thing he wanted. The man and his wife had already suffered more than their share of scandal and grief. Even now the man stood in front of him clothed in the black garments of mourning.

From the corner of his eye, Gray spotted a familiar small figure hurrying down the pathway toward them. She looked like Letty, but he knew she was nothing at all like the sweet creature who had made him burn for her last night.

She raced up and caught hold of his arm, and he ignored a thread of sympathy when he noticed the tears in her eyes.

"Please don't hurt him," she said. "You don't have to marry me. I told him I wouldn't marry you even if you asked. Just please . . . please don't hurt him."

He looked down at her and something moved inside him. She was Letty, but she was not. Anger burned like a hot poker in his stomach. An urge to make her pay for the lies she had told combined with a fierce desire to bury his hard length inside her.

"So you won't marry me even if I ask?"

She swallowed. "I am employed in London. Aside from that, there are things I wish to do, places I wish to see. I am not ready for marriage yet."

One of his eyebrows arched up. "Is that so?" He turned to her father. "See to the license. We'll be married as soon as arrangements can be made."

"What!"

He started striding toward the house, a surge of triumph expanding in his chest. He would pay her back for her deceit, and in the process he would satisfy this wild craving for her that one night of lovemaking had not begun to satisfy.

"I won't marry you!" she said, lifting her skirts and running along behind him.

He stopped and turned. "You'll marry me. I'm not giving you a choice."

Her mouth fell open as he strode away. He thought he heard a swear word slip from between her lips.

A grim smile arose. She was a cunning little baggage, but the passion he had aroused in her last night was real. Whatever sort of wife she made, he meant to enjoy her until he'd had his fill.

Then he would send her on her way, back

to London.

"I won't marry him!"

"You will, by God. You refuse and I swear I will take a switch to you, as I should have done when you were a child."

Corrie couldn't believe it. Her father had always indulged her. Now he was telling her she had to marry a man who despised her?

"I can't marry the earl," she argued. "I have a job. I am employed at *Heart to Heart.* Doesn't that matter to anyone?"

"You never should have taken that job. You are above that sort of labor. Besides, you would have to marry sooner or later. After last night, you have no choice but to do it now."

"But he hates me! Once I'm his wife, he'll probably beat me!"

"Good for him. If I had done that myself, I would have a quiet, respectful daughter instead of a willful harridan who is determined to ruin not only herself but her family, as well."

That shut Corrie up. She had seen what the gossips had done to her mother and grandmother and the rest of her family after Laurel had died. There was simply no way she could allow that to happen again to the people she loved. If Gray meant to punish her for her deception, so be it. She certainly couldn't deny she deserved it.

She took a deep breath and slowly released it. "All right, I'll marry him."

Her father's dark look slowly faded. "You wouldn't have given yourself to the earl if you hadn't cared about him, Coralee. You aren't that kind of woman."

She didn't argue. She was in love with Gray. Or at least she had been. She didn't know the hard-faced stranger he had become.

"In time it will all work out," the viscount said.

Corrie managed a halfhearted smile. "I'm sure you're right, Father."

But she was fairly certain it wouldn't.

Lately, nothing ever seemed to work out the way she had planned.

Seventeen

It took only three days for a special license to be obtained and hasty wedding arrangements made. She would marry Grayson Forsythe this morning in the gardens at Selkirk Hall, then return to the castle as Gray's wife, the Countess of Tremaine.

The thought chilled Corrie to the marrow.

"I don't think I can go through with this," she said to Allison, pacing frantically in front of the window. Only half-dressed, in frilly white undergarments and a blue satin wrapper, she turned and paced back the other way. "After what I did, I don't think I shall ever be able to face him and his family again."

She and Allison had arrived at Selkirk Hall shortly after the awful confrontation at Castle Tremaine. It was impossible to believe the days had rushed past, and Allison was there to help her dress for her wedding.

"You don't have any choice," her friend said, speaking out as she rarely did. "You owe it to your family. Laurel's death hurt them very badly. Your father may not show it, but he is still grieving. You don't want your parents to suffer another scandal."

"Oh, God." Corrie sank down on the tapestry stool in front of her rosewood dresser. The bedroom, done in white and mauve, was far more elegant than the shabby room Rebecca had assigned her at Castle Tremaine. Corrie's stomach churned at the realization that when she returned she would be sleeping in the countess's suite, which connected to Gray's bedroom.

"Perhaps after you are wed you will be able to make the earl understand why you behaved the way you did. In time, surely he'll forgive you."

She shook her head. "I don't think Gray is a very forgiving man. Perhaps if I were truly Letty Moss, in time he might forgive me. I think he cared for her in some way. Unfortunately, I'm Coralee. I'm outspoken and stubborn and determined. I am not the sort of woman Gray would wish to marry."

"Stop that right now. You are as much Letty as you are Coralee. You are kind and considerate. You are loyal and giving. In time your husband will see that, and he will realize you are everything he thought and more."

Corrie looked up at her, blinking to hold back tears. "Do you really think so?"

Allison wrapped her in a hug. "Yes, I do. You were willing to put yourself in danger because you loved your sister. And you love the earl. In time he will realize it and accept you for the woman you truly are."

Corrie's gaze lifted to Allison's face. "How did . . . how did you know I loved him?"

"We have come to be friends, Coralee. I do not believe you would have given yourself to the earl if you did not love him."

She dashed the tears from her cheeks. "Gray believes I've betrayed him, and in a way I did. I pretended to be someone I am not."

"You only pretended a little."

She sighed. "Perhaps. But he has been hurt before and he guards his heart above all things. I don't know if I shall ever get a second chance to reach him."

"If you love him, you have to try."

Corrie swallowed past the lump in her throat, realizing her friend was right.

"You need to get into your gown," Allison

said, reminding her how soon her life would change.

"I need a moment, Ally, if you don't mind."

Allison nodded. "Of course." She left to dress for the ceremony with a promise to return to help Corrie get into her wedding gown.

She had been gone only a moment when a soft knock sounded at the door. Corrie walked over to open it and cried out at the sight of her best friend in the world, tall, blond Krista Hart Draugr, standing in the doorway.

"Krista!" Corrie rushed into her arms and the women embraced. "I am so glad to see you! I knew you would arrive if you could, but I was afraid something might have come up and you wouldn't be able to make it."

"You shouldn't have worried. I left London as soon as I received your letter. The roads were still muddy after that dreadful storm and it took us longer than we thought to get here. Leif, Thor and my father are downstairs. All of us have been so worried. Are you sure about this? Are you certain this is what you want?"

Corrie sighed. "I have never been less certain of anything in my life."

"Then perhaps you should refuse the

earl's offer."

A near-hysterical laugh escaped. "It was more of a command than an offer. It is clear you do not know him. I shudder to think what he would do if I actually had the courage to refuse him."

"As I said, Leif and Thor are downstairs. If the earl were to cause any trouble —"

"It isn't really the earl. The truth is, this entire affair is my fault. Even if I were selfish enough to see my family embroiled in yet another scandal, I would not wish for that to happen to Lord Tremaine. Marrying me, whether he wishes it or not, will quiet the wagging tongues. He is not the awful man I believed him to be. He did not murder his wife or my sister, and his reputation doesn't deserve to be blackened any more than it has been already."

Krista took hold of her hand. "It sounds as if you care for him — at least a little."

Corrie looked up and tears welled in her eyes. "I love him, Krista. He is brooding and difficult and entirely too demanding, and I am hopelessly in love with him. Unfortunately, Gray doesn't love me. In fact, he hates me for deceiving him."

"I see." She seemed to mull that over. "The earl is angry — I suppose he has every right to be. But surely in time he will understand why you behaved as you did."

"Perhaps." Corrie looked at herself in the mirror, noticed the unusual pallor of her face. She took a shaky breath and turned back to her friend. "Aside from marrying a man who despises me, there is the not so small matter of my employment."

"Lindsey is doing a fine job in your absence. She wanted to accompany us to the wedding, but someone had to stay and oversee this week's edition. I am sure she will be willing to continue until you can figure out what you're going to do."

Corrie glanced up. "Do you think I might be able to come back? I like working at the gazette. I like working with you, Krista. I wasn't ready for marriage."

Krista took hold of her hand. "You weren't ready to fall in love, either. Sometimes these things just happen."

As they had to Krista, Corrie recalled. In the beginning, her relationship with Leif had been a disaster. Now they were incredibly happy. Corrie thought of Gray and ached at the loss she suddenly felt.

She walked away, over to the window. From the garden below, voices of the guests, just beginning to arrive, drifted up to her second-floor balcony. "I never found out what happened to my sister."

Krista joined her at the window. "I got your letter. I know you think one of the men at the castle was her lover. That doesn't mean he killed her."

"I know. I've told myself that again and again."

"Today is your wedding day. It's not a time to dwell on the past. Your sister would want you to be happy."

Corrie's heart squeezed. Laurel would have wanted her to marry a man who loved her. It wasn't going to happen.

"Gray will want some sort of justice. He lives by his own set of rules, but in his way, he is a very honorable man."

"As you are a brave and honorable woman. In time he will see that."

But Corrie didn't really believe it. Whatever Gray had felt for her was gone. It had vanished the morning Letty Moss disappeared.

Dressed in a three-tiered gown of dove-gray organdy trimmed with rows of mauve ribbon, her copper hair pulled into clusters of curls on her shoulders, Corrie stood just inside the French doors leading out to the garden. She planned to return to mourning for at least another month, as was the custom, and had chosen the gown with that in mind.

"He still isn't here." Her mother, a pretty brown-haired woman in her late forties, relieved of her mourning clothes for the wedding, stood at the window wringing her hands. "Dear God, perhaps he isn't going to come."

Corrie's chest tightened. It was possible. Perhaps leaving her at the altar was the earl's punishment for her weeks of deceiving him. For her parents' sake, she prayed he wouldn't make her humiliation so public.

"He is only a few minutes late," she said, trying to keep her mother from bursting into tears. "Perhaps there was a problem on the road." But in truth, she imagined he was making a point. If he arrived at all, it was clear he wasn't an eager bridegroom.

"He is here!" Krista turned away from the window and hurried toward them. "He is just walking into the garden."

"Thank God." Her mother was shaking. Corrie walked over and gave her a reassuring hug, though she wasn't sure which of them needed it more.

"Everything's going to be all right, Mother."

The older woman managed a trembly smile. "Yes, yes of course it will be. You are marrying an earl, after all. In time, people will forget how hastily you were wed."

Corrie felt a fresh rush of guilt. If only she had listened to Krista and stayed in London, none of this would have happened.

"It is time to go, Coralee." Her friend's soft reminder sent a wave of alarm rushing through her.

She took a calming breath and prepared to face the ordeal ahead. Krista knelt and straightened the train of her organdy gown, then opened the door. Though the guests were few, the church had been decorated with huge urns filled with white chrysanthemums and yards of mauve ribbon. A white runner pointed the way to the altar.

Leif and Thor both waited by the door, two very large men, one dark, one fair, both with the bluest eyes Corrie had ever seen.

Leif leaned over and kissed her cheek. "You look beautiful. Your earl is a lucky man."

She managed a wobbly smile. "Thank you."

"If he does not treat you well," Thor said darkly, "you only need come to me."

Tears burned her eyes. She was lucky to have such dear friends. "Thank you. I shall remember your offer, Thor." Which she very well knew he meant.

Thor Draugr had come from the same

undiscovered island as his brother. He'd been as backward and unschooled as Leif had first been. But Professor Hart was working the same miracle with Thor that he had worked with Leif. It was amazing the progress the big Norseman had made.

"You had better go." Krista gave her a last brief hug then returned to her husband. Seeing the way they glanced at each other made Corrie's heart ache with longing. If only Gray would look at her with that much love in his eyes. . . . But she didn't believe he ever would.

Her father stood waiting. "You make a beautiful bride, Coralee." He bent and kissed her cheek, his copper hair glinting, the same exact color as her own. "No matter how you feel about my actions, you know it doesn't mean I don't love you."

"I know, Father. I love you, too."

He lifted her white-gloved hand and kissed the back. "Whatever happens, I'm proud of your strength, Coralee. And your loyalty. The earl is getting a very fine wife."

She simply nodded. Her throat had closed up and she couldn't squeeze out the words she might have said. Then her gaze moved toward the front of the church and she saw the man who would soon be her husband, the tall, dark Earl of Tremaine. His jaw was set, his eyes as hard and dark as onyx.

She tried to recall the caring man who had searched for her in the pouring rain, the man who had made tender love to her, but there was no trace of him.

"Ready?" her father asked.

She nodded. It was all she could manage.

Corrie fought not to tremble as he walked her down the aisle. She spotted a few familiar faces: Allison next to Aunt Agnes, who worriedly wrung her hands; Rebecca and Charles next to Jason, who seemed almost amused.

Corrie had a grandmother she adored, but she was too frail to make the journey from London. Her mother waited at the end of the aisle for her husband to deposit the bride and join her. On the opposite side, Sir Paxton Hart, Krista's father, stood next to Krista, Leif and Thor.

Corrie's gaze swung back to the altar, where the earl stood waiting. Her father cast him a glance that held a trace of warning, then gave her into his care. Her hands felt like ice inside her gloves as she looked into the iron-hard lines of his face.

"I'm so sorry," she said softly. "I never meant for any of this to happen."

One of his black eyebrows lifted. "I suppose, in a way, I am sorry, as well. If I hadn't lusted after your lovely little body, you would still be a maiden and I would not be forced to marry you."

She recoiled at the reminder. He had always been blunt, but today she would prefer he save his well-deserved barbs until they were alone.

"Are we ready to begin?" Vicar Langston stood at the altar in front of them. He gave her a kindly, reassuring smile. "Sometimes the Lord works in strange ways. I hope you will both place your trust in him."

She felt the sting of tears, but steeled herself against them. She would not cry. Not in front of Gray. He thought little enough of her already.

"If you will please join hands."

Gray took her gloved fingers and she could feel the undisguised anger humming through him.

"Dearly beloved," the vicar began. "We are gathered together this day to join this man, Grayson Morgan Forsythe, sixth Earl of Tremaine, and this woman, Coralee Meredith Whitmore, in the bonds of holy matrimony according to God and the laws of England. . . ."

The minister continued, speaking the words that would wed her to Gray, but Coralee barely heard them. Inside, she was trembling, her heart aching for the uncertain future ahead of her. Gray believed that he had lost Letty.

When the ceremony ended and he dragged her into his arms for a hard, punishing kiss, Corrie knew for certain that she had lost Gray.

The wedding was over at last. The wedding party, small as it was, adjourned to the dining room, where a lavish buffet had been set out: a round of beef, roasted lamb with mint sauce, poached salmon and a medley of vegetables, cheeses and fruits. A separate table held desserts: gingerbread pudding, egg creams, custards, cakes and pies. Her mother had spared no expense and the guests seemed to enjoy the sumptuous array of foods.

Playing the role of solicitous bridegroom, Gray filled a plate for Corrie and brought it over to the linen draped table where they were seated, but she had no appetite. Not when each of the glances her husband cast her way seemed darker than the last.

His gaze skimmed over her dove-gray gown. He didn't miss the implication. "You look quite lovely today, but if you are thinking to return to mourning for your sister, you may think again. I'll not have my wife moping around the house, bringing the dirge of death to my family. You have grieved more than enough. Your sister is gone and the matter is over and done."

"But —"

"It is finished, Coralee."

She didn't argue. She hated wearing the depressing clothes that continued to keep Laurel's death at the forefront of her mind. In truth, for the first time since her marriage, she found something to be thankful about.

Gray leaned back in his chair. "At least your quarters will be better than the ones you occupied before."

"Yes . . . I had thought of that myself."

His mouth thinned. "Of course, Letty didn't seem to mind."

Corrie's temper inched up. She set her wineglass down on the table a little harder than she meant to, and several drops spilled over the edge. "I know you think the worst of me. But I am not the spoiled, selfish creature you seem to believe."

"Are you not?"

"No." She glanced around to be sure no one could hear. "I will not apologize because my family has wealth and position. I did not choose to be born the daughter of a

273

viscount any more than you chose to be an earl."

He was watching her with interest now, and she saw it as a chance to explain at least some of what had occurred.

"I know you are angry about a number of things, one of which is what I wrote about you in my column. In it, I mentioned what the gossips were calling you at the time. It was my *job* to report what I heard."

He leaned back in his chair. "And you did it so well. After all, you aren't the simple country wife you pretended to be." He frowned as a light seemed to suddenly dawn. "You named him Homer for the *Odyssey,* didn't you?"

"Yes."

His dark gaze sharpened. "Then you admit you read Latin."

Her chin inched up. "I also read Greek. It isn't a crime, you know."

"And you probably speak French!"

Jason must have heard the venom in Gray's voice. He walked up just then and rattled off his congratulations in the language. Corrie graciously accepted them, replying in perfect French, casting Gray a look nearly as black as the ones she'd been receiving from him.

Gray's hard gaze shifted to his cousin. "Be

274

careful what you say to my *wife,*" he warned. "Remember, I also speak the language."

Jason grinned, digging creases into his cheeks. "And here I thought you were only jealous of our ragamuffin little cousin. Interesting."

The earl's jaw hardened as the younger man walked away. "It appears my cousin still fancies you. Apparently whatever name you use doesn't matter to him."

"Don't be ridiculous. He was merely being polite."

"You're my wife now, Coralee. You had better remember that."

"I told you, I have no interest in Jason." She leaned closer. "If you recall, it was you, not him, I welcomed into my bed. Or have you already forgotten?"

His dark eyes seemed to glitter. "I have not forgotten. Nor will you, once we get home."

Corrie sucked in a breath. Perhaps rousing the devil's ire on his wedding night was not a good idea. Sweet God, when would she learn to hold her tongue?

The party ended far too early to suit Coralee, but from the hot looks he gave her, not nearly soon enough for Gray.

"Get your wrap," he said. "We're leaving."

"But —"

"Now!"

She jumped at the command in his voice. She wasn't Letty, she wanted to remind him. She didn't have to dance to his tune. But he had a right to be angry, and it was clear that tonight he intended to make her pay for the trouble she had caused.

A tremor of uneasiness went through her. She didn't know this man she had married, far different from the one who had made love to her in the storm. What plans did he have for her? What would he expect her to do?

Her uncertainly grew. She barely noticed when he wrapped her in her cloak and began to usher her toward the door, leaving only time enough for a brief farewell to her family and friends.

As she passed Thor, he caught her hand. "Remember what I said." The glance he cast Gray left no doubt as to what he meant, and Corrie felt a little tug of gratitude that he was her friend.

"I won't forget."

Gray began propelling her once more toward the door. In the carriage, he lounged against the seat across from her, his eyes burning with heat and anger, the face of the devil in a towering rage. It took all of her courage to meet that hard gaze and not look away.

"I'm your wife," she finally said. "I won't shirk my duties on our wedding night, but neither will I let you hurt me."

His sleek black eyebrows flew upward in surprise. "That is what you think? That I mean to hurt you?"

She trembled. "It is clear how much you hate me. I know you intend to punish me for the things I've done."

For the first time, his hard look softened. "I would not hurt you, Coralee, no matter how angry I was." He relaxed against the seat. "In fact, my plans for you tonight have nothing at all to do with pain . . . though I've learned there are times it can be used in interesting ways. Tonight, pleasure is the only thing I have in mind for you."

But the hardness had returned to his features, making his words difficult to believe.

Eighteen

The sun had set. Darkness settled in around the castle as a brutal wind howled outside. Corrie sat stiffly on the stool in front of the dressing table in the countess's bedroom, which adjoined that belonging to the earl.

She had her own suite of rooms, and as Tremaine had predicted, they were far more elegant than the shabby quarters she had occupied before. Furnished with graceful French rosewood furniture, and draperies and a counterpane made of pale green silk, the room was lovely, and yet she couldn't help feeling like an interloper in the bedroom that must have belonged to the earl's late wife.

With Allison no longer playing the role of her maid, Gray had promised to have one of the chambermaids assigned the task. The girl had not yet arrived, and Corrie fidgeted, nervously awaiting her. A fire burned in the hearth, warming the room, and yet she felt chilled inside.

Soon Gray would come.

She wasn't sure what he would expect of her, only knew that making love with him would be nothing at all the way it had been before. There would be no gentleness, no tenderness, no concern for her feelings.

The thought twisted her heart.

She was dreading the night ahead, wishing her maid would arrive, when the door swung open and Gray walked in without knocking. He glanced round the room and started frowning, as if for the first time realizing where he was.

"You can't stay in here. Not until the room has been changed. This bedroom belonged to Jillian, and there is nothing of you that reminds me of her."

He looked as if he had delivered the gravest of insults, and Corrie's heart squeezed harder, even as her chin went up. "The housekeeper brought me here."

He frowned again as he moved closer.

"It wasn't her fault," she quickly explained. "She was only doing what she thought you would want."

One eyebrow lifted. "Did you think I would beat her for a simple mistake? Is that now the opinion you hold of me?"

Corrie swallowed. "You were different

before. I don't know who you are anymore."

"As I don't know the woman I married." He ran a finger along her cheek. "Tonight perhaps we can change at least part of that."

He flicked a glance toward the door leading into his bedroom. "You may do whatever you wish in here. You will stay in my room until the necessary alterations are made."

Her stomach knotted. "I — I need at least a bit of privacy . . . and the maid you promised. Surely that is not too much to ask."

A hard smile lifted his lips. "Tonight I will serve as your maid. After that, I'll find someone to assist you." He held out his hand. "Come. It's time you made ready for bed."

She couldn't move. Her feet seemed rooted to the floor. She looked up at him and tried not to tremble.

"What is it?"

She had lied enough. "I'm frightened, Gray. I trusted you before. Now I . . ." She glanced away, struggling not to cry. She had never been a coward and yet tonight felt like the biggest coward on earth.

"Dammit to hell." Striding toward her, he bent and scooped her into his arms. Though her train had been removed, the tiered layers of her organdy skirt fell in frothy folds around them. Carrying her over the threshold into his bedroom, he set her on her feet in front of the dresser and began to pull the pins from her hair.

She stood stiffly as he sifted his hands through the curls, spreading them around her shoulders. He said nothing as he worked the buttons at the back of her gown, then helped her step out of her skirt and petticoats. She was left in her corset, drawers and stockings, while Gray remained dressed in the black trousers and white shirt he had worn to the wedding. His coat and waistcoat were gone, his black hair slightly mussed from the wind, and she thought of the highwayman who had stolen her heart.

If only he were here.

Gray bent and kissed the side of her neck, and Corrie started to tremble. It was insane. She was no longer a maiden. Gray had said he wouldn't hurt her, and yet . . .

She had loved the rogue who had taken her innocence that night in the storm. This was not the same man. She closed her eyes, but couldn't stop the tears from leaking from beneath her lashes. Gray saw them and his head came up.

"For God's sake, Cora, you're no longer a virgin. I told you I wouldn't hurt you. What the devil is wrong?"

She swallowed, found a handful of courage. "You aren't him — that is what is wrong. You wanted Letty. Well, I want the man you were before." A bubble of hysterical laughter escaped. "It is poetic justice, is it not?"

Those dark eyes drilled her. He whispered a curse she couldn't quite hear, turned away from her and stalked over to the sideboard along the wall. A few moments later, he returned with a small glass of wine. "Drink this."

"What is it?"

"In India, they call it the *divine elixir.*"

"What is in it?"

"It's a powder made from crushed priyala seeds and kumhara — that's prickly pear — and something they call murahari. I mixed it with wine to help you relax."

When she looked up at him, he reached out and cupped her face. It was the first tenderness he had shown since the morning he had discovered her true identity.

"There's nothing in it that will harm you. You have my word."

She eyed him with suspicion. "As a soldier or a gentleman?"

His lips twitched, just the faintest crack in the armor he had built around him.

"As a soldier," he said softly, and she

upended the glass and drank every drop of the slightly bitter wine.

By damn, he'd meant to punish her, pay her back in some way for the lies she had told and the damage she had done. But when she looked at him with those lovely, tear-filled green eyes, when her soft lips trembled, all he could think of was how much he wanted her.

He didn't understand it. She wasn't the sweet country wife he had fantasized about, the simple young woman whose innocent passion he craved.

Instead she was a shrewd, calculating creature who had schemed and lied her way into his affections. He looked down at her, all soft curves and lovely, feminine features, hair like silk and the color of flame.

She had the beauty of a goddess, the sensuous pull of a siren. She was Maya, the Hindu goddess of illusion. She was nothing at all what he had believed, and yet he ached for her as he never had another woman.

But Maya was also a demon, the creator of the magical arts.

This woman must be a demon. How else had she managed to enchant him to the point where punishing her, hurting her in any way, would be far more painful for him than for her?

He reached toward her, ran a finger along her cheek, felt the creamy smoothness of her skin. His blood heated. He wanted to taste her, to touch her all over, to bury himself inside her.

She handed the glass back to him with a hand that no longer trembled, and he could see the power of the aphrodisiac already beginning to work.

Her eyes no longer looked frightened, but languid, soft and welcoming. The stiffness was gone from her body, and as he set the glass down on the dresser, she swayed toward him, her gaze drifting up to his mouth. When she moistened her lips with her small pink tongue, his stomach contracted and his shaft went iron hard.

The potion had done its work. She was his now, a more than willing partner to do with as he pleased. He turned her toward the mirror and watched her face as he prepared to strip away her remaining garments.

The nape of her neck beckoned, slender and pale, dusted with fine burnished hair. He pressed his mouth there, felt the soft tickle of silken strands against his cheek, and hardened even more. Reaching down, he propped one of her feet on the stool, knelt and removed each of her stockings, kissing his way along her calf. He licked the arch of her small foot and heard her moan.

Her drawers and corset remained. Remembering his fantasy the day she had sprained her ankle, he slid his palm up her shapely leg, her thigh, until he reached the slit in her drawers. He slipped his hand inside and gently began to stroke her, finding her wet and slick, as he knew he would.

The drug would do his work for him. He tried not to think how much he preferred her natural responses to those conjured by one of the potions Samir had made from ingredients brought back from India.

She began to move against his hand and he stopped, unwilling to give her release so soon. Instead, he came to his feet, slid his hands into the heavy weight of her hair, tipped her head back and kissed her. At his touch, she pressed herself full length against him, went up on her toes and kissed him back. When her tongue dipped into his mouth, a shudder of lust tore through him.

He wanted to drag her down on the floor, to open his trousers and take her, pound into her until he could no longer hold on to his seed.

Instead, he removed the rest of her garments, kissing each section of bare skin exposed, inhaling her soft floral scent mingled with the musky odor of her desire. Lifting her into his arms, he carried her over to the bed, leaving her only long enough to remove his own clothes, then returning to join her on the mattress.

The moment he reached for her, she went into his arms and kissed him wildly, and Gray nearly lost control. He knew the power of the drug, had given her only the mildest dose. It occurred to him that it wasn't merely the potion, it was the woman he had given it to. Her name might be Coralee and not Letty, but this was the same passionate creature who had responded so avidly to him before.

Something loosened inside him. He didn't really know her, wasn't sure he could make any sort of life with her. He wasn't a man who gave his trust lightly and what little he had given to Letty, Coralee had destroyed.

Still, when he entered her lush, welcoming body, when he moved inside her and she lifted her hips to take more of him, he felt a stirring deep inside he hadn't expected to feel.

He kissed her hungrily, as if he couldn't get enough, and she kissed him with equal abandon. Heavy strokes took him higher, his hips pumping, driving him closer to the edge. He didn't give in to his powerful need until she reached her peak and cried out his name, didn't give in until she peaked again. Then desire overtook him and pleasure surged through him, so fierce his teeth clenched and his muscles knotted.

It was a long time before he spiraled down. Gray lay beside this wife he did not know, felt his erection stir to life once more, and told himself he could not possibly want her again so soon.

The fear was gone. Instead Corrie felt a burning fire she couldn't seem to put out. She had expected Gray's anger, his need for revenge, not this wild passion he couldn't seem to control. Her own passion burned. She couldn't seem to douse the flames.

She told herself it was the drug, but in her heart, she knew it wasn't. The potion was merely an excuse for her to do what she wanted. Since that first night, she had dreamed of kissing him, touching him all over, of feeling the movement of muscle over bone, learning the texture of his skin.

As he lay beside her, she came up over him, her breasts brushing against the curly black hair on his chest, his flat copper nipples, her own pebbling into diamond-hard crests. She kissed him deeply, kissed his brow, his eyes, the line of his jaw.

"Coralee . . ." he whispered, saying her name as she had yearned to hear him do, making her heart leap with hope.

Lacing her fingers in his thick black hair, she bent over him, ravished his mouth in a burning, hungry kiss, and Gray kissed her back, driving his tongue inside, setting her body on fire.

She loved the taste of him, the heat and masculinity, the strength in the arms that surrounded her. She felt his hands at her waist, lifting her on top of him, her hair swinging forward, forming a curtain that seemed to block out the rest of the world.

"Gray . . ." she murmured. She had loved him once . . . when he was a different man and she a different woman.

He kissed her deeply and lifted her again, and she felt the hard length of him probing for entrance. Understanding dawned and she took control, began to lower herself onto his shaft, to feel the exquisite fullness inside her.

Heat spiraled through her, a fierce burning desire to reach the pinnacle he had taken her to before. She moved, lifted herself up, then sank down again, felt a rush of triumph and an incredible surge of pleasure when he groaned. Gray's muscles tightened as he fought for control, and for the first time she recognized the power she held over him.

Corrie shifted, beginning to learn the rhythm, moving steadily toward the goal both of them longed to reach. The wind howled, her breathing heightened and pleasure sharpened inside her. Gray hissed in a breath as she took more of him, began to move faster, plunge harder, deeper.

"Mother of God," he growled, gripping her hips to hold her in place, thrusting into her again and again until he drove both of them over the edge.

Fulfillment came swift and hard, a shattering release that again forced his name from her lips. Gray reached the pinnacle an instant later and both of them careened off the cliff.

She slumped onto his powerful chest and was surprised to feel his lips press against her forehead. He eased her off him, then curled her against his side.

Gray said nothing and neither did she, both of them afraid of destroying the fragile moment.

Slumber beckoned. Her last thought was that whatever happened between them, she was no longer afraid.

■ ■ ■ ■

Corrie awakened as the first faint light of dawn purpled the lands outside the window. Her mind felt a little muzzy, her muscles a little sore. A hard male body pressed against her. *Gray.*

She turned her head to look at him, recognized the thick black lashes fanned out against his lean cheeks, the hard line of his jaw, the faint shadow of his beard.

The covers were bunched around his hips, leaving him naked to the waist, and her attention moved there. He had the most magnificent body, all hard muscle and sinew, his abdomen flat, except for the slight rise of his hip bones. He had made love to her last night, and though it wasn't the same as before, he had given her the pleasure he had promised.

The potion had done its job and she had relaxed. No, more than relaxed. She had responded like the tigress he had once called her. She blushed to think she had practically attacked him.

Her insides tightened with the thought. Perhaps that would be his punishment. When he awakened he would ridicule her behavior, remind her of the wanton creature she had become.

Corrie sighed. Whatever he had put in the wine had helped dissolve her fears, but she couldn't blame her wild responses completely on that.

She flicked a glance at the man she had married. As much as she had enjoyed the pleasure he had given her, she liked their lovemaking better when the passion between them had sparked to life by simple desire.

That hadn't happened last night, but perhaps they might have reached some unspoken agreement. He was a man and she a woman. They desired each other. It would have to be enough.

"Sleep well?" he asked from the opposite side of the bed and the edge was back in his voice.

Corrie steeled herself. "Very well, thank you."

"Are you still frightened?"

"No."

That same eyebrow arched. To test her, he reached over and cupped a breast, began to rub her nipple. It tightened instantly and an ache began to throb between her legs. His hand moved there as if he knew, and a soft moan escaped.

"Well, at least we have this." There was no taunt in his voice, no hint of reproof, and she relaxed as he came up over her, kissing her deeply, arousing her with an ease that should have surprised her but did not. She gave in to the fires he stirred, letting him catch her up, beginning to pick up the rhythm of his movements, thinking perhaps he was right.

At least we have this.

But in her heart, she knew it was not enough.

Nineteen

Sunlight probed for entrance through the curtains at the windows of Gray's bedroom. Corrie stirred and reached for him, but his side of the big four-poster was cold, Gray already gone. She lay back against the pillow, staring up at the heavy gold velvet canopy above her. Though part of her was glad she didn't have to face him, another part wished he had been there to make love to her when she awakened.

A light knock sounded, drawing her attention, and a young woman in a black skirt, white blouse and mobcap entered the bedroom.

"His lordship sent me," she said. "I'm Anna. I'm to be your new maid." Tall and amazingly thin, with fine brown hair and pale skin, Anna smiled pleasantly. "If that be all right with you, milady." She was perhaps a little over thirty, her features plain but not unattractive.

"Very well, Anna. My clothes are in the countess's suite. Why don't we go in and you can help me pick out something to wear?"

"Yes, milady."

Half an hour later, Corrie was dressed and sitting in the breakfast room across the table from Rebecca, the two of them engaged in their first private conversation since the wedding.

"So you are now here for good. Or at least until Gray tires of you."

Corrie stiffened. From the moment she had filled her plate from the array of foods at the sideboard, Rebecca had been as unpleasant as Corrie had feared.

"What are you talking about? We are married. I am now Gray's wife." Which he had made abundantly clear with his fierce lovemaking last night.

"Surely you realize his interest in you is only temporary. He meant to make you his mistress, not marry you."

It was true. He had married her because her actions had left him no choice. "Even if that is so, he is still my husband."

Rebecca sipped the robust dark tea in her porcelain cup. She was dressed as extravagantly as always, in a gown of pale blue silk that set off the blue of her eyes. A cluster of gleaming blond curls rested on each of her shoulders.

"Gray is a man of powerful sexual appetites," Rebecca said. "For a time after Jillian died, he felt guilty. He buried his desires, but Bethany put an end to his celibacy. Then you came along. Surely, you realize you won't be the last."

Corrie managed to swallow the bite of eggs she had taken, though she was no longer hungry. "As I said, we're married. I'll expect him to uphold his wedding vows." And as she repeated the words, she realized she meant them. If Gray could not be faithful, she would leave him. The thought stirred an ache in her heart.

Rebecca just laughed. "If fidelity is what you expect, then you, my dear, are a fool. What man holds to his marriage vows? Sooner or later, another woman will catch Gray's fancy and he will ship you off to one of his other estates. Perhaps if you are fortunate, you can take up residence in his town house in London. At least you would be able to continue writing that ridiculous column of yours."

Corrie gritted her teeth. Now that she was married to Gray, the last shreds of Rebecca's civility had faded. The woman was clearly furious that she was no longer mistress of Castle Tremaine.

"Writing for the paper is my job. But I suppose you would see any kind of work as beneath you." Which reminded her that if she expected any sort of privacy, she would have to see to the refurbishment of the countess's bedroom.

She rose from her chair, her plate barely touched. "I'm afraid I have to go. I have a number of things to do this morning. If you will excuse me . . ."

A tight smile stretched across Rebecca's face. It didn't matter. They had never been friends and that wasn't going to change.

As Corrie made her way along the hall to retrieve her cloak, she thought of the project ahead. This morning, as she dressed for the day, she had noticed how dismal Gray's rooms were — the massive wooden furniture, the heavy draperies that hid the sun, the dark brown carpet on the floor.

After being in his sunny office — the India Room, she called it — where he kept his most personal belongings, she was certain the bedroom did not suit him. She would ask him first, of course, but if he gave her permission, she would change the dismal suite along with hers.

She found him in his private study, working on a set of ledgers lying open on his desk. She had never seen him in the room, and now that she did, she realized the extent to which his travels were a part of him. He looked perfectly natural seated at the light rattan desk, comfortable amid the jewel-toned colors, the brass urns, the pots of sandalwood incense. In fact, he seemed more at home in the room than anywhere else in the castle.

Girding herself for whatever mood he might be in, she knocked on the open door, pasted on a smile and walked in.

He glanced up from the ledgers, saw her and frowned. Not an auspicious beginning.

"Good morning, my lord."

His eyes ran over her apricot gown. "I thought only Letty dressed in simple muslin."

Corrie tried not to feel the barb. "I have work to do. That is why I am here. Silk and satin would hardly be appropriate."

"What is it you need?"

"You suggested I make some changes in the rooms that are mine upstairs. I was wondering . . . if you would agree, I should also like to make some alterations in your rooms, as well. Of course, if you prefer them the way they are —"

"Do whatever you please." He returned to his work, bending his dark head to the task as if she were already gone.

Letty might not have minded being so summarily dismissed, but Coralee Whitmore wasn't used to such rude treatment. Rounding the desk, she marched to where he sat.

His head came up as he realized she was still there. "Was there something else you wanted?"

Not when she had first come into the room. Now, seeing the tight lines of his face, the twist of his lips that made it clear he wanted her gone, there were any number of things she wanted.

"Perhaps there is." She pondered only a moment. "I am your wife, am I not? We have been wed but a day. I believe as a bride, I deserve a good-morning kiss."

She caught the shocked expression on his face as she leaned down and pressed a warm kiss on his lips. Gray sat there stunned as she turned and walked away.

"Have a good day, my lord," she called to him over her shoulder.

As she sailed out of the room, she smiled, unable to contain a small feeling of triumph.

The refurbishing project was under way. As soon as she left Gray's office, Corrie set off for the village to hire workmen and order new furnishings for both of their bedroom suites.

Earlier, she had considered having the carriage brought round — she was, after all, the Countess of Tremaine. But the day was simply too pleasant, the sun the perfect temperature on her shoulders.

She was passing the stable on her way to the path leading into town when Homer came bounding toward her.

"Homer!" She knelt in front of the scruffy gray dog and threw her arms round his neck. "I missed you, boy." She petted his shaggy coat. "Want to go for a walk with me?"

He barked as if he understood, and she laughed as they set off for the village. At least she could count on one friend at the castle.

The path was even more overgrown than it had been last month, the long grasses brushing against her full skirts. Her first task as Lady Tremaine was begun, but there was a far more important matter on her mind, one she had tried to set aside but realized she simply could not.

I have not forgotten you, sweet sister.

For the past few days, she had managed to ignore thoughts of Laurel. With the forced marriage and dealing with Gray,

Corrie had had little time to think of anything else.

Now that she was actually a resident of the castle, it occurred to her that she had accidentally fallen into the perfect situation. Though it was nearly impossible to believe Charles or Jason capable of murder, finding Laurel's book had convinced her one of the men had been Laurel's lover.

Rebecca had remarked on men's infidelity. Perhaps she knew firsthand.

And Jason . . . Jason was boyish and charming, exactly the sort of man her sister might have fallen in love with.

As a member of the household, Corrie could go wherever she pleased. A little more snooping might tell her which of the men she should pursue. Once she knew for certain who it was, she would press him for answers, find some clue as to what had really happened to Laurel and her baby.

Corrie hurried her pace. As soon as she returned from the village, she was going to continue her quest for the truth.

Gray stood at the window in his bedroom. After his encounter with Coralee in his office, he had found himself climbing the stairs, thinking that if kisses were what his little wife wanted, he would give them to her — and far more than that.

But the room was empty, and he tried to tell himself he wasn't disappointed. Looking down from the window, he spotted his bride in the courtyard of the stables, behind the house. He was annoyed to see her kneeling, wrapping her arms around her big gray mutt of a dog.

What the hell was she doing? She wasn't Letty Moss. She was the hardhearted female who had slandered him in her column, a woman who made a living by digging up people's secrets and flaunting them in front of the world. She had lied to him, pretended to be sweet and naive when clearly she was not.

And yet . . .

Gray watched her with the dog and wondered. Was it possible Cora and Letty weren't as different as he believed?

The thought was disturbing. It was one thing to indulge a favorite mistress, to care for her in some distant fashion. It was another thing entirely to become enthralled with one's wife. During the year he was married, he had managed to keep Jillian at arm's length, had never really desired any sort of closeness. But there was something different about Coralee, something that drew him and filled him with a strange sort of yearning.

Gray steeled himself against the urge to join her on her walk to the village. He was a solitary person. He had been since he was a boy, and he intended to keep on that way. He wasn't about to let the deceitful little redhead charm her way into his heart.

He turned away from the window as a soft knock sounded on the door. He walked into the sitting room just as Samir turned the knob and walked in.

"I am sorry to disturb, *sahib,* but visitors have arrived downstairs. Your friends, Mr. Petersen and Colonel Rayburn. They wait for you in the study."

"Colonel, is it now?" Timothy Rayburn had been a major when Gray was in India, one of his closest friends.

The little man grinned, exposing two gaping holes in his teeth. "Yes, *sahib.*" Samir had always liked Rayburn.

Gray found himself smiling, as well, a rare occurrence these days. "Tell them I'll be right there." He was glad for the unexpected arrival of his friends, though a little surprised they were traveling together. Timothy Rayburn was military through and through, a major — now colonel — in the 99th Infantry stationed in India, where Gray had first met him. Dolph was retired from whatever unofficial position he'd held in the War Office.

Then again, perhaps it wasn't so surprising.

Gray headed downstairs and found the men lounging in deep leather chairs in front of an empty hearth, sipping from snifters of brandy Samir had provided them.

"Timothy. Dolph. It's good to see you." The men rose and shook hands with him. "Congratulations on your promotion, Colonel. You certainly deserve it."

Rayburn grinned. "Yes, well, it took long enough." He was a barrel-chested man with a freckled face, thick red hair and a quiet disposition. He was also the sort of soldier a man could trust with his life — as Gray had done on more than one occasion.

"What brought you two all the way from London?" he asked.

"Business in Bristol," the colonel answered. "A new trade agreement that involves the East India Company and the army's need for gunpowder."

Gray nodded. Saltpeter, a necessary ingredient, had been shipped from India since the early 1600s.

"Trade and a chance for a little advice from a friend," Dolph added.

Gray leveled a hard look at the tall, dark-haired man with the rugged face and weathered complexion. "Advice, is it? It seems I got a bit from you. As I recall, I received a message telling me not to be concerned about Letty Moss."

Dolph just smiled. "The lady is hardly a threat. You wished to hire me to investigate her, but at the time, I had already been hired on her behalf to investigate *you.* I've been away from London for a bit, but from your manner, I presume you've discovered Mrs. Moss's true identity."

Gray walked over to the sideboard, lifted the stopper off a crystal decanter and poured himself a drink. "Perhaps you should have told me. Had I known, the lady might not now be my wife."

Dolph choked on the sip of brandy he had just taken. "You married her?"

He shrugged his shoulders. "Letty Moss was a delectable little morsel. I planned to make her my mistress. The viscount had a different notion — since the girl was his daughter."

Dolph bit back a grin. "Congratulations."

"Hear, hear!" Timothy Rayburn said, raising his brandy glass in salute.

Dolph's expression turned serious, laugh lines fading from the corners of his eyes. "She's a fine young woman, Gray. She'll make you a very good wife."

Gray made no reply. He didn't want a wife. He'd had one already, and losing her had brought him endless pain.

He carried his drink over to the sofa and sat down across from his friends. "So . . . what sort of advice are you looking for?"

The colonel replied. "You know India, Gray, better than any Englishman I know. Rumor is, trouble may be brewing there. We'd like your opinion on the subject."

"You say *we*." He turned, fixed Dolph with a stare. "I thought you were retired."

"I am. Occasionally I do a little work for the East India Company . . . matters here that might pertain to their interests over there."

"I see." Gray leaned back in his chair as the colonel picked up the conversation and began to fill him in on the situation in India as it was today, five years after Gray's departure.

He listened intently. From the moment he'd set foot on Indian soil, the instant he had inhaled his first breath of hot, pungent air scented with frangipani, sat and watched the dark-skinned children with their wide white smiles, the women with their kohl-rimmed eyes, he had felt a special bond with the country.

Samir had been assigned to him a few weeks after his arrival, and the frail little man had sensed his passion for the land. The Hindu had introduced him to Talika, a beautiful, exotic Indian woman whose husband had died, and a week later, she became his mistress.

Talika was well schooled in her duties, the skills she had learned from the *Kama Sutra,* the Hindu guide to living and the art of love. She had guided him, instructed him and taught him how to achieve the ultimate pleasure from a coupling. He'd been younger then, hot-blooded and eager, and he had learned well.

Through his Hindu mistress, he had also learned about India, experienced the sights and sounds, the colors and diversity of a place unlike any other in the world.

"We have concerns, Gray," the colonel was saying. "There are rumors, whispers of mutiny. The Bombay and Madras commands are a bit worrisome, but it is the Bengal forces that make us the most uneasy."

Gray lounged back in his chair. "In my opinion — which apparently is the reason you gentlemen stopped by — I think the army has every reason to be concerned. Until that fiasco in Kabul two years ago,

the British Army was considered uncon-
querable, almost godlike in its power. The
annihilation of Elphinstone's garrison and
the retreat from Kabul put an end to that
thinking."

The colonel's russet eyebrows slammed
together. "For God's sake, man, you know
what that place is like. The terrain is abomi-
nable, the weather unbearable. Along with
the fighting, the troops died of heat, disease
and lack of supplies."

"Not to mention," Gray added dryly, "the
senior officers were poorly chosen and
incapable of conducting a proper campaign."

Rayburn did not deny it. "Even so, I
should think the stiff retribution the army
dished out would have redeemed us in the
opinion of the Indian population."

"I wish it were that easy. They're a people
with long memories. I fear the damage will
not be so easily repaired." Gray took a sip
of his brandy. "Whatever happens, I don't
think it's going to occur right away. Waves
of dissension move slowly. It could take
years before the army sees the result of its
ill-advised war with Afghanistan."

The colonel sipped from his own glass. "I
appreciate your speaking your mind as you
have. I was not overstating when I said you

know India better than any man of my acquaintance."

Certainly better than most of the men in England. In the three years he had lived there, Gray had made it a point to learn as much as he could, to understand the people and their customs. Since he had left, he'd stayed abreast of what was happening as much as possible.

He smiled. "I am no longer in the army. My opinions won't get me clamped in irons."

Rayburn chuckled. "You make a point."

"I hope you're planning to stay the night. Rebecca spent a fortune on the cook she hired. The food is incredible. And Derek is due in sometime this afternoon. I imagine it's been a while since you've seen him."

Derek Stiles was Gray's half brother, a man whose existence he had discovered only after his father had died.

"We'd love to stay," the colonel said. "It's a bit of a ride on to Bristol."

"I haven't seen Derek in years," Dolph added. "Besides, I had a second reason for coming. I'd like a word with your wife."

Gray looked at his friend, at his carved features and swarthy complexion. He was a hard man, as his face betrayed, and yet there was something about him women found attractive. Gray decided their meeting would not be private.

"She went into the village. I'll see if she has returned." Gray left the men, wondering what Dolph had to say to Coralee. He wished he weren't so glad to have an excuse to seek her out.

His thoughts settled on the woman he had married. His Indian mistress had taught him patience, a skill essential to the art of making love. But when it came to Coralee, Gray's practiced skills seemed to elude him. Each time he made love to her, he was consumed with desire unlike any he had known since he was a youth.

Tonight, he was determined that would change. He intended to regain his legendary control, use his skills instead of letting his emotions guide him. He wondered if, without the influence of the drug he had given her, his wife would be as eager a pupil as she had been last night.

TWENTY

Finished with her errands, Corrie headed back to the house, stopping briefly to leave Homer at the stables, where he was most content. She was surprised to see young Georgie Hobbs, the boy who had stolen the bread, busy cleaning one of the stalls.

"Hello, Georgie."

The lad's dark head came up. He looked around warily, as if searching for the earl.

"He isn't here. You don't have to worry."

The boy released a breath. "I've been comin' every day. I'm not sure 'e knows."

"I imagine he does. He seems to know most of what goes on around here."

He lifted another forkful of dirty straw and dumped it into the wheelbarrow. "You think . . . if I was to keep workin' real hard and pay off me debt, he might give me a job here at the castle?"

She bit her lip. It wasn't her place to interfere in Gray's decisions. Then again, she was his wife, and to her husband's chagrin, not nearly as timid as he wished. "I think he might. Why don't you ask him?"

His face went a little pale. "He pro'bly don't need no help, anyways."

"Actually, I could use another stable boy." Gray strode toward them, tall and masculine and incredibly attractive.

A memory arose of his hard body pressing her down in the mattress last night, the driving strength in those lean, muscular hips, and her stomach contracted.

"How is your mother?" Gray asked the boy.

"She's feelin' much better, milord. Did ye mean it about the job?"

"You've already worked enough to repay your debt. I'll give you a little money out of your first week's wages, enough to last you and your mother until you get paid again."

A watery sheen appeared in the young boy's eyes. "Thank you, milord. Ever so much."

"You keep working the way you have been, Georgie, and in time you'll earn a permanent position here at the castle."

The boy looked at Corrie and smiled so widely she caught sight of a missing tooth. She smiled back at him, an odd fullness in her chest. Georgie returned to work, and when she glanced at Gray, she saw him gazing at her in a way he hadn't since his discovery that she wasn't Letty Moss.

"Stray dogs and stray boys. I admit I am surprised, Countess."

He was surprised that she would be kind to a ragamuffin boy? That she wasn't the coldhearted shrew he believed her to be? "Is that supposed to be a compliment?"

He reached out and touched her cheek. "I suppose in a way, it is." He took hold of her hand. "Come. We have guests. One of them is a friend of yours."

"A friend?"

"As it turns out, he is also a friend of mine. Randolph Petersen." The edge returned in his voice. "The man you hired to prove me guilty of murder."

Corrie walked with Gray into the drawing room where Dolph Petersen waited. She wasn't actually the person who'd hired him — Leif and Krista were responsible for that — but she had written Krista and asked that the investigator continue his work even after he'd discovered Gray was innocent.

Her heart kicked up. Perhaps Mr. Petersen had brought news.

She spotted him as she walked through the doorway, her full skirts swishing around her ankles. He was nearly as tall as Gray, as rugged and attractive as she remembered.

"Mr. Petersen. It's good to see you." She took his hand in both of hers, and he bent and kissed her cheek.

"Your husband told me the news of your marriage. I wish you both the very best."

She flushed to think what else Gray might have told him. "Thank you."

"I had hoped to speak to you in private." He cast Gray a glance, must have read the implacability in his face. "Since you are now a married woman, I find myself in a bit of a dilemma."

"Perhaps not. Perhaps it is time my husband understood why I remained here even after I knew he was not involved in what happened to my sister."

One of Gray's black eyebrows arched. "And here I thought you stayed because you were so enamored of me."

She ignored the sarcasm. "I stayed because I wanted to find out the truth. To do that, I needed to discover whether it was Charles or Jason who was my sister's lover."

Gray's jaw hardened. "What the hell are you talking about?"

"I am talking about the man who got my sister with child, then abandoned her. If you gentlemen will please follow me, I will show you the proof I have found."

Corrie left the drawing room and the men fell in behind her. She could feel Gray's anger radiating in waves, and wondered what damage she had done to their already fragile relationship by accusing a member of his family of such heinous behavior.

Making her way into the study, she drew up a step stool to retrieve the book she had found. She frowned as she felt the empty space where it had been. Scanning the shelf, she read the gold printing on the spine of volume after volume, then moved the stool and looked again, though she knew in her heart the book had been removed.

"It was here. Only a short time ago, I found it. I returned it so no one would know what I had discovered."

Gray's features looked tight. "What are you searching for? You're making no sense, Coralee."

"I found a book that belonged to Laurel, a volume of sonnets she prized. She had given it as a gift to the man she loved. It was inscribed to him inside the front cover."

"If it was inscribed, then you know the man's name."

"She didn't pen his name. She called him her beloved. She mentioned they had read the book together. She said that she loved him."

Gray said nothing. She was sure he didn't believe her, and turned away so he wouldn't see the tears that sprang into her eyes.

She wiped them away with the tip of her finger, took a deep breath and turned back to him. "Since you can't be the man who took her innocence, then it has to be Jason or Charles."

"It could have been any number of men," Gray argued. "Dozens of people visit the castle. Perhaps your sister fell in love with one of the guests."

"If you knew Laurel, you would understand that she would never give her affections lightly. She had to have known the man, come to respect and love him. That takes time."

Dolph Petersen's voice was gentle. "That is what I wished to tell you." He looked up at Gray. "I know you don't want to hear this, but as your wife says, perhaps it is time you did."

Dolph returned his attention to Corrie. "There was another man at the castle quite often, during those months before your sister became with child. In fact, he spends a good deal of time here. Derek Stiles, Gray's half brother. Apparently, he will be arriving sometime this afternoon."

A long silence fell. Only the ticking of the clock on the mantel broke the silence. Why hadn't someone told her? Why had she never heard the name?

But she had, she began to recall. Several years back, she'd heard gossip about Derek Stiles, the bastard son of the late Earl of Tremaine. Derek had the same reputation Gray had with women. It had simply never occurred to Corrie that a son born out of wedlock would be welcome at the castle.

"Both of you are insane." Her husband cast her a piercing glance, then started for the door.

"I think your wife is right," Dolph said, stopping him before he reached it. "I believe the countess found the book, as she claims, and if she did, then one of the men in your family fathered Laurel Whitmore's child. Now that Laurel is dead, whether it matters remains to be seen."

A muscle ticked in Gray's cheek. "What are you implying, Dolph?"

"Nothing. But Coralee believes her sister was murdered. If that proves to be true, she deserves to see justice done. If Laurel had an affair with one of the men in your family, perhaps he knows something that would lead to the truth of what happened to her sister and her infant that night."

Gray pinned Corrie with a glare. "What happened is that Laurel Whitmore committed suicide. It can't be undone. If one of my brothers or my cousin was involved with her in a physical way, rest assured he has suffered for his indiscretion. But none of them are murderers." He turned to Dolph. "What's been said in this room stays among the three of us."

"That goes without saying."

Gray turned back to Corrie, his features even harder than before. "You're my wife, Coralee. I want this madness ended here and now. You and your obsession with your sister's death have caused more than enough trouble already."

He stalked out of the room, and Corrie fought to hold back tears. Her heart was aching, her throat too tight to swallow. *More than enough trouble.* That was how he thought of their marriage — as trouble. A problem she had thrust upon him.

She felt Dolph's hand on her shoulder. "I'm sorry, my lady. Perhaps I should have handled this in a different manner."

She shook her head. "It wasn't your fault. I was going to tell him, anyway. I thought he might be willing to help me."

"Give him a little time. Gray's a hard man,

but fair. And justice is important to him."

She thought of all the good he had done in the time that she had known him. Gray was fair and he was just. Perhaps in time, he would understand why discovering the truth was so important.

As she made her way out of the study, she tried without success to convince herself.

As expected, Derek Stiles arrived at the castle that afternoon. He was about Gray's age, probably no more than thirty, another handsome man who might have been Laurel's lover. Derek shared the same blond hair as Charles, only a richer shade of gold. He had the same straight nose as Gray and the same brown eyes, though Derek's were more tawny.

On their first meeting, he was as charming as his half cousin Jason, as solicitous as Charles, both of whom were there to greet him.

"So you managed to tear yourself away from the ladies long enough to come out and meet your new sister-in-law," Jason teased during the introductions made in the Sky Room.

Derek drew Corrie's gloved hand to his lips. "I'm sorry I missed the wedding. Somehow my invitation got lost."

Corrie colored faintly. "There wasn't much time."

Gray just grunted. "It was a small affair, and besides you hate weddings."

"Only the thought of my own," Derek said with a roguish grin. Corrie thought of Laurel and wondered how far the man would go to avoid being forced into marriage. She tried not to think that Gray had done the honorable thing only because her father had made it nearly impossible for him to refuse.

Rebecca floated forward just then, her blue eyes finding Derek. "Stop it, you scoundrel. As Coralee said, there was scarcely time to make arrangements, but you will be invited to the reception I am hosting in the newlyweds' honor."

Gray opened his mouth, but Rebecca cut him off before he could protest. "Come now, Gray. You know it's an old tradition to invite the village for a celebration of the nuptials when the lord of the castle is wed."

And Rebecca would want to squelch any gossip that might arise from Gray's actions — or Corrie's stupidity in not stopping his seduction when she had the chance.

"You don't really mind, do you, Gray?" his sister-in-law pressed. "It truly is a custom and it will help still the wagging tongues."

"Do whatever pleases you," he said darkly.

"Thank you." She smiled. "We shall make it an afternoon affair two weeks hence. Oh, and I almost forgot — an invitation arrived just this morning to Lady Devane's costume ball. It is going to be held the last Saturday of the month. I have already sent our acceptance."

Gray scowled. "You might have asked."

"You're married now. You have an obligation to present your wife to society — such as it is out here." Her smile looked brittle. "You wouldn't want anyone thinking you have already grown tired of your bride."

Gray's gaze found Coralee's and she saw the heat, the hunger. He had certainly not tired of her yet.

His mouth edged up. "No, we wouldn't want that. Tell the countess we'll be there." He looked at Derek. "How long are you planning to stay?"

"Until you tire of my company. I thought at least until the end of next week."

Something shifted in Rebecca's features before her smile slipped back into place. "You know you are welcome for as long as you wish."

Charles smiled. "We have other guests in the house, as well. Dolph Petersen is here and Colonel Timothy Rayburn. I believe you're acquainted with them both. They'll be joining us for supper. Perhaps we can convince them to stay a bit longer and we'll get up a bird-hunting party. What do you say?"

"A splendid notion," Derek agreed. "We'll make a point of it."

Corrie left the men to their discussion of the week's activities. As she headed for the library in search of something to read, she tried to form a picture of Derek Stiles with her sister.

Aside from his comments about marriage, it wasn't that difficult to do.

In a gown of emerald silk that bared her shoulders and exposed a bit of her cleavage, Corrie sat across from Gray in the dining room. Beneath gas chandeliers, the guests dined at a linen-draped table set with gilt-rimmed plates, ornate silverware bearing the Tremaine family crest, and shimmering crystal goblets. A pair of footmen served the sumptuous meal prepared by Rebecca's French chef.

"You were right," the colonel said as he dipped his spoon into an exquisite cream of oyster soup. "The food is delicious. Of course, a military man is grateful for anything more than bread and boiled meat."

Jason grinned and Charles chuckled softly. Even Gray managed to smile.

Petersen and Rayburn were interesting men, Corrie saw as the evening progressed, well-educated and not afraid to discuss topics beyond fashionable London parties and the weather. As she had hoped it might, eventually the conversation turned to India.

"Gray lived among the natives," the colonel said, "something few Englishmen are willing to do. I think he fell a little in love with the place. He was determined to learn as much about the country as he could."

"It's unlike anyplace else in the world," Gray said between bites of roast lamb and parsley potatoes, bringing up a topic Corrie had longed to hear him discuss. "It's wildly primitive, some of its customs incredibly barbaric. At the same time there's a wisdom among the people I've never witnessed anywhere else in the world."

Corrie began asking him questions, and Gray surprised her by answering. A lively discussion ensued about the future of India and what should be done to insure British interests.

"They won't wear the yoke forever," Gray said. "One day they'll demand their independence and England will be forced to give it to them."

"Nonsense," Rayburn declared. "They're a colony and always will be. They're like children, dependent on the British to take care of them."

By the time the debate was over, Corrie had seen a side of her husband she hadn't yet discovered. He was far more open in his beliefs than she would have believed, and powerfully persuasive in presenting his views. He should take his seat in the House of Lords, she thought, but doubted that she could convince him to do so.

The evening was more enjoyable than she had expected — except for the dark, penetrating glances she received from Gray. Clearly, he was still brooding over her earlier accusations. But the other men made up for his occasional silence, keeping the women entertained.

In deference to the ladies, the men declined brandy and cigars, and Derek suggested a game of cards.

"I'm afraid we'll have to pass," the colonel said, having already declined an invitation to stay and join the bird-hunting party. "Our business in Bristol can't wait, which means we'll need to get an early start."

"We appreciate your hospitality, Gray," Dolph added. "Good evening, ladies and gentlemen."

The two men headed upstairs, but the rest of the household agreed to the card play. As they moved into the game room, Gray stayed surprisingly close to Corrie's side, even partnering her at whist.

With him seated to her left, she couldn't help noticing how handsome he looked in his perfectly tailored black evening clothes, the way his white cravat set off his dark hair and swarthy complexion. She could feel his masculine power, feel the force of his gaze as if he touched her, and her hand shook as she picked up her cards.

"All right, let's get started, shall we?" Charles began to arrange his hand, eager to get under way.

Turning her thoughts from Gray, Corrie forced herself to concentrate on the game.

She was good, she knew, and it showed when she won her first hand. Silently, she thanked Leif Draugr, a master player, for helping her improve her skills. As the evening progressed and Corrie chalked up another winning hand, Derek teasingly made mention of her prowess.

"Are you certain you aren't a sharper, my lady? You play cards like a man."

Gray glanced her way. "Another of your hidden talents, sweeting? I wonder what other interesting abilities you've kept hidden from me."

She ignored the subtle jibe. Letty had pretended to be a very poor card player. Corrie was better than most men. It was another reminder of her deception.

She pasted on a smile. "My friend's husband, Leif Draugr, helped me improve my game. He is very good at cards. The three of us played in the evenings quite often."

"I know Draugr," Derek said, his blond hair gleaming in the lamplight, the color of pirate gold. "Made a fortune at the gaming tables. No one knows much about him."

"His wife, Krista, is my best friend. We work together at *Heart to Heart.* It's a ladies' magazine. Perhaps you've heard of it."

Derek looked amused. "I've read it."

"You have?" She was only a little surprised. A number of men read the gazette, or at least portions of it.

"I have a lady friend who's a dedicated fan. Whoever writes the editorials does a damn fine job."

Corrie's smile this time was sincere. "That would be Krista mostly. I wrote a number of them last fall when she was away. I did a series of interviews with reform leaders, including one with Feargus O'Conner, mostly as a means of lending support to the various bills before parliament."

Gray's dark eyes fixed on her face. "Becky subscribes to the gazette. News is hard to come by out here, so I read it often. You wrote that series?"

She steeled herself, certain he would have something viperous to say. "Yes . . . As I said, I managed the gazette for a time while Krista was away."

"They were very well written," he said softly, drawing her gaze to his. "You made some extremely valid points."

She stared at him, her heart squeezing painfully. "The gazette isn't just about fashion and gossip. We also do some very important work. In time I hope I'll be able to contribute again in some way."

Derek shot Gray a roguish grin. "Didn't know you married a reformer, eh, Brother?"

Gray stiffened, his grim look returning. "There is a lot I don't know about my wife. I do, however, know what a delightful bed partner she is, so if you will excuse us, it is time the two of us retired."

"Gray!" Her face flushed with embarrassment as he slid back his chair.

"Your wife is a lady," Charles said. "I shouldn't need to remind you."

Gray made a slightly mocking bow, not

326

the least repentant. "My apologies, madam." Tugging on her arm, he urged her to her feet, her cheeks still flaming.

It was clear Gray was making a point. She had noticed his possessiveness all evening, but had no idea what it meant.

Leaving the others in the game room, they headed up the stairs. Even before they reached the master's suite, she sensed a subtle change in him, the control he seemed to draw around him like a protective cloak.

Uneasiness settled over her as he opened the door and waited for her to walk in.

TWENTY-ONE

The bedcovers on the large four-poster were neatly folded back, the lamp on the dresser turned low in preparation for the lord and his lady wife. A soft yellow glow permeated the room and the faint scent of sandalwood hung in the air.

Corrie's heart beat softly. She knew what lay ahead and her senses sharpened in awareness.

"I need to ring for Anna," she said, hoping to give herself a little time. She started toward the gold-tasseled bell-pull, but Gray caught her arm.

"You don't need your maid." He shrugged out of his black evening jacket and his waistcoat and tossed them over a chair. "Turn around," he commanded, the husky note in his voice sending a curl of heat through her middle.

She did as he asked, allowing him to undress her. Anticipation mixed with trepidation as he pulled the pins from her hair. He took his time, kissing her shoulders, her neck, biting an earlobe as he unfastened the buttons at the back of her emerald silk gown. His warm breath fanned her skin and heat pooled low in her belly.

Gray peeled away each layer, kissing the areas he exposed, and yet there was an odd detachment to each of his movements, a control he seemed determined to keep.

He knew exactly where to press his mouth to make her tremble, exactly how to caress and mold her breasts, how hard to bite down on her nipple to make her breath catch. The heat was building, her body responding. Pleasure rolled through her, so powerful she bit her lip to stifle a moan.

She looked at Gray, saw the hard ridge of his sex outlined at the front of his black evening trousers, knew he was aroused and wanting her as much as she wanted him.

And yet there was something missing, some element that had been there when he had made love to her that night in the storm, and now seemed almost imagined. Her wedding night had been fierce and abandoned, but there had been little emotion in her husband's practiced lovemaking. Apparently tonight would be the same.

Unless she did something about it.

The moment he removed the last of her garments, Corrie turned and slid her arms around his neck. Pressing herself against him, she pulled his mouth down to hers for a deep, burning kiss. For an instant, he resisted, clasping her arms as if he meant to push her away. Corrie just kept kissing him, running her fingers into his silky black hair, dislodging the velvet ribbon, pressing her breasts into his chest.

Gray softly groaned.

And then he was kissing her back like a madman, parting her lips with his tongue, driving deeply inside, cupping her bottom and pulling her against his arousal. The stiff ridge thickened even more, began to pulse insistently against her. Corrie worked the buttons on the fly of his trousers, reached down and caught his hard length in her palm. It felt big and hot and male, heavy against her fingers. When she tightened her hold, Gray jerked backward, surprise and passion darkening his face.

"I'm sorry," she said, "did I . . . did I hurt you?"

"No, I . . ." He shook his head. "God, I want you." And then he was kissing her again, deep savage kisses that left her breathless and pliant, hot wet kisses that left no doubt as to his intent. For an instant, she recognized the man he had been that night in the storm. The fiery, passionate man who took what he wanted, but gave of himself in return.

Lifting her up, he carried her over to the bed and settled her in the middle of the deep feather mattress. For a time, he simply stood there, staring down at her. He drew a shuddering breath, fisting his hands as if he fought for control, then moved away from her to strip off his clothes.

He disappeared for a moment, then reappeared, striding naked toward the bed. Hard muscle rippled in his shoulders and the broad width of his chest. Ridges tightened across his stomach, and long sinews flexed in his thighs as he approached.

There was something in his hand, she saw. Several lengths of red silk floated from his palm, almost touching the floor. He came to the bedside, caught both her arms and looped the silk around her wrists. She didn't resist when he drew them over her head and tied them to an ornate post in the headboard.

"What . . . what are you doing?"

"Just let yourself relax. You'll enjoy it, I promise."

The distance had returned. Dear God, would she never be able to reach him? She stifled a sob, thinking of the man she had fallen in love with, the man she might never know again.

Gray leaned over and kissed her, a soft, deep, sensuous kiss with none of the wild abandon of moments before. For the first time, she realized how tightly he held himself in check, how carefully leashed each of his movements was.

Gray kept kissing her, arousing her body, taking complete control. In a flash of insight, she realized that in tying her up, he was able to keep himself apart from her. That he was protecting himself from his response to her.

That in his arms, he was in danger of losing control.

And knowing she could affect him so deeply made her heart leap with hope.

He climbed onto the bed and his mouth covered hers. Long, deep, erotic kisses followed, and Corrie gave herself up to his practiced skills. It wasn't what she wanted, wasn't what she needed from him, but she wouldn't deny herself the pleasure those hot looks promised.

She arched upward at the feel of his mouth on her breasts, the sharp tug of his straight white teeth. His hands worked their magic, teasing and caressing, skimming over her body, sliding hotly between her legs.

She shifted restlessly on the bed, tugging at her silken bonds, crying out at his gentle penetration, the heated stroke of his fingers. Desire swelled, twisted like a hot coil in her belly.

She wanted him, wanted to feel him inside her.

"I need you, Gray . . . please . . ."

"Not yet."

She trembled as his mouth moved lower; his tongue slid into the indentation of her navel. He settled himself between her legs, kissed the inside of her thighs, and she squirmed.

"I need . . ." She moistened her lips. "I want to feel you inside me."

"Soon," he said, and set his mouth to an entirely new task.

Corrie writhed and arched against the sweet invasion of his tongue, her body tightening, the sensations sharpening until she couldn't stand an instant more. She cried out as a powerful climax shook her, stalled her breathing. Pleasure washed through her, so fierce she bit back a scream.

She was beginning to spiral down when he entered her, the bonds still holding her wrists, making it impossible for her to escape. Impossible for her to touch him. Dear God, she wanted to. She had never wanted anything so badly.

Perhaps that was the reason her body tightened instantly, began to climb to the pinnacle she had reached before. She could feel his hardness inside her, feel the breadth and length of him, the power of his maleness. Gray plunged into her again and again, and waves of sensation crashed through her.

Corrie bit her lip to keep from crying his name, and then she was soaring, arching upward, Gray pounding deeper and harder until he reached his own release.

She drifted, floating in a sea of contentment. She didn't notice when he untied the silk scarf, only roused a little when he curved his hard body around her.

She must have slept for a while. It was the middle of the night when she awakened to the feel of his mouth on her breast, his hands stroking gently between her legs. Passion flared and she welcomed him into her body.

Afterward, she slept again.

In the morning, Gray was gone.

It was early, though the servants were already up and about their daily tasks. In the kitchen, Gray accepted a linen bag filled with cold meats, bread and cheese that Cook threw together for him. Then he headed for the stable. What he needed was a brisk morning ride, a long run with Raja over the glistening dewy fields. He needed to escape his uncertain feelings for the woman in his bed.

Dammit to bloody hell.

He couldn't believe what had happened, couldn't believe how close he had come to losing control. He didn't understand it. As lovely as his wife was, he had been with more beautiful women, been with far more skillful lovers. What was it about her?

He strode along the stone path to the stable, his mind on Coralee and how best to deal with the woman who was now his wife, when he spotted Dickey Michaels racing toward him.

"Milord! Thank 'eavens ye've come. I was only waitin' till a decent hour to fetch ye."

Gray frowned. "What is it, Dickey? What's happened?"

"I need to show ye. This way, milord." The lanky youth raced ahead of him into the barn. "It's your lady, milord. The day after she took that spill, I went to fetch 'er sidesaddle, like ye told me. Didn't think nothing o' it at the time. This mornin', I took it down to put a new cinch on and this is what I found."

Dickey held up the broken cinch for

Gray's inspection. "It's been cut, do ye see? Weren't just a break, like I thought. It were meant to come apart the way it did."

Gray examined the cinch, saw it wasn't torn raggedly as a break would have been, but sliced almost all the way through. A chill slid down his spine. "Who else uses this saddle, Dickey? Maybe my wife wasn't meant to be the target."

"No one uses it, milord. Your sister-in-law used it before she got 'erself a fancy new padded one some months back. Ain't no one used it till I saddled Tulip for your lady-ship the day the two o' ye went ridin'. Since it didn't break that day, someone musta cut it right after."

Someone who figured Coralee would be us-ing it again. "Aside from you and the other grooms, who has access to the tack room?"

"Door ain't kept locked. Coulda been just about anyone, maybe someone passin' by from the village."

And Coralee had been in the village asking questions. For the first time Gray considered that perhaps his wife was right, and someone had indeed murdered her sister. He didn't believe for an instant it was anyone in his family. Even if one of his brothers or his cousin might have seduced the girl, none of them would murder a woman and her in-

336

nocent child.

More likely, the killer — if there was one — was a footpad or criminal of some sort. Maybe someone from the village had committed the murder and was sending a warning that Coralee should stop asking questions.

"Thank you, Dickey. From now on, keep the tack room door locked, will you? And keep an eye out for anyone you see who shouldn't be around here."

"Aye, milord. Ye can count on Dickey."

Gray just nodded, his mind shifting from escaping the house to worry about his wife. The woman had been nothing but trouble since the day she arrived. Nothing but trouble since the day he'd been forced to marry her.

And his stomach knotted with fear that something might happen to her.

During the day, Corrie worked on her plans to remodel the upstairs suites, which gave her the chance to spend time with a number of the servants. Determined to continue her search for information, she subtly questioned the housekeeper, the butler, the upstairs and downstairs chambermaids, even the kitchen maids. If one of the male members of the family had been involved with Laurel, the servants did not know.

Surprisingly, gleaning the information was more difficult than Corrie had expected. Every time she looked up, Gray was somewhere near. He was there in the master suite when the draper, with the help of a pair of footmen, hung new silk curtains at the windows. He appeared outside the door of the kitchen when she went in on the pretense of getting a glass of milk.

She was heading for the village to check on the arrival of the furniture she had purchased when her husband pulled up beside her in his two-wheeled phaeton and insisted she let him drive her.

He had never been more solicitous. She would even go so far as to say he was cordial. Still, at night he was the same remote lover he had been since their wedding. As intense as the pleasure was, there was always something missing.

The odd thing was, she believed Gray felt it, too.

Nearly a week had passed when the first shipment of furniture arrived at the castle. Movers cleared the heavy oak pieces out of Gray's suite, replacing them with lighter teak and bamboo ones she had purchased with the help of a dealer in London.

There was a rosewood dresser inlaid with

intricate designs in brass, a mahogany chest delicately carved and inlaid with ivory, a teak writing desk with ebony drawers.

Screens with lacy filigree were scheduled to arrive later in the week to decorate the walls, along with brass lamps and several antique urns.

At Corrie's instruction, one of the workmen rolled up the ugly brown rug on the floors, and new carpets of a paisley pattern in rich blues, deep greens and burgundy went down in its stead.

The amber walls and draperies, tied back to let in sunlight, went well with the burgundy silk counterpane and the decorative pillows in colorful patterns of blue and deep green she'd had made to accent the massive four-poster bed, the only original piece of furniture she had kept.

She was helping one of the men move the heavy oak dresser and replace it with a teakwood writing desk, when she tripped over an ottoman that hadn't yet been placed, and fell back against the paneled wall on one side of the room.

When she stepped away, the panel popped open, and to her amazement, revealed a passage behind the wall. Looking around to be sure no one had seen it, she quickly set the ottoman in front of the panel. When the workmen had finished placing the furniture and gone to fetch another load, she hurriedly examined the latch so that once the panel was closed, she would know how to open it again.

Where in heaven's name did the passage lead?

Corrie vowed that as soon as she got the chance, she would find out.

Gray decided not to tell Coralee about the cinch. He wasn't certain the broken strap meant she was truly in danger, and he didn't want to worry her for nothing.

And he didn't want her jumping to conclusions — even if they were the same ones he had jumped to. He didn't want the entire matter of her sister's death stirred up all over again.

Instead, he wrote to Dolph Petersen in Bristol, telling him about the cinch and the possible threat to Coralee, asking him to return to Castle-on-Avon and continue his investigation into the possibility of Laurel Whitmore's murder.

In the meantime, Gray began asking a few questions himself, snooping around a bit in the village, seeing what he could find out. He spoke to Vicar Langston and discovered that Laurel Whitmore had come to see him after her return from East Dereham. She'd been troubled, the vicar said, though at the time, he didn't believe she was in any way suicidal.

At the Green Dragon Tavern, a barmaid named Greta told him — for a price — that gossip had it one of the men at the castle had been having an affair with Viscount Selkirk's daughter.

"Thought it was you, 'andsome," she said, grinning up at him. "Ye'd surely be the one I'd pick."

Gray paid her for her help, a little extra for the compliment, and headed back to the house. He had tried to convince himself neither his brothers nor his cousin had been involved with Laurel Whitmore. But Cora believed it was so. Dolph was fairly convinced, and local gossip agreed.

It bothered Gray to think that one of the men in his family might have seduced an innocent young woman and abandoned her.

Still, seducing a woman was far different from murder.

If it hadn't been for the broken cinch, Gray would have remained convinced the girl had killed herself. But he couldn't ignore what Dickey Michaels had found, and now he wondered . . .

Had a footpad come upon the young

woman that night, as she wandered with her child beside the river? Perhaps he had tried to rob her, and the attempt had gone sour. If Laurel was anything like Coralee, she would have fought her attacker. In the tussle, Laurel and her child could have fallen into the water.

Or the man could have pushed her.

Coralee had been asking questions. Perhaps the man responsible was afraid he would be discovered. He would hang for the crime, no doubt.

How far would a desperate fellow go to escape the gallows? With two deaths behind him, another would hardly be a concern.

Gray thought of Coralee and his stomach twisted into a knot of fear.

The announcement, completely unexpected, came at luncheon the following day and sent the entire household into a tailspin. Corrie, Gray and the rest of the family sat round a table placed on the terrace to enjoy the sunny June afternoon. There were guests in attendance: Squire Morton and his wife, Mary, as well as two of their sons, Thomas and James.

Corrie studied Thomas carefully, since Aunt Agnes had made mention of his visits to Selkirk Hall. He was the second son, perhaps thirty-five, a large man with thick brown hair and skin slightly weathered by the work he did out-of-doors. Even with the faint scar on his chin, he was handsome. He was polite and well-mannered, the sort of man Laurel might have found attractive.

But the book Corrie had found in the study made it clear that Laurel had been in love with one of the men at the castle.

As the group sipped white wine and enjoyed dilled salmon and a fresh cucumber salad, Rebecca leaned toward Charles and whispered something in his ear. He rapped his wineglass to draw the company's attention.

"We've news to share," he said at her urging. "Why don't you tell them, my dear?"

Gowned elegantly in cream-and-rose silk, Rebecca surveyed the table of family and friends and smiled. "We're going to have a baby. For years, Charles and I have been hoping . . . praying it would happen. Now, after all of this time, God has finally blessed us." Tears brimmed in her brilliant blue eyes and she wiped them away with the tip of a finger.

"Why, that is marvelous news!" said beefy Squire Morton.

Gray rose from his place at the head of the table, dark and forbidding, looking nothing at all like the rest of his fair-haired family. "This is quite an occasion. Congratulations to you both. I know how much you've wanted a child."

There was something in his expression Corrie couldn't quite read, something deep and troubled. He had wanted children once. Perhaps he still did, but had vowed never to have them.

"I . . . my wife and I," Gray corrected, "couldn't be happier for both of you."

"A toast," Jason said, lifting his wineglass, "to the future Mama and Papa Forsythe."

"Here, here!" Derek chimed in. "To a healthy babe and many more to come."

The toasts were accepted graciously, Rebecca smiling all the while, Charles a bit more reserved, but smiling along with his wife. Corrie added her own good wishes, happy for Rebecca, though they were not friends, and delighted for Charles, who was certain to make an excellent father.

After luncheon, the group dispersed, heading off in different directions to entertain themselves.

"What are your plans for the afternoon?" Gray asked Corrie, solicitous as he had been all week.

"I need to take a few more measurements in the rooms upstairs." It was only a tiny lie. She meant to explore the secret passage, which meant she truly would be upstairs in the suite. "Why do you ask?"

"No plans to run off to the village?" There was a trace of worry in his expression. It had been there all week.

"No, but —"

"Fine, then I'm going for a ride. Stay out of trouble, will you?" For an instant, she thought he might kiss her. Instead, he turned and strode toward the back of the house.

Corrie watched his tall dark figure disappear, a feeling of yearning in her heart. She had tried to tell herself she was no longer in love with Gray, that the man she had married was an altogether different one, but it wasn't the truth. Day after day, the need she saw in her husband's face, the longing he tried to hide, stole a little more of her heart.

She thought of the lonely man he was and the lonely life he led. She thought of all he had lost, and believed it was his fear of losing even more that made him unable to love.

With a sigh, she crossed the terrace and entered the house. The mystery of the passage lured her, the possibility of where it might lead and what she might find once she got there.

Corrie picked up her pace as she climbed the wide staircase.

Twenty-Two

Thankfully, both Samir and Anna were busy somewhere else, so the master's suite was empty. Corrie breathed a sigh of relief. Hurrying over to the dresser, she lit a candle, placed it in a silver candlestick and quietly moved toward the wood-paneled wall.

The newly arrived furniture was draped with white sheeting, hidden from Gray until the project was complete. She wanted to surprise him, hoped so much that he would be pleased with what she had done. But there was no way to know until he saw it.

In the meantime, the passage beckoned. Corrie pressed on the spot she had carefully marked, and a portion of panel silently swung open. She expected cobwebs and spiders, but when she thrust the candle inside the opening, the narrow passage seemed merely dusty and inky dark.

Taking another quick look around, and a breath for courage, she stepped into the space, but didn't close the panel. She planned to be back in the room long before Gray returned from his afternoon ride. Aside from that, the last thing she wanted was to be trapped in the narrow, confining passage with no way to escape.

As she began to move down the pitch-dark corridor, the candle threw faint yellow light in front of her and cast shadows along the walls. She couldn't tell how far the passage went, but along the route, the candle revealed what appeared to be several openings . . . if she could figure out how to unlock them.

Ignoring the chill that invaded the passage and slowly crept up her spine, she continued along until she came to a set of stairs. The candle flickered and she paused, her heart racing at the thought of the flame going out, leaving her in total darkness.

The full skirts of her apple-green day dress swished against the walls as she descended to the floor below. She wasn't sure where she was, only that the faint sound of voices began to reach her.

Corrie moved toward the sound, stopping when she could hear what was being said. But the thick walls muffled the voices so much she couldn't tell who was speaking, only that they seemed to be a male and a female.

"It's mine, isn't it?" the man was saying.

"Of course it is, darling. Charles was never man enough to father a child."

Corrie sucked in a breath. *Rebecca.* It had to be.

"I knew I wasn't the one to blame," she said, "and you have proved it. I shall be forever in your debt for such a gift."

Corrie heard the muffled sound of footfalls — the man pacing back and forth across a carpet. "He doesn't suspect, does he?"

"Of course not, darling. He wants a child too badly to examine the matter overmuch. The last thing Charles would wish to know is that the child isn't his."

Corrie felt a pang of sympathy for Charles Forsythe, to be duped in such a manner. She also felt a trickle of relief. Laurel's baby wasn't Charles's. Though he and Rebecca had tried to have children, Charles hadn't been able to father a babe. Which meant he couldn't have been Laurel's beloved.

Corrie liked Charles Forsythe. She was thankful to know he hadn't seduced an innocent young girl and then abandoned her.

"He'll raise it well," the man was saying. "Charles was meant to be a father, as I never was."

Who are you? Corrie silently asked, still unable to actually recognize the speaker's voice. *Jason or Derek?*

The ugly thought arose — perhaps it was Gray.

She bit her lip. It couldn't be. She refused to believe it. Gray had never shown the slightest interest in Rebecca. And Corrie didn't believe for an instant he was the sort of man who would cuckold his brother.

"I miss being with you. I want us to be together again." The man's voice barely reached through the wall.

The idea arose: *What about Thomas Morton?* He was an attractive man, a friend of Rebecca's. Perhaps more than a friend. And he had just been there at the house.

"We've discussed this," she said. "It's over. You know it had to end."

"I don't want it to end. I don't see why we can't go on the way we were."

Corrie strained to hear Rebecca's reply, but the pair was moving away from the wall. All Corrie could hear now were whispers, and soon after, only silence. She thought she heard a door open and close, but she couldn't be sure.

For a moment, she stood there in the passage, the candle flickering, threatening to go out. With a calming breath, she turned back the way she had come. When she reached the tiny staircase leading upward, she picked up her skirt and petticoats and hurriedly climbed, anxious to leave the dismal corridor and consider what she had learned.

Things at Castle Tremaine weren't as they seemed and never had been.

She wondered what Gray would say if he knew.

Then again, perhaps he already did.

As he had done every afternoon this week, Gray rode Raja as fast as he could across the fields. Still, he couldn't escape thoughts of Coralee. Worry that something might happen to her made him physically ill.

Except for the few hours he took for himself when Cora was inside the castle and he knew she was safe, he stayed close by. Even now, worry nagged him. He drew Raja to a halt atop a hill, turned the horse and started back toward the house.

As he crossed the fields, his thoughts shifted from Coralee to the announcement his sister-in-law had made that afternoon. Before this time next year, Charles would be a father. If the infant was a boy, the Tremaine title and fortune would be secure. And Charles would make a very good father.

For the first time, Gray was forced to ponder the notion that Coralee might also be with child.

It was a frightening thought.

Terrifying.

Gray had never had a loving, supportive father of his own. He had no idea how to be one. Bloody hell, he wouldn't know where to begin. He thought of Jillian and the short time they had been married. As a newly titled earl, he'd believed it was his duty to provide an heir. He had been certain that in time it would happen, but beyond that, hadn't given the matter much thought.

Then Jillian had died and the guilt had set in. Her death had been his fault. If he had gone boating with her that day, he could have saved her. He didn't doubt it for a moment.

A wave of nausea rolled through him. He had failed Jillian, and if he had a child, he might fail again. For an instant, he thought he might be sick.

He couldn't take the chance of failing a daughter or son, of failing Coralee. It wouldn't be fair to any of them.

From now on, he decided, he would take measures to prevent Cora's womb from quickening. He certainly knew how to do it, though there was always a chance it might not work. He didn't think she had yet conceived. There was still time to prevent it from happening.

By the time he reached the house, Gray had mostly convinced himself. Leaving the stallion with Dickey, he headed toward the castle. His worry built as he went in search of her, hoping she was still involved in her refurbishing project and out of any possible danger.

"Have you seen the countess?" he asked Samir.

The little Hindu smiled. "She awaits you upstairs, *sahib.*" Samir had said little about the woman Gray had married. He was a patient man and not quick to judge another human being, but Gray was sure he'd just caught a hint of approval in the weathered lines of the man's dark face. If he had, Gray wondered what his wife had done to win such a wise man's favor.

Calling Coralee's name as he opened the door and stepped into his sitting room, Gray knew in an instant why Samir seemed so pleased.

His own chest tightened. For an instant, he thought he had stepped out of England and into a world from his past. Nothing of the old suite remained. The massive oak furniture and heavy gold draperies, always so oppressive, had disappeared and with them, dark memories of his father seemed to lift away.

With sunlight streaming through the windows, he saw furnishings of teak and bamboo, a rosewood dresser decorated with shiny brass ornaments, a carved mahogany chest inlaid with ivory, an ebony-fronted bureau. Screens of lacy filigree lined one wall. There were beautiful brass lamps and the kind of antique brass urns he hadn't seen since he had left India.

He walked into the bedroom, his heart beating oddly, and saw that both rooms had been done in royal blue, deep green and rich burgundy, the walls and draperies of a soft honey color.

Only the bed remained, and with its burgundy silk counterpane and decorative pillows in colorful blue-and-green paisley patterns, even that looked different. It was as if his wife had looked into his soul, as if she understood the world that had made him most happy.

"Do you like it?"

He followed the sound of her voice and turned to see her standing a few feet away. She looked so lovely that a lump rose in his throat.

"You read my heart," he said.

Tears welled in her eyes. She walked to where he stood and leaned toward him, gently slipped her arms around his neck.

"I hoped you would like it. I wanted you to feel as if you were home."

He held her. Just held her. Her small body curved into his and it filled him with warmth. He knew he should let her go. Knew it was dangerous to allow these feelings he held for her to grow into something more. He took a deep breath and stepped away, but he couldn't let go of her hand.

"It's beautiful. I couldn't be more pleased. Thank you for such a wonderful gift."

She simply nodded. With her hand still holding his, she led him toward the door between their bedrooms and pushed it open. The suites were nearly identical. The tones in hers were a little softer, but there was no mistaking the Indian influence.

"You don't mind, do you? You make it sound like a very special place."

"I don't mind."

"I should like to see it someday."

He shook his head. "It's an amazing country, but not a place for an English-woman."

She merely shrugged. "I've always wanted to travel. I had hoped to write a book one day about the places I had seen." She let go of his hand and glanced away. "That was before, of course."

"Before you married me."

She returned her gaze to his. "Yes."

"I guess we both gave up something."

"Some of our freedom, I suppose."

That was what he had thought, but now he wondered. . . . Perhaps he had gained something even more valuable in return.

He cleared his throat. "I love the rooms," he repeated, simply to have something to say.

"I'm glad."

Her smile was so sweet his heart squeezed. Bloody hell, he couldn't let this continue. He had to do something before he slid completely off the precipice that seemed only inches away.

"Your rooms are nice, but I like having you in my bed, nearby in case I want you. When we retire, you will continue to sleep with me."

She bristled, as he knew she would, and the tender moment was lost.

"I have my own bed. Just because I'm your wife doesn't mean you can command me as you once did your troops."

Grateful to be on more familiar terrain, he stood his ground. "Nevertheless, you'll sleep in my bed. If you refuse, I will simply carry you in and tie you to the bedposts as I did the other night."

She made a low, growling sound in her throat, and he almost smiled. She was so full of fire.

Nothing at all like Letty.

Yet in the ways that counted, exactly like Letty.

The thought disturbed him, considering the feelings he had harbored for the little country waif. Instead of dragging his wife into his arms, carrying her over to the bed and making love to her as he dearly wished to do, Gray turned and walked away, leaving her alone in the suite.

It occurred to him, as it had before, that perhaps he should tell her about the broken cinch. If he didn't hear from Dolph in the next day or two, he would. Gray was coming to appreciate Coralee's intelligence. It might be interesting to hear what she had to say.

In the meantime, he would keep her safe.

He cast a last glance at the door to her bedroom and forced his feet to keep moving away.

Supper was over. The men suggested a game of cards, but Rebecca pleaded a headache and declined. Corrie seized the opportunity and also declined, then headed upstairs to renew her investigation of the passage. She had secured a prying tool from one of the workmen who had helped with the refurbishing, and hoped to use it to open the panels along the secret corridor.

Anna helped her change out of her dinner gown into her nightgown. Corrie stood fidgeting as the maid pulled the pins from her hair and ran the bristle brush through it.

"Thank you, Anna, that will be all for tonight."

"Don't you want me to braid it?"

"I'll take care of it this evening." She didn't have much time. She would plait it the moment she got back.

"Good night, milady." The thin woman slipped quietly away, and the moment she was gone, Corrie lit her candle and headed for the passage. Pressing on the spot she had marked, she stepped back as the panel swung open, then quickly ducked into the shadowy space.

The last time she had entered it had been daylight. The corridor was no darker now, yet it seemed so. Each of her creaking footsteps tightened her nerves a notch. The eerie whisper of air that blew through the passageway sent a shudder down her spine.

She moved along the corridor, holding the candle out in front of her, searching the walls to find any cracks that indicated there might be an opening. The air shifting past her felt colder, the darkness more dense. She shivered and wished she had put on a robe. Some ways down the passage, she found the first opening and tried to think which bedroom it might lead to.

She pressed on the wall, ran her hand up and down each side and over the top, but found no way to get it to open. She tried the prying tool, pulling back firmly, but not hard enough to crack the wood, yet the door remained solidly closed.

She was debating whether to use more force when the candlelight reflected on a shiny piece of metal she hadn't noticed before. She lifted the inch-long latch and the panel popped open neat as you please.

She could see the glow of lamplight and flattened herself against the wall of the passage, fearful someone might be in the room. A lamp burned on the dresser, the wick turned low, but when she leaned forward to peek into the room, she saw that it was empty.

Unsure how much time she would have, she ducked through the opening, which was not quite as tall as she, and made a quick survey of the bedroom.

A leather traveling satchel sat on the floor, and she recognized some of Derek's garments in the armoire. A hat and gloves, black evening clothes and shiny black shoes . . . There were several well-made frock coats and trousers, but nothing that might be a clue to a connection with Laurel. Corrie moved to the satchel, opened and searched inside for something — anything — that might prove telling.

Nothing.

A riding crop lay on the dresser, and a pair of leather riding boots stood nearby. It was clear Derek traveled lightly and also clear she wasn't going to find any pertinent information here.

She wasn't sure how much time had passed or how long the men would continue their card playing, but she felt fairly safe in trying one more door. Returning to the secret corridor, she ducked inside and closed the panel, then continued through the inky blackness. The second door seemed miles away, and yet she knew it must access one of the other bedrooms along the upstairs hall.

Being even more careful this time, she pressed her ear against the wall, straining to hear anyone moving about. Relatively certain the room was empty, she found the metal latch, then held her breath as the panel popped open.

No lamp burned this time. She crossed the room, set her candle on the dresser and began to search the place in its soft yellow glow. She was busy looking through the armoire when the bedroom door swung open without the least amount of warning, and Jason Forsythe walked into the room.

"I'll see you in the morning," he said to someone in the hall, then turned and stopped dead at the sight of her in her nightgown standing in front of his armoire.

"Well, *chérie,* I admit you are a treat I hadn't expected to find. However, we both might have been better served if you had come when your husband was not standing in the doorway." Amusement curved his lips. "As it is, we shall both be lucky to escape with our lives."

Corrie gasped as Gray stormed into the bedroom, his dark eyes blazing with damnation. "What the bloody hell are you doing in my cousin's room?"

Jason held up a hand. "Easy, Gray. Perhaps she merely lost her way."

He pinned her with a glare. "Surely you can do better than that, sweeting."

Corrie swallowed. Gray was already furious, but the truth was better than what he was thinking now. "I was . . ." She turned, pointed toward the open panel leading to the secret passage. "I found a hidden corridor behind the wall in your sitting room. I wanted to see where it led."

He looked over at the black, forbidding hole that was the opening of the passage, and frowned. "You expect me to believe you traveled through that dismal tunnel merely to see where it went?"

"Well, I — I was . . ."

"The truth, Coralee."

"All right! I was looking for clues. I thought you would all be busy playing cards, and while you were downstairs I would see what I could find out."

"Your sister, again! Dammit to bloody hell!"

"Would one of you mind telling me what is going on?" Jason walked over to examine the opening, enjoying the situation now that he was sure Gray wasn't going to kill him.

Of course, Corrie thought, her husband might still do his wife bodily harm.

Gray focused his attention on Jason. "Coralee came here to prove I had murdered her sister — which you already know. Apparently, she discovered my innocence or she wouldn't have allowed me to bed her."

Corrie blushed.

"Unfortunately, she is now convinced one of the other men in the house was Laurel Whitmore's lover. She is trying to discover which one of you it is."

Jason's light brown eyebrows went up. "Interesting. I had trouble imagining you leg-shackled, Gray, but I think I'm beginning to understand. You certainly don't have to worry about your marriage being dull."

Gray's features tightened. "Since we're discussing seduction, I might as well ask — were you and Laurel Whitmore involved in an affair?"

Jason shook his head. "I knew her. I liked her. I wouldn't have minded taking her to bed, but I am not ready for marriage and knew well enough that is what it would mean."

Gray shoved back a lock of black hair, loose from its ribbon. He turned a dark glare on Corrie. "Satisfied?"

"I suppose I shall have to be."

He walked over to the passage, leaned down to peer inside, then shut the panel. As he walked back across the room, he grabbed Corrie's wrist and started tugging her toward the door.

"I'd appreciate it if you would keep my wife's little adventure to yourself."

Jason chuckled. "Of course."

Gray dragged Corrie out into the hall and along the carpet toward the master's suite, her nightgown billowing out around her ankles as she ran to keep up. He hauled her into the sitting room and slammed the door.

"You little fool, I swear I ought to give you the thrashing of your life." His gaze sliced down to her bottom, protected only by the thin white nightgown. "But I'd probably enjoy it too much." Angry strides carried him over to the panel she had left open as a means of escape.

"Did you know it was there?" she asked.

"No." He tried to see inside the passage, but it was as black as pitch inside. "Where does it lead?"

"I've only gone partway. It travels along the bedrooms on this side of the hallway, opens into some of them, and also goes downstairs. I went down and looked around a bit, but you can see how dark it is. I wasn't sure where I was, so I came back up."

His jaw clenched. "You could have been hurt, Coralee. If you had been injured while you were in there, we might never have found you." He paced back to where she stood. "Dammit, promise me you won't do anything that foolish again."

"I left the door open. I wasn't really in

364

danger."

"You might have been." He sighed, dragged the tie from his hair and ran his fingers through it. The thick black mass fell around his shoulders, making him look like the highwayman he sometimes seemed. "The day you rode out in that storm, your cinch didn't break — it was cut."

"Cut? I don't know what you mean."

"Someone wanted you to take that fall. You'd been asking a lot of questions. Perhaps it was a warning, I don't know. Until we do, we have to be careful nothing like that happens again."

Corrie glanced toward the window, thinking of the day she had taken the fall in the rain. "You're saying someone tried to kill me?"

"Or at least hoped to see you hurt."

She mulled the information over and lifted her chin. "If that is so, it proves I am right. My sister was murdered, and whoever cut my cinch wants to stop me from finding out who killed her."

Gray released a slow breath and, to her amazement, agreed. "It's possible." He glanced toward the passage, pointed to the ominous dark opening. "And if you're right, with a stunt like that you're playing right into his hands."

He was angry again. And he was worried. She could see it in his eyes.

The anger won out. "It's time for bed." After shutting the panel, he grabbed her hand and hauled her across the carpet into his bedroom. "I want you from behind. Get up on the mattress."

She had no idea what he was talking about and simply stood there staring.

"The bed," he demanded, as if he had the right. Which, as her husband, he did.

She flicked a glance in that direction, but still didn't move. He might have the right, but she didn't like his tone of voice and wasn't about to be bullied. "I am not yours to command, and besides, I don't know what you want me to do."

He seemed only a little surprised by her defiance. Perhaps he was beginning to know her, after all. He was a difficult man, moody and often brooding, but she didn't believe he meant to hurt her.

His hard look slipped away. "I'll teach you," he said softly. "I'll make it good for us both. Trust me."

She did, she realized. Certainly, she trusted him in this. She started to pull the string at the neck of her nightgown, but Gray caught her hand.

"Leave it," he said gruffly.

366

Intrigued now, she did as he asked, climbing up on the high four-poster, watching as Gray stripped off his clothes. He turned away for a moment, then joined her naked on the bed. Catching her face in his hands, he kissed her, a long, wet, demanding kiss that sent heat into her stomach and desire sliding through her limbs.

Gray came up behind her, molding his powerful body against her back and hips. Through the nightgown, she could feel the heat of his groin against her bottom, and silently cursed the fabric that formed a barrier between them. One of his big hands slid into her hair where it fell in soft curls around her shoulders. He combed the heavy strands with his fingers, exposing the column of her neck.

She felt his mouth against her nape as he reached around to caress her breasts, to tease and mold them through the soft white cotton, and her nipples stiffened against his palms.

She yearned to be rid of the nightgown. "I need to feel you, Gray."

"Soon."

"But I need —"

He leaned over and caught her chin, settled his mouth over hers, silencing her protests.

"I'm going to give you exactly what you need," he promised in his deep husky voice.

But instead of removing the nightgown, he lifted it over her hips, bunching the fabric around her waist. His hands smoothed over her bottom, then moved between her legs, where he began to caress her.

Her insides tightened. The man knew every trick, knew that the longer the cumbersome nightgown stayed on, the greater was her need to take it off, and the hotter she became.

She moaned as he parted her burning flesh and began to stroke her. "You're mine," he said. "No more trips into another man's bedroom."

She tried to concentrate on his words, but the pleasure was building. She bit down on her bottom lip to keep from begging him to take her. "I wasn't . . ."

He nipped her bare bottom and a warm shiver went through her. "You are the most vexing female." The stroking increased. "Damn, but I want you."

Guiding himself into her damp heat, he filled her slowly, until he impaled her completely, then gripped her hips and began to move.

Hot sensation poured through her. Sweet God, it was heaven. Corrie arched her back to take him deeper still, and Gray hissed in a breath. His pace increased, the heavy thrust and drag infusing her with heat. She knew his desire was as strong as her own. Still, she could feel his determined control.

Her own control faded, caught up in the heat and need, the desire that scorched through her like a flame. The muscles in his buttocks flexed as he drove into her. Hard arms reached around her. He gripped the nightgown in his fists and tore the fabric away.

A whimper escaped. She was naked at last and she wanted to sob with relief. Instead, she gave herself over to the hot feel of skin against skin, the deep stroke of flesh into flesh.

She cried out Gray's name as a powerful climax shook her, but he didn't stop. Not until another wave of pleasure rolled through her, melting the last of her need. Then his muscles tightened and he reached his own release.

Seconds passed. Slowly they spiraled down. Gray settled himself beside her, and as she curled against him, she saw him removing something from his still-firm erection.

"What is that?"

"French letter," he said absently.

369

Corrie stiffened. "You . . . you told me they were used to prevent childbirth."

He looked up at her. "That's right."

"But we're married now. Children are a normal part of marriage."

He glanced away. "I'm not ready to be a father, Coralee. I'm not sure I ever will be."

She swallowed. She couldn't believe she had heard him correctly. Tears welled in her eyes. "You're my husband, Gray. Would you deny me the joy of having your child?"

His gaze swung back to hers, turbulent and for the first time uncertain.

Corrie pressed on. "What about your duty as an earl?"

"Charles's son can carry on the title."

"But I love children, Gray. And I think you would make an excellent father. Please don't take this away from me — from us."

His gaze found hers. "I didn't think it would be this important to you."

He didn't think it would be important? A lump swelled in her throat. She loved him. He was her husband. Of course it was important. "I want your child, Gray — more than anything in the world."

He reached out and touched her face, and she was surprised to feel a tremor in his hand. Leaning over, he very softly kissed her. "All right, if that's what you want. I'll give you a baby. Or at least make a damn good try."

And then he came up over her, filling her again and stirring her blood. Corrie gave herself into his care, feeling love for him expanding in her heart.

She wasn't sure she could ever make him love her in return, but tonight they had touched on the future, spoken of children and family.

It just might be a start.

TWENTY-THREE

It was a sunny afternoon in June, the day of the celebration being held in honor of the marriage of the Earl and Countess of Tremaine. Rebecca had worked tirelessly for nearly two weeks, and as Corrie looked out on the wide green lawns surrounding the castle, where the party would be held, everything appeared to be in perfect order.

The gathering was scheduled to start at four o'clock and continue into the evening. Colorful paper lanterns hung from the trees. The candles would be lit as soon as it was dark. Great kegs of ale had been brought in for the villagers, along with lemonade and jugs of wine. Long rows of tables had been set up under the trees, laden with outrageous quantities of food: roast pig, a haunch of beef, succulent pigeons browned on a spit. There were breads and cheeses, platters of vegetables and puddings, and an astonishing array of desserts.

It was a day when commoners would mingle with the aristocracy, a celebration not to be missed.

Though Corrie's parents had decided not to make the tedious journey, Aunt Agnes and Allison would be there. Since Corrie's marriage, their visits had been few. They didn't want to take her away from her husband.

Corrie scoffed. All Gray really cared about was having her close by whenever he wanted access to her body, which he did with amazing frequency. Of course, she couldn't deny she enjoyed his skillful attentions. She just wished he would share a bit of himself beyond making love.

The party progressed and the ale flowed. More platters of food were brought out and consumed by the festive crowd on the lawn. Krista, Leif and Thor had been invited, but with Corrie gone and Lindsey still new to her job as editor, Krista was needed at the gazette. Reluctantly, she and Leif had declined the invitation, but promised a visit next month, which Corrie preferred, since they would be able to spend more time together.

The afternoon moved toward evening, perfectly choreographed by Rebecca, who was dressed like royalty in a confection of cream-and-amber silk. Corrie had chosen a gown of pale green moiré, the skirt swept together in long pleats up the front, and trimmed with green silk cord around the bodice and hem. Her full petticoats brushed against her ankles as she moved through the crowd of guests on her husband's arm.

In a navy-blue frock coat, satin-collared waistcoat, light gray trousers and white silk cravat, Gray looked elegant and handsome. His wavy black hair, tied neatly at the nape, shone like jet in the afternoon sun. Corrie didn't miss the provocative glances he received from several women.

If he noticed, Gray didn't let it show. He was playing the dutiful husband, and if she pretended, she could almost imagine him that way. In truth, it was only a performance. He had yet to accept her as more than a bedmate. She had to keep that firmly in mind.

Corrie studied the sea of guests milling about on the manicured lawns. All the important neighbors for miles around were there: the town magistrate, the vicar and his family, Squire Morton, his wife and sons, two of whom were married and had children of their own.

The Forsythe family was well represented, with Charles and Rebecca, Gray's half brother, Derek, and his cousin, Jason all in attendance. Corrie flicked a glance at the handsome man with the deep dimples and light brown hair. Jason had denied any involvement with Laurel, and he had been extremely convincing.

Which left Derek Stiles the likely suspect.

Corrie sighed, no longer certain that any of them were involved. Without the book she had found as proof, she had begun to doubt her own judgment. Perhaps she was wrong about it all.

Then again, there was the sabotaged cinch and the fall she had suffered.

It was several hours after the party had started and introductions had all been made that Gray allowed her to escape into the company of her friends.

"I am so glad to see you!" Corrie hugged Aunt Agnes, then Allison. "We live so close to each other and yet it seems there is never time enough to visit."

"You are newly married," said bulky Aunt Agnes, out of mourning along with Allison for the occasion of Corrie's wedding celebration. After Gray's edict, Corrie had never returned to wearing the dismal black garments. She couldn't say she was sorry.

"You are busy with your husband," Aunt Agnes continued, "as is to be expected. You need time to get to know each other."

Corrie just smiled. "Even so, I shall come by and see you next week. I should love an excuse to get away for a bit."

Allison reached over and squeezed her hand. "How are you doing? Are you and the earl . . . beginning to settle your differences?"

Corrie's gaze shifted to where Gray stood in conversation with Jason. "I suppose. He is no longer angry, at least. Though I don't think he has altogether forgiven me."

"Give him time," Allison said.

Corrie nodded. What other choice did she have?

Her friend looked exceptionally pretty today, a bit too thin, but attractive with her very dark hair and high, carved cheekbones, elegant in a way Corrie had never really noticed before.

Derek did. As the afternoon progressed, he homed in on Allison, and Corrie saw the two of them sharing a plate on a blanket down by the river.

Her stomach twisted. What if Derek had been Laurel's lover? What if he had seduced and abandoned an innocent young woman, had perhaps been involved in her death and that of her infant son?

Was Allison in danger?

"You are frowning." Gray's deep voice reached her. She turned to see him walking up beside her. "What's wrong?"

"Nothing. I just . . ." She looked up at him. She wasn't sweet little Letty. She didn't have to pretend anymore. "I am worried about Allison. Derek seems to have taken an interest in her and there is a chance he was the man who fathered my sister's child. I don't want Allison getting hurt."

Corrie thought Gray would be angry. Instead, his dark gaze moved off toward the couple on the blanket.

"Derek has always enjoyed the company of a beautiful woman. Without her mobcap, your friend Allison has quite an arresting face. I'll speak to him, make certain he understands that the girl is family and therefore off-limits." He cast Corrie a glance. "I'll talk to Derek. I suggest you speak to your cousin."

She nodded, knowing he was right, though it might not do a bit of good. Derek was blond, handsome and charming. What woman wouldn't be attracted to him? Then again, perhaps Corrie was jumping to conclusions. "I shall. Thank you."

He reached out and touched her face, then turned and walked away.

She saw him again when he arrived to

escort her to supper. Filling their plates with all sorts of delicious treats, Gray seated her at a table that had been set up for the bride and groom.

The meal was delicious. When she had finished as much as she could possibly hold, she leaned back and sighed with contentment. The wine was as good as the food, and she drank a good bit, which made her notice the hot looks Gray began to cast her way. She yearned to slip off with him, to have him take her upstairs and make love to her.

Feeling a little bit wicked, she'd leaned over to suggest exactly that when a wave of dizziness hit her. Reeling a little, she sat back in her chair.

Gray's eyebrows drew together. "What is it? Are you feeling unwell?"

"No, I . . . I'm sure I am fine. I just . . ." Another round of dizziness hit her and she braced herself against the table. "I think I must have drunk too much wine."

He nodded. "I'll make our excuses and we'll go upstairs." His burning glance told her exactly what he had in mind once they got there. Corrie smiled as he made his way to Rebecca and Charles to express his thanks for the party and take his leave.

By the time he returned, Corrie was no

longer smiling. "I am feeling unwell, my lord. I am extremely sorry."

"It's all right. I've noticed you aren't much of a drinker." Helping her to her feet, he guided her back to the house. Thankfully, the company, many of them feeling the effects of the food and drink themselves, paid little heed to their leave-taking.

Unfortunately, by the time Corrie reached her suite, she was well and truly ill. Hurrying into her bedroom, she lost the contents of her stomach into a chamber pot. The world swirled around her and she fought not to be sick again. Catching sight of Gray walking toward her, she felt embarrassment war with misery.

"Here, drink this." He handed her a glass of water. She drank it, then used the towel he handed her to wipe the perspiration from her face.

"I — I didn't realize I had drunk all that much." She sat down in a chair, suddenly exhausted. "I'll be all right in a minute. I just . . . just need to rest for a while." Her eyes slid closed. She was asleep in an instant, leaning against the back of the chair.

Gray shook her shoulder, but she barely stirred.

"Coralee? Coralee, are you all right?"

She tried to nod, but her head lolled

sideways. All she could think of was sleeping. She couldn't remember ever being so tired.

"Dammit, Coralee, wake up!"

Gray shook her again and her eyes slowly opened. She stared up at him blearily. "I'm sorry . . . I'm just so . . . sleepy." Her lids drifted closed once more and she heard Gray curse.

Corrie moaned as he hauled her to her feet.

Gray examined her pupils, must have seen something that he did not like. "I don't think you drank too much." He tipped her chin up and looked into her heavy-lidded eyes. "I think someone drugged you." He shook her again and her eyes fluttered open. "Did you hear what I said? You've been drugged."

"Drugged . . . ?"

"Given a dose of opium. The drug acts this way when a person has too much. Someone must have doused your wine or your food with laudanum or something similar. If you go to sleep, odds are you won't wake up."

She roused herself a bit at that, forcing her head up, her heartbeat sluggish inside her chest. "Someone is trying to kill me?"

His jaw hardened to steel. "It isn't going

to happen." He settled her in the chair for a moment, strode over to the bellpull and gave it a single hard yank.

"On your feet," he said, hoisting her up again, forcing her eyes to open. "Sooner or later, the stuff will wear off. Until then, you have to stay awake."

"I — I don't think I can."

His hand was gentle on her cheek. "I'm going to help you, love. Just lean on me." And so she did, her body as limp as soggy bread, her feet barely willing to move round the floor.

She didn't remember exactly when Samir arrived in the bedroom, only dimly heard Gray speaking to him in a deep, worried voice.

"She's been given an overdose of opium," Gray said. "Can you do something to help her?"

Before her eyes closed again, she caught the little man's nod.

"I will do what I can. I will need time to mix the herbs."

"Do it as quickly as possible." As the dark-skinned Hindu shuffled away, Gray's grip on her tightened. "Let's go," he commanded, urging her to move again, holding her up as if she were an oversize rag doll.

She was so unbearably tired. She felt limp,

her body out of control. "Can't I just . . . can't I rest . . . just for a moment? I'll get back up . . . I . . . promise."

She started to sink down, but Gray hauled her erect. "Keep walking. I'm not letting you die, dammit."

And so she did. Walking and walking, her body leaden, her eyelids barely open. She wasn't sure how long they went on that way, Gray moving her around the floor, his hard body and firm arm all that kept her from sliding into a puddle at his feet.

"Come, love. Drink this." He held a glass to her lips and tipped it up, forcing her to swallow the bitter liquid Samir had brought. "Finish it." She did as he commanded, knowing he wouldn't allow her to refuse.

They walked some more, on and on, an endless march as the hours slipped past, the hands on the clock moving even more slowly than her legs. Eventually, little by little, she was able to hold her head up, able to lift her feet a little more easily. The hours continued toward morning, but still Gray did not give up. She knew he must be as exhausted as she, but he was relentless.

It was after four in the morning when she finally looked at the clock and the numbers were no longer blurry. "I need to sit down, Gray. I promise I won't fall asleep."

"Are you sure?"

She nodded, her eyes for the first time completely open.

Gray leaned over and kissed her forehead. "Sit for a while. I'll be right beside you."

He settled her on the settee in front of the hearth and sat down next to her, keeping an arm around her, watching for any sign she might slip into an unconscious slumber.

Corrie reached over and caught his wrist. "You saved my life tonight. If you hadn't been here —"

"I *was* here and that's what matters." He lifted her hand to his lips and placed a soft kiss in her palm. Then his jaw tightened and he glanced away. "I'm going to find out who did this. And when I do, the bastard is going to pay."

The sun was finally up when Gray put Coralee to bed. He left her maid sitting in a chair beside her, with instructions to awaken her every hour. If there was a problem, Anna was to find him immediately.

Even then, Gray worried. As he sat behind the desk in his private office and recalled what had happened, perspiration broke out on his forehead. What if he hadn't gone upstairs with her? What if he had been distracted and hadn't noticed her drug-induced state until it was too late?

Coralee might now be dead.

Gray's chest constricted at the thought of losing her. He told himself it was just that she was his wife and it was his responsibility to protect her. He reminded himself that he had failed Jillian and didn't want to fail again.

He was lying to himself and he knew it. Somehow, in the weeks Coralee had spent in his household, she had begun to reach him in a way no one ever had. She had told him she wanted to have his baby. *His.* As if no other man would do.

He didn't believe in love. He told himself he didn't love Coralee. And yet he would kill to protect her. He had known it the moment he had seen her in the bedroom, barely able to stay on her feet, vulnerable as he had rarely seen her.

As he headed downstairs, Gray thought of the way she had trusted him to take care of her, the way that trust had made him feel. Coralee was in danger — of that there was no doubt. But when he looked at her and felt the soft pulsing of his heart, he realized so was he.

"What on earth were you thinking? For God's sake, that was an idiotic, unbelievably stupid thing to do." Rebecca paced one way and then another, paused and looked out at the fountain at the rear of the garden.

"She needs to be stopped. Sooner or later, she's going to stumble onto someone who saw or heard something. She's going to put the bits and pieces together and figure out what happened to her sister that night."

Rebecca turned to face him. "You said we should do something that would warn her away, and I agreed, but I didn't agree to this."

The man sipped his brandy. "If it had worked, she would no longer be a threat."

"But it didn't work — and I am coming to believe you have lost sight of our goal."

They stood on the terrace. Just a polite conversation with a friend. They were safe, since Charles had gone into the village.

"It isn't Gray's wife we need to dispose of," Rebecca continued. "It is Tremaine himself. Once that distasteful bit of business is finished, Charles will be earl and I will be his countess. With the Tremaine fortune at my disposal, I shall be able to pay you the very sizable sum I promised."

The man swirled the brandy in his glass and took a drink. "Believe me, I haven't forgotten."

"What do you intend to do?"

He drained the snifter and set it down on a wrought-iron table near the balustrade. "I intend to do exactly as I agreed."

Rebecca eyed him with speculation. "You know, these attempts that were made on Gray's wife might actually work in our favor. If he were to die in an accident that appeared to be meant for her . . ."

For the first time, her companion smiled. "You are not only beautiful, but smart."

"Or better yet, both of them might perish."

He nodded. "Yes, that would be safer. I'll speak to Biggs, figure out how best to proceed. I believe you have hit on exactly the right solution."

Rebecca hoped so. For years she had run the earl's household, assumed the duties of countess with none of the respect or financial rewards. Now her place was being usurped by an interloper who had snared Tremaine through a web of deception, and sooner or later Rebecca would lose everything.

She was tired of being dependent on her brother-in-law's charity. Fortunately, the man at her side enjoyed living well and he was in need of money.

And he was tired of waiting, too.

■ ■ ■ ■

Corrie slept the entire next day and all through the night. She didn't go down for meals. Instead, Anna brought a tray up to her room.

Corrie wasn't in the mood to face Gray and his dark, worried glances, or listen to Rebecca discussing London gossip. She wasn't interested in Jason's flirtatious banter or what Derek might have to say about his afternoon with Allison. Only Charles's kindness would be missed. He had always been the one who seemed to ease the discord between her and Rebecca, to try to lighten the tension between her and Gray.

So far, none of them had been told the circumstances of her illness. She had decided to leave it to Gray whether or not to tell them. She knew he was doing his best to discover the culprit, and prayed he would succeed. Odds were the man had already committed a double murder, and so far he had gotten away with it. Corrie was his biggest threat.

A chill went through her.

Once she was dead, he would be safe.

As the afternoon progressed, she wrote a letter to her parents, leaving out mention of the attempts on her life, wrote a similar letter to Krista, then retrieved her journal from the trunk beneath her bed.

She never quite knew where to start, but it didn't matter. It was the writing itself that was important. She loved the play of words, loved to fashion them into interesting sentences. She loved writing her column for *Heart to Heart,* but her real ambition was to pen a novel.

She would, she vowed. Now that she was married, she would never get to travel as she had planned, but there were other things she could write about.

One day, she thought with an inward sigh.

Dipping the quill pen into the inkwell, she began to scratch out the dark events swirling around her: the secret panel and the conversation she'd overheard about Rebecca's baby, the broken cinch and the overdose of opium.

Corrie shuddered as she tried to think who might be guilty of the attempts on her life.

And what the man might do next to see her dead.

Twenty-Four

Corrie received a summons from her husband to appear in the study at three o'clock that afternoon. When she walked through the door, she saw Gray standing behind the desk, while his half brother, tall, blond Derek Stiles, stood on the opposite side next to Charles, who stood next to Jason. Along with the fair-haired men was Dolph Petersen.

"Coralee," Gray said, rounding the desk to join her. His gaze turned worried as he noticed she was still a little pale. "Are you feeling any better?"

"Much better, thank you." She didn't say more. She was hoping he would tell her the nature of the meeting, but instead, he simply seated her and returned to his place behind the desk. The others took seats in the same row of chairs lined up across from him.

"I appreciate all of you coming. As you

may know, my wife has been ill for the past few days. What you don't know is that someone tried to kill her."

"What?" That from Charles, who rose halfway out of his chair.

"Those are very strong charges," Jason said. "Are you certain, Gray?"

"Very certain. She was given an opium overdose sometime during our wedding celebration. When I was stationed in India, I saw the effects of the drug on several occasions. A man in my regiment died from a similar misuse of it."

"Perhaps it was some sort of accident," Charles suggested. "Somehow the drug got into her food by mistake."

"I might believe that . . . except this was the second attempt on her life."

Charles sat back in his chair, clearly shaken.

"Do you know who did it?" Derek asked, his jaw hard. He was the most hot-tempered of the Forsythe men.

"Not yet. I asked you here because I am hoping you might be able to help."

"Of course," Charles said. "Whatever you need us to do."

"Why would anyone want to kill Coralee?" Jason inquired, his tone still a little uncertain.

"From the time of her arrival at Castle Tremaine, my wife has been convinced that her sister was murdered. She has been trying to find the man who did it."

"I thought that matter was resolved," Charles said with some surprise. Like everyone in the household, he had assumed she had given up her quest after her true identity was revealed and she had been wed to Gray. "There was never any suggestion of foul play in Miss Whitmore's death," he added. "The authorities believe it was suicide."

"That is what I believed, as well," Gray said, "before the second attempt on Coralee's life. Now I think my wife is very likely correct. Dolph Petersen agrees."

Petersen turned in his chair, fixing his attention on the others. "I think this latest attempt speaks for itself. As long as the countess is alive, the villain is in danger of exposure. The penalty would surely be death."

Charles just sat there.

Jason and Derek seemed to ponder the notion.

The silence lengthened until Gray spoke again. "The reason I asked you here is because I need to know the truth. I would have sought each of you out in private, but

I believe the matter is too important. I also believe Coralee has the right to hear what you have to say."

Gray's dark gaze swept the room. "Jason has already addressed the matter. That leaves you, Charles, and you, Derek. Both of you were in residence during the months before Laurel Whitmore left for East Dereham, carrying an illegitimate child. What I want to know is if either of you was the father of that child."

Coralee sat forward in her chair. Since Charles couldn't father a child, it had to be Derek. She wondered if he would be man enough to admit the truth.

But it was Charles who spoke up, a gruff note in his voice. "It didn't happen the way you are thinking." He swallowed so hard his Adam's apple bobbed up and down. "I loved Laurel and she loved me. I never meant to see her hurt in any way."

It wasn't possible. Rebecca had said Charles couldn't father a child. Yet with one look at his pale, haggard expression, Corrie knew it was the truth.

Anger forced her out of her chair. "You're a married man, Charles! How could you seduce an innocent young woman? How could you do it?"

"I never meant for it to happen." His voice

was hoarse with emotion. "We came upon each other one morning while we were out riding. Laurel's horse had picked up a stone. I walked with her as she led the animal back to her house. We started chatting. She was so easy to talk to and we had so much in common." Tears welled in his eyes. "I rode to the same spot the following day, hoping I would see her again, and there she was. We talked and talked. It seemed as if there was so much to say. We started meeting whenever we could. I don't think either of us ever thought it would go further than friendship."

He shook his head and the tears in his eyes rolled down his cheeks. "And then one day it did."

He looked at Corrie, and there was so much pain in his face, her heart squeezed with pity.

"Your sister was the loveliest, kindest person I have ever known. I would have died in her place if I could have."

Corrie forced the pity away. "You abandoned her, Charles. You left her alone when she needed you most."

He stiffened. "I didn't know about the child. She never told me. She knew I was married. She didn't want my family to suffer for what we had done. She said she needed time to sort things out. I thought perhaps she was right." He swallowed. "I should have stopped her from leaving. If I had, she might still be alive." He started crying then, great sobs that shook his shoulders and were completely unlike him.

Corrie's heart went out to him. She had lost Laurel and grieved for her, as Charles must have done. She stood up and went to him, put her arms around his neck and simply held him. For a moment, Charles clung to her. "I'm sorry," he whispered, "so very very sorry."

Taking a deep breath, he straightened away from her, spoke to Gray and the rest of the men in the room. "I never meant to bring about such tragedy. Laurel and I . . . we never meant for anyone to get hurt."

Gray took control, allowing his brother to regain his composure, and Corrie sat back down.

"So you didn't know about the baby," he said.

Charles shook his head. "I only saw Laurel once after she came back from East Dereham."

"What happened?"

"It was just the way it was before. I still loved her and she still loved me. I told her I wanted to leave Rebecca and marry her."

Corrie's heart twisted. She should have known it was Charles her sister had loved. She should have realized Charles would have loved her in return.

"What did Laurel say?" Gray asked.

"She said I had to be sure it was what I wanted, be certain that it was the right thing to do. I told her making her my wife was exactly what I wanted. That I knew it was the right thing to do."

"Who besides Laurel knew what you intended?" Corrie asked.

"No one. It was only discussed between the two of us."

"So you never mentioned the possibility of divorce to your wife?"

Derek rose out of his chair. "Surely you aren't implying . . ."

"She didn't know," Charles said. "I was hoping to hear from Laurel, to meet with her again to finalize our plans. Instead, word came from the constable that she . . ." He swallowed and a fresh glaze of tears appeared in his eyes. "That she had drowned and there was a child." Charles squeezed his eyes closed and Corrie could feel his pain as if it were her own.

"No one is perfect," Gray said gently. "Your marriage to Rebecca was arranged when you were both children. You and

Laurel fell in love. Sometimes things just happen."

Jason spoke up just then. "It's clear Charles had nothing to do with Laurel Whitmore's death. He was in love with her. He would certainly do her no harm. It seems to me that if, as your wife is convinced, Laurel was murdered, she must have been the victim of a footpad or a thief from the village."

"Jason is right," Derek agreed. "During your wedding celebration, the entire village was present. The person who drugged Coralee could have been any one of a hundred different people."

"Do you know what Laurel was doing at the river that night?" Corrie asked Charles.

He shook his head. "She wasn't that far from Selkirk Hall. Perhaps she just wanted to think things through, clear her head. Perhaps she had decided to tell me about the baby, I don't know. The entire chain of events could be purely happenstance, a footpad coming upon her, a struggle and then . . ." He swallowed hard and glanced away.

"Whatever happened," Gray said, a fierce gleam coming into his eyes, "my wife is not going to become another victim. I'm going to find out who the killer is and stop him from doing it again."

At Gray's insistence, Corrie spent the week close to the house. Her visit to Selkirk Hall was postponed. Even on a long walk in the garden, Gray accompanied her. In the meantime, Dolph Petersen was staying at the Green Dragon Tavern, trying to dig up information in the village.

Corrie wondered if Greta would offer the hard-faced man comfort, and if so, whether he would accept her invitation. She wondered what new information he might be able to charm out of the woman if he did.

Rebecca had been told of the attempts on Corrie's life, but she was not completely convinced.

"It could just be some sort of coincidence, you know. Your cinch broke. Later you ate something that didn't agree with you and had some sort of reaction."

Corrie didn't argue. Rebecca's opinion didn't really matter. She'd been informed out of necessity, but she had not been made aware of Charles's involvement with Laurel.

Corrie had pondered whether or not to tell Gray about Rebecca's affair and the child she carried, but Corrie had no idea who Rebecca's lover might be, and it seemed to have no bearing on the matter at hand. Even if she told him, she wasn't completely sure Gray would believe her. With so much turmoil in the household, she finally decided keeping silent, at least for the present, would be best.

She was considering her decision when Charles approached her on the terrace after supper.

"I asked Gray if I might have a moment with you in private," he said, stepping out of the shadows into the light of the torches.

"What is it, Charles?"

"I wanted to speak to you about your sister. I wanted you to know how much I loved her, and how truly sorry I am for everything that's happened."

Corrie looked up at him. She could still see the lines of grief in his face. It must have taken immense control to hide it for so long. "I'm glad it was you," she said. "I am glad you were the man my sister fell in love with."

"Do you mean that?"

"You're a good man, Charles, no matter the circumstances of your relationship with Laurel."

His eyes misted. "She meant everything to me. Everything."

Corrie nodded. "Yes, I can see that."

"When you came here, I thought you were merely distraught, grief stricken, as I was, over her loss. Now . . . to discover Laurel truly might have been murdered . . . it is nearly unbearable."

"We'll find him. All of us working together . . . we'll find him."

Charles stared down at his feet, as if there was something of importance he wished to say, and was trying to find the courage to do so. "I never asked before. I suppose I couldn't bear to know. Was the child a boy or a girl?"

She felt a tug at her heart. "You had a son, Charles. Laurel named him Joshua Michael."

Charles's blue eyes filled with pain. "That was my best friend's name. He died of an influenza while we were at boarding school. Laurel knew how close we were, how often I thought of him." There was overwhelming sadness in Charles's face. "You're very brave. If I had been a more courageous man —"

"You didn't kill her, Charles. It wasn't your fault."

He didn't say more, just nodded as if trying to convince himself, then turned and walked away. He left her on the terrace staring after him, feeling his pain and grief.

Gray joined her a few moments later. "My brother is a good man."

"Yes, he is."

"Then you no longer believe he had any part in your sister's death?"

"No. I just wish the information he gave us could have been more useful."

A muscle tightened in Gray's cheek. "So do I."

It was several days later when Dolph Petersen returned to the house. Unfortunately, Corrie wasn't invited to join him and Gray in their closed-door meeting in Gray's private office.

Still, she couldn't resist a bit of eavesdropping. As soon as the men were inside, she hurried over to the door and pressed her ear against it. She was surprised to hear them discussing the Countess of Devane and her upcoming costume ball.

"I think the two of you should go," Dolph was saying.

"Are you insane? You saw what happened at the last affair Coralee attended."

"This time we'll have men both inside and outside the house. Your wife will be completely protected."

"No. It's out of the question."

"If you don't find this man, Gray, sooner or later he is going to succeed. You need to catch him before he does, and unless you have a better idea, we are going to have to draw him out."

"With my wife as bait. The answer is no."

Corrie opened the door and walked into the office. "I am sorry to intrude, my lord, but Mr. Petersen is right. I can't live like a prisoner forever. Presently, I can't go riding, can't visit my family. I can't even walk out to the garden. I won't go on this way. I simply will not."

"Since you were eavesdropping, you heard what I said. It's just too dangerous."

"So is not finding him."

Gray blew out a breath. For several long moments, he said nothing. Then he turned a hard look on Dolph. "Fine, we'll do it your way. But if anything goes wrong —"

"Nothing is going to go wrong. We won't let it. If our theory is correct, the culprit is someone from the village. That means he will not be among the guests, but someone hired by the countess's staff to help with preparations for the ball."

"Which means it could be a footman or a groom or a housemaid. Bloody hell, it could be the cook!"

"As I said, we'll be careful. And you will be with your wife the entire duration of the ball."

Gray cast a firm look Corrie's way. "You

may be certain of that."

Still, it was obvious he was worried. She knew he felt guilty for the death of his first wife. He was determined it wouldn't happen again. Certainly it wasn't because he held any special feelings for Corrie herself. Since Charles had confessed his deep love for Laurel, Gray had been more remote than ever. Even his desire seemed to have waned.

On the occasions they did make love, his passion was carefully controlled. He used his skills to pleasure her and himself, but his emotions remained locked away.

Only the concern she saw in his eyes gave her the faintest degree of hope.

TWENTY-FIVE

The plans were set, arrangements made. Dolph brought men in from London, a small army of protectors. Though the footmen and serving staff would be wearing Lady Devane's pale blue livery, Petersen's men, dressed in simple peasant garments, were meant to go unnoticed among the stable hands and grooms outside, the belowstairs servants working behind the scenes in the house.

So many extra people had been hired for the occasion the men should be able to mingle without being noticed. It gave Corrie some comfort, but still she was worried.

So was Gray, she knew, though she hadn't seen him since earlier in the day. He was checking things over, making last minute changes, doing everything in his power to insure she would be safe. Charles, Jason and Derek all knew the plan and had agreed to watch for anything that might look suspicious.

By seven o'clock that evening, their whole party was costumed and ready to depart in the carriages that would take them to Parkside. All but Corrie, who was a little late getting dressed.

"Are you certain, my lady?" Anna was looking at her worriedly. "You said you planned to dress as Julia Augusta, the empress of Rome."

She had meant to. She had worn the slim white robes and gold sandals at a ball in London, and had found the costume in one of her trunks. "I changed my mind."

"But surely the wife of an earl —"

"I am going as a country maid. What is wrong with that?"

Anna bit her lip. "Why . . . nothing, my lady."

But gowned in worn apricot muslin and a simple straw bonnet, she didn't really look like anyone but Letty Moss — which was exactly her intent. She had no idea where the notion had come from, but once it stole into her head, she couldn't make it go away.

She had no idea what Gray would be wearing, no idea what his reaction would be when he saw her. Perhaps that was the reason she was so determined to go through with it.

She left Anna in the bedroom and headed down the hall to the stairs, her simple muslin skirts and ruffled petticoats whispering against her legs. When she reached the top of the steps, she paused.

Standing at the bottom of the staircase was the handsomest man she had ever seen, and her heart began to throb. He was tall and broad-shouldered, dressed in tight black riding breeches tucked into knee-high black boots, and a full-sleeved, white lawn shirt. His hair was in a queue. A mask of black silk hid the top half of his face, covering all but his intense dark eyes.

He was costumed as a highwayman, the man she had imagined him to be the day she had first seen him.

The man she had fallen in love with.

Her knees felt weak when he looked up to find her standing at the top of the stairs. She wondered if he would be angry at the clothes she had chosen, but instead, the edge of his mouth faintly curved. He waited in silence as she made her way toward him, then took her hand as she stepped down from the bottom stair.

"I believe we have met somewhere before," he said, making her a sweeping bow.

"Mrs. Moss," she said. "Letty Moss, my lord."

Through the holes in his mask, his dark eyes glinted, seemed to drink her in. Did she really look so different? Or was it just the memory of the woman she had been that softened his gaze when he looked at her?

"I believe our party is waiting," he said. "Shall we, Mrs. Moss?" Extending his arm, he led her out to the row of carriages lined up in front of the house. The others were already there, and at their appearance, began to climb aboard the coaches. Petersen's men rode front and back, and armed men posed as footmen at the rear of each carriage.

Inside the coaches, the entire party was costumed, Rebecca garbed as Marie Antoinette in a blue satin gown encrusted with brilliants and decorated with ropes of gold. Her skirt was wide, draped over a wire-mesh farthingale, the fashion of that day, and she wore a tall silver wig also laced with gold.

Charles was garbed as the French king, Louis. Jason wore a red hunting jacket and cap and looked as if he intended to ride to the hounds, and Derek was a pirate with a gold earring in his ear, a patch over one eye and a sword belted at his waist.

All of them were dressed for the ball and ready for the evening ahead, and yet there was an unmistakable tension among the men. They were acting as Corrie's guardians.

She didn't believe they would shirk their duties tonight.

It took the better part of an hour for the party to reach the next village and find its way to Parkside, Lady Devane's magnificent Georgian estate. As their carriages pulled up in front, Corrie noticed the glow of lamplight in every room of the house. A half-dozen liveried footmen rushed to assist the guests up the red velvet carpet into the foyer of the mansion.

"I want you to stay close to me," Gray said. "No wandering off on your own."

She nodded absently, caught up in the pomp and extravagance of the event. She was carrying a feathered mask on the end of a stick. She held it over her face and peered through it at her surroundings.

Gray caught her chin, forcing her to look at him. "Promise me."

"I promise."

"If you see anything, notice anything, I want you to let me know."

"I'm not a fool, Gray."

His mouth edged up. "No. You've never

been a fool." He took her hand and rested it on his arm, and they made their way toward the receiving line.

Gowned as the goddess Diana, Lady Devane stood in the foyer. Her gaze sharpened on Gray. "Darling — it's good to see you. I'm so happy you and —" She broke off in surprise at the sight of Corrie's simple clothes. "I'm so happy you and your *wife* could attend."

Gray just smiled. "I'm sure we're going to enjoy the evening." He urged Corrie inside, leaving the countess staring after them, stanching whatever vitriolic words she might have said.

The decorations were lavish, the mansion made to look like an ancient Greek city, with white-painted columns scattered about and ivy draping the walls. It was clear the countess had spared no expense. A ten-piece orchestra, the musicians garbed in white togas, began to play, and Gray led Corrie toward the sound as the strains of a waltz drifted to them.

"Would you like to dance?"

She looked up at him in surprise. She had never danced with her husband. It seemed odd, and yet, knowing Gray, she was surprised he would ask.

She smiled at him with delight. "I would

love to dance with you, my lord."

His eyes ran over her face, came to rest on her lips, and a soft warmth spread through her. He settled a hand at her waist, led her onto the dance floor, and she followed him in the steps of the waltz.

He danced with the same grace she had noticed when he rode his horse, and though he was a great deal taller, they moved easily together, their rhythm well matched. Beneath her hand, she could feel the hard muscles in his shoulder and when she caught the faint scent of sandalwood, desire flared. Gray must have sensed it, for when she looked up at him, heat was there in his eyes.

She caught that same look off and on through the evening. Though he kept a close watch over her, the night was filled with subtle touches and hot, burning glances. A little after midnight, the rest of their party joined them as they went in to the long gallery to enjoy the lavish supper set out for the guests.

"Seen anything?" Gray asked Jason.

"Not a thing."

"Derek?"

He shook his head, moving the shiny gold hoop in his ear. "I almost wish I had."

Gray's jaw flexed. "I'd like to put my

hands around the bastard's neck and squeeze the life out of him."

Corrie shivered and Gray's expression softened. "Sorry, love. I didn't mean to sound so bloodthirsty."

But she was sure he meant every word.

They dined on pheasant and lobster, served buffet style, which meant the food would be safe for her to eat. They enjoyed champagne from a communal fountain, though none of them drank very much.

As the evening progressed, Corrie began to relax. She didn't think the man they searched for was here. Perhaps he couldn't find a way in, or simply wasn't ready to try again so soon. Some of Gray's tension eased as he came to the same conclusion, and each of his glances seemed to burn hotter than the last. In his highwayman's costume, he was the most handsome man in the room, and Corrie felt the pull of attraction, the surge of love for him that she had felt that night in the storm.

They were standing near the staircase, taking a momentary break from the dancing, when she leaned toward him. "I want you to make love to me."

Surprise appeared on his face. "You don't mean here? Now?"

She cast him a wicked glance. "There are

so many people. Surely we can disappear somewhere for a little while without being missed."

His eyes turned the color of jet and a fire seemed to burn inside them. He hadn't looked at her quite that way since the night of the storm.

Grasping her hand, darting a glance both ways, he led her up the sweeping stairs. A few guests were paired off together in the hallway, some she recognized, enjoying trysts of their own. Gray led her past them to the end of the corridor, to another hallway that was completely empty. He opened a door, checked to be sure the room was unoccupied, then hauled her inside and turned the lock.

Corrie reached up and pulled the ties of his black silk mask. "Kiss me."

Gray's gaze turned fierce. He took the feathered mask from her hand and dragged her mouth up to his for a deep, burning kiss.

"I want you," he said, kissing her until she was nearly too weak to stand.

She tugged at the black velvet ribbon tying back his hair, freeing the long black strands. "I want you, too. I want you the way you were that night in the storm."

He reached out and cupped her cheek. "How was I that night?"

411

Corrie's eyes filled with unexpected tears. "You were fierce and you were tender. You were the man of my dreams."

Gray's chest tightened. For long moments, he just stood there, staring down at the woman he desired above all others. "Sweet God, Coralee."

His hands shook as he reached for her, pulled her into his arms. She looked so beautiful tonight, so artless and sincere. And he wanted her so damn badly. Cradling her face in his hands, he kissed her, softly at first, then more deeply. A force burned inside him and the kisses turned wilder, hotter, became a fierce plundering that seemed to have no end.

For weeks he had held himself back, forced himself to keep his distance even when they were in bed. He knew their lovemaking had been different than before; he had purposely made it so by keeping himself under tight control. But he hadn't understood that his wife felt that difference, too. That she had been as dissatisfied as he.

Now her softly spoken words and the yearning in her eyes reached him as nothing else could have. Inside his chest, his heart squeezed and his breathing turned harsh. He felt shaken, completely off balance, as if he could no longer ignore his fate.

As if he no longer wanted to.

Grasping her shoulders, he ravished her mouth, drove his tongue inside to claim the sweetness within, kissed her the way he hadn't allowed himself to do since before their return that morning after the storm. He gazed down at her, thought how much he wanted her, how much he had come to need her.

Taking her lips in another burning kiss, he drank in the taste of her, inhaled her soft rose scent until his body ached and demanded release.

Backing her against the wall, he lifted her skirts, found the slit in her drawers and began to stroke her. She was wet and ready, her need as fierce as his own.

"We haven't much time," he said against her mouth, nibbling the corners before he kissed her again.

"We don't need much time," she said breathlessly, reaching out to unbutton the front of his breeches. Gray helped her free his erection, lifted her against the wall and wrapped her legs around his waist. He plunged himself deep inside her, felt her hands in his hair and heard her soft moan of pleasure.

Again and again, he drove into her, completely out of control. He no longer cared. This was what he wanted, what he needed from the woman in his arms, this unleashed passion that was so different from the practiced lovemaking they had shared since their wedding. A hot, wild consummation he hadn't known since that night in the storm.

"I need you," he said, driving into her again. "I've never wanted a woman so badly."

"Gray . . ." She kissed him as if she couldn't get enough, slid her small tongue into his mouth.

A deep groan rose from inside him. He tried to hold on, told himself it was too soon, but when he felt her passage tighten around him, felt the first sweet ripples of contraction, he couldn't hold back any longer. A powerful climax hit him, shook his body and tightened his muscles until he clenched his teeth to hold back a primal scream.

"Letty . . ." he groaned, driving into her one last time, holding her tightly against him. "My sweetest love . . ."

Gray felt her stiffen. She drew away from him, dragged in a shaky breath and struggled to get free.

It was then he realized she was trembling,

fighting not to cry. Easing her legs from around his waist, he set her back on her feet.

"What is it, sweeting? Did I hurt you?"

She looked up at him and tears rolled down her cheeks. "You hurt me, Gray. You broke my heart." And then she turned, twisted the key in the lock and ran out of the room, slamming the door behind her.

For an instant, Gray just stood there, completely stunned. What in God's name had he done?

You called her Letty, you fool.

The name had just slipped out; he had no idea why. Surely it wasn't so important.

Whatever had occurred, his wife was under his protection and he had to find her.

Hurriedly rebuttoning his breeches, he ran out of the room and down the hall. Coralee was nowhere to be seen. At the bottom of the stairs, he spotted Charles next to Jason and ran toward them.

"Have you seen Coralee? She was with me and now I can't find her."

"We'll help you look for her," Jason said. "I'll go upstairs. You two search down here."

"We've got to find her!" Gray exclaimed. "There's no telling what might happen if we don't."

His brother must have read the panic in his face. Charles caught his arm to steady him. "We'll find her. We'll get Derek to help us."

But they had only begun to search when Coralee walked up to Gray as if she had returned from an afternoon stroll. She looked shaken and pale, and his heart squeezed inside him. Worry turned to anger.

"For God's sake, Coralee, where the hell have you been? You scared me to death."

She drew a shaky breath, her face even paler. Her expression tore at his heart. "I'm afraid I'm not feeling very well, my lord. I would like to go home."

Concern shot through him. "Are you ill? Has something happened?"

"It's nothing like that. I just . . . I want to go home."

"All right. Yes, that's a good idea." He took her with him to retrieve her cloak, made his farewells to his brothers, Rebecca and Jason, and the two of them left the house. The guards fell into their places around the carriage as the couple climbed inside.

All the way back to Castle Tremaine, Gray watched Coralee, but she made no mention of what had happened in the room upstairs.

Perhaps he had injured her in his furious, unrestrained lovemaking.

"Tell me what I did," he said as the carriage rumbled through the darkness. "If it was the way we made love —"

She shook her head. "You were wonderful. You were exactly the man I remembered." But when she gazed up at him, fresh tears gathered in her eyes.

"Tell me."

"You were just as I remembered. But I am not Letty and I never will be." And she said no more, not even when they retired upstairs to his suite, not until she told him she wanted to sleep in her own bed that night.

Gray let her. Inside his chest, an ache had formed around his heart. She had dressed as Letty and he had called her that. He didn't understand why the name had hurt her so badly. And he had no idea how to repair the damage he had done.

Whatever it took, he would fix it, he told himself. He would apologize and make things right.

But in the morning, when he asked her maid if she was feeling better, he discovered Coralee was gone.

TWENTY-SIX

London teemed with activity as the sleek black carriage rolled through the crowded streets. Corrie had forgotten how noisy the city was, how sooty the air. She had traveled all day, hoping to reach London before nightfall, but darkness had settled in an hour ago.

She sighed as she leaned back against the velvet seat. When she had left the castle early that morning, all she could think of was getting away from Gray and the hurt she had suffered. On the long journey, she'd had time to ponder what she should do once she got back to the city.

Gray had a town house in London. As the Countess of Tremaine, she would certainly have the right to use it, but Gray might come after her. He was, after all, a very protective man. Whatever his feelings for her, she was his wife and he would feel responsible.

Corrie wasn't ready to face him.

By leaving the country, she would likely be in far less danger. But there was always a chance she might be followed, and the only place she would truly feel safe was with Krista and Leif. Corrie hated to ask them for help, but she needed her best friend's advice, and she knew with Leif and Thor close by, she wouldn't have to be afraid.

It was after supper when the coach pulled up in front of the Draugr's two-story brick town house. Corrie climbed the steep front steps and knocked.

The butler opened the door. "May I help you, madam?"

She managed to smile. "You may remember me . . . Coralee Whitmore? I am now the Countess of Tremaine."

"Why, of course, my lady. Please do come in." He was a middle-aged man whose hair was turning gray. Simmons was his name, she recalled.

"If you will please follow me into the drawing room, I will tell Mr. and Mrs. Draugr that you are arrived."

"Thank you." She followed the butler into a salon done in red and gold, with fringed lamps on small ornate tables, shelves filled with an astonishing amount of bric-a-brac, and bins that held a number of London weekly magazines.

It was decorated in the latest Victorian fashion, probably furnished by someone other than Krista, who was always too busy to worry about such things.

As Corrie stood in her best friend's home, she realized that she was nervous. For an instant, she wished she hadn't come.

Then Krista came striding into the room on those long legs of hers and pulled her into a warm, comforting hug. Corrie clung to her, grateful for their enduring friendship, and fought not to cry. Krista must have felt her tremble, for she eased a little away.

"Coralee, what on earth has happened?"

Across the room, Leif stood in the doorway. Corrie caught a quick glimpse of Thor's tall dark figure just before Leif closed the drawing room doors, giving them the privacy he must have sensed they needed.

"Is it the earl?" Krista asked, leading her over to the sofa, where both of them took a seat. "He hasn't hurt you, has he? If he has —"

"He hasn't hurt me. Not in the way you mean."

Krista reached out and caught her hand. "Tell me, dearest. What has happened that has made you leave your husband?"

For the next half hour, Coralee told her friend about Gray and how deeply she had fallen in love with him. How, after they were married, she had tried to convince herself he was no longer the man she had believed him to be and that she no longer felt as she had before. How she had finally admitted the truth.

"I love him so much," she said, accepting the handkerchief Krista handed her to wipe the tears from her cheeks. "He's a hard man, but he can be gentle. Gray is intelligent and loyal. He is lonely and in so much need of love. He touches me and I . . ." She glanced away, blushing at the thought of what Gray could do with a single kiss or the touch of his talented hands.

She took a shaky breath. "The problem is he is not in love with me. He is in love with a woman who doesn't exist. He is in love with Letty Moss."

"Oh, Coralee . . ."

"It is true, Krista." Corrie next told her friend about how it had been before they were married. Krista listened patiently, though it was clear she wasn't completely convinced.

Not even when Corrie told her about the night they had gone to the costume ball. "For the first time since our wedding, he let down his guard and made love to me as if he truly cared. Then he called me . . . Letty, his *sweetest love*."

Krista squeezed her hand. "That is not so hard to understand. You said you were dressed as Letty. Perhaps, for a moment, he was confused."

"I'm sure he was. I'm also sure he was wishing Letty Moss was truly there instead of me."

They talked for several hours, Leif kind enough to leave them alone. Then a brisk knock sounded and Krista's huge blond husband slid open the drawing room doors.

"Ladies, I am sorry to interrupt. But Coralee, your husband is here, and if I do not let him in to see you, he and Thor will soon be brawling in the entry."

Corrie came up off the sofa. She had thought Gray would follow her. He would feel obliged to protect her. But she didn't think he would arrive in the middle of the night!

The door slid open farther and Gray strode into the drawing room. He was dressed in his riding breeches and high black boots, both of which were mud-spattered and wrinkled. His black hair was tied back, but strands fell loose around his shoulders as if the wind had torn them free.

It was clear he had ridden hard to make up for the head start she'd had before he discovered her gone.

She ignored a little thrill that he had come so quickly, told herself he was merely doing what he felt was his duty.

Gray stood in front of her, his dark eyes blazing. "What the bloody hell are you doing in London?"

So much for his concern.

"I needed some time to think. This is the only place I could imagine where I would be able to do it."

"What about the danger, Coralee? Did you give any thought to what might happen to you when you took off on your own?" Before she could answer, Gray turned to Leif and Thor, who stood behind them, long legs splayed as if they were prepared to do battle. "Has she told you her life is in danger? Did my hotheaded little wife happen to mention that twice she has nearly been killed?"

Leif frowned, his golden eyebrows drawing together. "You should have told us, Coralee."

Thor pinned her with a disapproving glare. "If this is so, you should not have gone off by yourself. But you need have no fear. We will make sure you are safe."

Leif's blue eyes fixed on Gray. "Why does someone wish to kill Coralee?"

"Because of her damnable determination to find the man who murdered her sister."

Krista's head came up in shock. "I thought you were through with all of that, Coralee!"

"Tell them, Gray. Tell them I was right — that Laurel was murdered."

"I imagine it's true, though we've yet to find proof. The fact that someone wants Coralee dead gives credence to the theory. Dolph Petersen has continued his investigation and he believes it is so." Gray returned his angry gaze to her. "And the last thing you need to do is run off by yourself without the least protection!"

He stalked toward her. Corrie backed up until her shoulders brushed the red flocked wallpaper.

"Enough of this foolishness. You're coming home with me. I am not about to leave you here."

"I'm not going with you, Gray. Krista says I am welcome to stay, and that is what I'm going to do."

"I'm not giving you a choice!" Reaching out, he caught her arm and started hauling her across the room toward the door.

Thor stepped in his way. "Your wife does not wish to leave."

"I told you, her life is in danger. I'm her husband. It's my duty to keep her safe."

"Coralee will be safe here, with my brother and me."

Corrie felt a swell of affection for the handsome, dark-haired Norseman. In the months after Krista's wedding, Corrie and Thor had become friends of a sort, though much of the time he had been at Heartland with Professor Hart, studying the English language and customs.

Corrie had come to like him very much, and he seemed to like her. On top of that, she was Krista's friend and therefore part of his extended family. Like Leif, Thor was very protective of his family and friends.

"I'm not leaving without her," Gray said, ready to go head-to-head with Thor, who was at least four inches taller and a good deal heavier than he.

Corrie stepped between them. "I need some time, Gray."

"You're my wife, Coralee."

"I'm your wife, but you don't love me. I need some time to come to terms with that."

His mouth opened, but no words came out. She could read the turbulence in his expression, the responsibility he felt to keep her safe. But he wasn't a liar, which left him with nothing to say.

"These men are warriors," Corrie continued, tamping down her disappointment. "Surely you can see I'll be safe as long as I am with them."

"You belong with me."

"I'm not ready to leave."

He turned away, paced across the drawing room and back. "I don't like this — not one bit."

"I'm staying, Gray."

He turned, fixed a hard look on Thor. "If I leave her in your care, do you swear to keep her safe?"

"I give you my word as a warrior."

Gray would accept that. "And do you also give me your word that you will treat her with the respect she deserves as my wife, and make no advances toward her?"

The edge of Thor's mouth curved. "She is beautiful, but she is yours."

Gray turned to Coralee. "I'll be here tomorrow. There are things that need to be said."

She wondered what he could possibly have to say and tried not to be hopeful. "All right."

Gray started for the door, stopped and strode back. He hauled her into his arms and very thoroughly kissed her. It was a fierce, possessive kiss, and by the time he let her go, her knees were weak.

"I'll be back," he said gruffly, and then he was gone.

Corrie just stood there, blushing furiously at his outrageous behavior.

Krista walked up beside her. "I'm sorry, Coralee, but I don't believe a man who kisses a woman that way doesn't love her."

A lump rose in her throat. "Gray doesn't know how to love."

Krista looked up at her handsome blond giant of a husband, a man who had come to London unable even to speak the language. He'd known nothing of English customs and had no idea how he was going to earn a living. Today, he was married to the grand-daughter of an earl, was the father of an eight-month-old son and the owner of a successful shipping firm.

Krista just smiled. "It's amazing what a man can learn."

Gray lay awake well past midnight, trying unsuccessfully to read himself to sleep.

He was surprised when a light knock sounded and the door swung open. Samir moved so quietly across the bedroom, he seemed to appear by magic. "I traveled quickly. I thought you might have need of me."

The man was amazingly intuitive. "Thank you for coming, Samir. I had only planned to stay one night and return with my wife on the morrow. It doesn't appear that is going to happen."

"She refuses to come back with you?"

He nodded. "She's a woman. She is behaving exactly like one."

"And yet you do not force her, as you could."

Gray sighed into the quiet. "She says she needs time. Considering all she's been through, I didn't think it was too much to ask."

"She loves you."

He glanced away. He didn't even know what love was. His mother had loved him, but that had been so long ago, he didn't really remember. And yet when Samir said the words, Gray's heart swelled with hope that it was true.

"You must show her you have feelings for her, as well."

Gray shook his head. "I wouldn't begin to know how."

"You could tell her the way you feel."

"I won't lie to her. It wouldn't be fair."

"That is so, but also do not lie to yourself."

Gray said nothing. Whatever he felt for Coralee was unlike anything he had felt for a woman before. Was it love? He scoffed. He wasn't the kind of man who loved.

"If you cannot find the words to tell her, you must show her. Your woman has never been . . . what do you English call seducing a woman with gifts and small pleasures?"

He smiled. "Courting."

"This you must do."

"I'm worried about keeping her alive, Samir. I hardly have time to pay her court." •

The little Hindu shrugged his thin shoulders. "That is for you to decide."

But by morning, Gray had come to the conclusion that Samir, as usual, was right. First he wrote to Charles, Jason and Derek to tell them he would be staying in London for at least a week. He knew they would be worried, would be on their way to join him if they didn't get word. Instead, he asked them to stay in the country and continue working with Dolph to find the man who had threatened Coralee's life.

His next piece of business was a stop at the florist shop. There he ordered half a dozen bouquets of yellow roses and had them sent to the Draugr's town house, then bought a bouquet of red roses to take with him.

The soft scent reminded him of Coralee, and he held them to his nose as he finished his shopping and made his way toward the residence where she was staying. He wasn't sure what he would say, how he was going to get his wife back, but he knew he wanted her home. She belonged in his house, in his bed.

And Gray was a man who went after what he wanted.

Corrie made her way downstairs to join Krista in the breakfast room and found the entry filled with yellow roses. More sat in vases in the drawing room, and when she went in to breakfast, a vase of red roses graced the middle of the table.

Leif's deep voice reached her from his place at the head of the table. "It is clear your husband cares for you more than you believe."

Her heart stumbled. Was it possible?

"Gray sent . . . sent all of these?" She indicated the other bouquets spread throughout the house.

"I looked at one of the cards," Krista said, smiling. "I was dying of curiosity."

"But he isn't the type of man who would send a woman flowers."

"Apparently, he is," her friend said smugly. "And as I recall, roses are your favorite."

"He couldn't possibly know that."

Thor scoffed. "You smell like roses. Any man would know." With his thick black hair neatly trimmed, if a little long over his collar; with his square jaw and incredible blue eyes, he was one of the handsomest men Corrie had ever seen.

But it was Gray who drew her, Gray she loved.

As they breakfasted on eggs and sausage, Corrie told them about the attempts that had been made on her life, and their efforts to catch the man who might still want her dead.

"We tried to draw him out at the Countess of Devane's costume ball. It didn't work, but the party was quite spectacular." She took a sip of her tea. "I, um, thought I might write an article about it for the next edition of the gazette."

Krista uttered a small yelp of glee. She came out of her chair, hurried over and hugged her. "Oh, Coralee, that would be wonderful. Lindsey is doing a marvelous job, but she's working extremely hard. The article would give her a bit of a break."

Thor made a sound in his throat. "The woman needs more than a break. She needs a man who will take her in hand."

Krista rolled her eyes. "They fight like

children. I don't know why they can't get along."

"She doesn't know her place," he grumbled.

"And you are still living in the sixteenth century, Thor Draugr."

He didn't bother to argue. He had arrived with his brother from an island far to the north of Scotland, a place not found on any seaman's map. They had lived there in the same manner their Viking ancestors had been doing for more than three hundred years.

It was only by chance that Corrie and Krista had come upon Leif, who had survived a shipwreck and been washed up on English shores, and the pair had helped him escape the men who had taken him prisoner. Krista's father, Sir Paxton Hart, had helped him make a new life here in London, and during that time she and Leif had fallen in love.

Thor had eventually joined his brother in England, and Sir Paxton was schooling him and helping him become a gentleman — no easy job for Thor. For the moment, he was working at *Heart to Heart,* but he was also working with his brother in the shipping trade.

The butler appeared in the doorway, his

attention focused on Corrie. "I am sorry to bother you, Lady Tremaine, but your husband —"

"Needs a word with you," said Gray as he walked into the breakfast room. "I'm sorry to intrude," he said to the others, not looking sorry at all, "but I need to speak to my wife." Seeing that her plate was nearly empty, he urged her up out of her chair. "If you will all excuse us . . ."

It was more a command than a request. He was, after all, the Earl of Tremaine and used to getting his way.

"Of course," Krista said diplomatically, while Thor looked daggers at Gray.

Corrie didn't protest. She wanted to hear what he had to say. "Excuse us," she repeated, and let him lead her toward the door of the breakfast room.

"He reminds me of someone I know," Krista whispered to Leif as the two walked out into the hallway.

Her husband just grunted.

As Corrie entered the drawing room, Gray tossed a look back over his shoulder. "The Draugr brothers are quite unusual. I imagine they have an interesting story. Perhaps in time you will tell me."

"Perhaps." But at the moment, there were other things she wished to discuss. She led him over to the sofa and both of them sat down. "Thank you for the flowers. I was surprised you would send them."

He glanced away. "I've watched you in the garden. I thought you would like them."

"Roses are my favorite."

His mouth edged up. "I guessed."

So he *had* noticed her perfume. "So what did you want to talk to me about?"

Gray met her gaze squarely. "Letty Moss."

Corrie tried not to wince. Gray had always been direct. "What . . . what about her?"

"Why did my saying her name upset you so much?"

She glanced down, plucked at a fold in her skirt. "Because it's always been Letty you wanted. Always her and not me. I had hoped that would change, but obviously it hasn't."

Gray caught her hand. His fingers felt warm around hers and his gaze was intense on her face. "Letty Moss was a woman I wanted to bed. I would never have married her."

"You wouldn't?"

"No."

"Because of her social status? I didn't think you were the sort of man who would be concerned."

"It wasn't *who* she was. It was who she

434

wasn't. The Letty you portrayed would have satisfied me in bed, but nothing more. I need a woman who's intelligent and interesting, one who is loyal and steadfast, a woman I can count on. I need a woman who isn't afraid to stand up to me. I know I am not an easy man."

She smiled. "No, you are stubborn and difficult. You're possessive and far too domineering."

He grinned. "But I am extremely skillful in bed."

Corrie blushed. "Yes, you are, you rogue, though I like you better when you let down your guard and allow your feelings to show."

"I like you better that way, too."

"You could tell?"

He brought her hand to his lips and pressed a kiss into her palm. She could feel the heat all the way to her toes.

"Come home with me, Coralee. We'll start over, get to know each other as we should have done before."

Hope soared inside her. And yet she didn't quite trust him. "Give me a little more time."

"Dammit, Coralee."

"Please, Gray."

"I want you in my bed. Just sitting here, I find it's all I can do to keep my hands off you." As if it were true, one of his hands unconsciously fisted.

"I want to go with you, Gray — you'll never know how much. But I'm just not ready yet."

He studied her face. "You're that determined?"

"I need this, Gray."

He nodded. "All right, I'll give you the time you need on one condition."

"What is that?"

He smiled, making him look so handsome her breath caught. "You agree to go for a carriage ride with me this afternoon."

Pleasure moved through her, along with a hint of worry. "Do you think it's safe?"

"I won't come alone. I'll have at least two men with me."

She nodded. "Then I would love to go for a carriage ride with you."

Gray leaned over and kissed her. What started as a gentle brush of lips turned into a deep, openmouthed, soul-bending kiss that left both of them breathless and wanting.

"I'll see you at four," he said gruffly, rising to take his leave.

As she watched him walk out the door, Corrie thought how much her husband had surprised her. He was giving her the time she wanted. She hadn't believed her wishes were important to him.

I want you back in my bed, he had said. But she needed to be certain she was the woman he truly wanted, and not a phantom who had never existed.

As she recalled the events of the past two days, it occurred to her that Gray might not love her, but it appeared he cared more than she had believed.

Corrie clung to that hope as she headed upstairs to begin her article on the costume ball at Lady Devane's.

TWENTY-SEVEN

As he did each afternoon, Gray took Corrie for a carriage ride round the city. He was attentive as she had rarely seen him, taking her shopping, buying her gifts and sweets. He refused to buy her perfume except for the rose fragrance she usually wore, and somehow she found that charming. It felt wonderful to be with him, to enjoy the attention he lavished upon her.

It worried her only a little that she was falling even more in love with him. He was her husband. If she wanted her marriage to work, loving him was a risk she would have to take.

Gray came in the afternoons, but in the mornings before he arrived, while Leif went to work at his company, Valhalla Shipping, Thor would accompany her and Krista to *Heart to Heart.* Corrie finished the article on the countess's costume ball, refraining with only a bit of difficulty from hinting at the names of the people involved in the trysts she had stumbled upon upstairs. Then she wrote a piece on the joys of living in the country — something she never would have imagined until she journeyed to Castle Tremaine.

Though she enjoyed working again, it occurred to her that she had changed in the months she'd been gone. She was no longer as fascinated with society and the social whirl as she had once been, and because of Gray, she now knew the damage unfounded gossip could cause.

As always, it was fun working with Krista, and interesting to watch Thor and Lindsey Graham, the school chum who had taken over Corrie's job. Lindsey and Thor studiously avoided each other, as if neither could stand to be in the same room.

Lindsey, slender, with honey-brown hair and tawny eyes, was energetic and dynamic, a woman who clearly had goals and ambitions. Thor believed a woman's place was in the home — skinning furs, Corrie imagined, weaving or winnowing wheat.

And yet there was a certain sizzle in the air between them whenever they were accidentally forced together.

Interesting, she thought as she walked out of the office with Gray, who had come to pick her up for their afternoon in the city. Though the summer weather was lovely, warm but not too hot, and the flowers in the park bloomed in brilliant shades of pink and gold, he refused to put the top down on the low-slung Victorian that carried them about the town.

"It would make you too easy a target," he said. "I'm not willing to take any chances." And so there were two armed guards posing as footmen at the rear of the carriage, and she knew that Gray was also armed.

They settled themselves comfortably inside and let the relaxing whir of the wheels set the mood.

"I've enjoyed the time we've spent together this week," Corrie said, trying not to notice the way he watched her, the heat in his eyes he made no effort to hide. "Since our wedding, it's been the first chance we've really had to get to know each other." She glanced over to where he lounged in the carriage seat. "But we have yet to speak of your late wife, Gray. Will you tell me about her?"

For several long moments he said nothing. Then he sighed and let his head fall back against the squabs, reluctant, she could tell, but somehow resigned.

"Jillian was young and she was beautiful. I had just come into the title. I felt I needed a wife and Jillian seemed suitable."

"Suitable? That is the reason you married her?"

He shrugged. "It seemed reason enough at the time."

"What happened the day she was killed?"

He glanced away, toward the shops lining the street. A young boy darted after a ball, then returned to where his playmate waited.

"Rebecca had planned a boating party," Gray said. "A number of people had been invited. At the last minute, I decided not to go. I was feeling restless. I couldn't stand the idea of spending the day being polite and pretending to be interested when I wasn't in the least. I went riding instead. When I returned to the castle near dark, Charles was waiting. He told me the boat had sprung a leak shortly after leaving the dock and gone down very quickly. Everyone made it out safely except Jillian."

"Oh, Gray, I'm so sorry."

He stared out the window, but seemed not to notice the carriages they passed or the people hurrying along the street. "Charles said she went under and never came up. Her skirts must have caught on a sunken log or something, I don't know. The men searched for hours. We didn't find her body until the next day."

Gray looked up and she could see the pain in his face. "If I had been there, I could have saved her. I was her husband. I was supposed to protect her."

Corrie leaned toward him, reached out and cupped his cheek. "You are no more to blame for Jillian's death than I am responsible for what happened to Laurel. For months, I blamed myself for not being there when she needed me. I thought that if she had confided in me about the baby, I could have helped her in some way. But the truth is, life is full of misfortune. We can only do the best we know how. That is all God expects of us."

Gray gazed down at her. There was something in his eyes, a vulnerability he rarely let show. He glanced away, and when he looked at her again, his expression had changed and so did the subject.

"It is time you came home."

She didn't like the determination she saw in his fierce dark eyes. "But I've so enjoyed your courting — that is what you've been doing, is it not?"

A flush rose in his cheeks. "I am trying to make you happy. These are the things a woman likes, are they not?" He cast her a smoldering glance. "Of course, there are far better ways I might please you." His gaze lowered to her breasts. "All you have to do is come home."

Corrie gasped as he hauled her into his arms and very thoroughly kissed her, a searing promise of what would happen if she gave in to his demands. She was tempted. Very tempted — and light-headed by the time he let her go.

Still, she wasn't quite ready to return. "I can't, Gray. Not yet."

"I warn you, Coralee. I'm not a man known for his patience. And you are testing mine sorely."

She knew she was. She felt as if she faced a lion on a very short leash. "Just a few more days."

He made a growling sound in his throat that somehow seemed fitting.

"I know the words you want to hear . . . what every woman wants to hear. But I know nothing of love, Coralee. I only know I care for you deeply. I need you, Corrie. Please come home."

I care for you deeply. The words wrapped around her heart. Coming from a man like Gray, so unsure of his emotions and completely uncertain how to deal with them, they were words she cherished. He had given her more than she had ever believed he would.

She swallowed past the tightness in her throat. "All right. I'll come home with you, Gray."

His eyes closed in relief. "Thank God." He drew her into his arms and kissed her. She could feel his hunger, his powerful need, even as he slowly released her. He reached over and brushed a loose tendril of hair from her cheek.

"As much as I'd like to go back to the castle, I think we should stay in the city a little while longer. My family and Dolph are searching for the man who tried to kill you, but until they find him, I think you're safer here."

She had thought the same thing. "Probably."

"Since we're staying, we might as well enjoy ourselves. I made arrangements to take you to the theater tonight . . . if you would like to go."

"The theater?"

He must have read the surprise in her face, for he smiled. "I don't spend all of my time in the country, you know. I never expected you to do that, either."

She had always loved the city. She found herself smiling in return. "I adore the theater. I would love to go."

He seemed pleased. "We'll have men with

us, so you won't have to worry." He settled back in his seat. "Tonight the theater. Afterward you return to my bed."

A tremor of heat slipped through her. She had missed his lovemaking, missed sleeping next to him at night.

Tonight she was going home.

She wondered when she had come to think of any place with Gray as being home.

The theater was crowded with ladies and gentlemen elegantly gowned for the evening. Corrie hadn't been to the Theater Royal since the interior had been redone with gold-flocked wallpaper, gilded ceilings and crystal chandeliers.

The earl's private box sat on the second floor, the interior draped with heavy gold velvet and furnished with matching velvet chairs. As soon as they were safely inside, the two guards who had escorted them upstairs returned to the carriage to await the end of the performance.

Corrie let Gray seat her, then he took the chair beside her. Wanting to please him, she had chosen a gown of aqua silk that left her shoulders bare and displayed a good bit of her bosom. The full skirt had a deep vee in the front that made her waist look exceedingly small, and she was wearing a lovely string of pearls Gray had bought her at Harrington's, an expensive shop in Bond Street.

She had taken extra care with her hair, curling the coppery strands into clusters against her shoulders. She seemed to have chosen well. Gray's eyes slid over her breasts again and again, making her nipples harden against the stays of her corset. She trembled at the hunger he so boldly displayed, and felt an answering hunger rising inside her.

Her need built with every second she sat next to him in the box. Dressed almost completely in black, with his onyx hair and intense brown eyes accented by the snowy cravat at his throat, he was so handsome she could barely keep her mind on the play. Tonight he carried a silver-headed cane, giving him an even more dashing appearance, which clearly impressed the ladies as he walked by.

The play, a comedic farce called *The Lark,* first performed in Vienna, was wildly entertaining and actually had Gray laughing. Corrie felt a swell of love as she looked up at him, and he leaned over and kissed her.

He ran the pad of his thumb across her bottom lip. "Thank you for what you said today."

That he shouldn't blame himself for what had happened to Jillian. Perhaps it was the reason he was able to laugh tonight. Perhaps he had taken the first step in forgiving himself, the first step toward healing.

The play was a delight, but by the time it was over, Gray was no longer laughing. Instead, he was looking at her as if he would ravish her right there in the box, and making her want him to do just that.

"I enjoyed the play," he said, "but as soon as we get home, there is something I intend to enjoy far more."

You, his dark eyes said, and a delicious warmth slipped through her. She was smiling when they pushed through the heavy velvet curtains into the crowded hallway. Then a man walked up beside her and pressed something into her ribs. She glanced down and gasped at the sight of a pistol.

He prodded her again. "When ye get to the end of the hall, ye'll see a door. It'll take ye out to the rear o' the buildin'."

Her heart set up a clatter. Was this the man who had tried to kill her? Dear God, how had he known where to find her?

"I'm not . . . not going anywhere with —" A fierce jab cut off her words.

"Ye'd best do as I say." He had bony hands and dirty hair and he smelled of stale liquor.

She trembled as she looked up at Gray.

"Do exactly what he says, Coralee." A second man, bigger than the first, stood next to Gray and she glimpsed a second weapon. Gray squeezed her hand where it trembled on his arm, warning her to stay calm. His eyes said not to fear, that he was biding his time, looking for the moment to strike.

They moved undetected through the crowd, though the men were dressed more shabbily than the rest of the theater patrons exiting their expensive boxes. It was late and everyone was tired, eager to get home, just as Corrie had been only a few minutes ago.

Gray pushed open the door at the end of the hall and she caught sight of a stairway outside, leading down to the alley behind the theater. They made their way to the bottom, and the instant Corrie's feet touched the ground, Gray shoved her hard out of the way.

"Run!" he shouted. A pistol shot rang out and Corrie screamed as Gray and the big man hit the ground rolling, one of them groaning in pain.

Please God, not Gray, she prayed, and saw him spring to his feet at the same instant the second man aimed his weapon.

"Gray!" Corrie cried, and launched herself at the man, knocking him off his feet, the gun flying out of his hand. He spun her around and slapped her hard across the face, sending her into the rough brick wall. Then Gray was on him, slamming a fist into his face, knocking him backward onto the ground. Gray retrieved his silver-headed cane from where it had fallen, turned the handle, and a blade popped out the end. He pressed the knife against the man's neck, the blade glinting in the light of a gas lamp next to the stage door at the rear of the building.

Corrie stood shaking, her hand over her mouth, watching the drama unfold as if it were part of the play.

"Are you all right, love?" Worry lined Gray's face.

She nodded, all she could manage as she wiped a trickle of blood from the corner of her mouth with a shaking hand.

He returned his attention to the man on the ground. "Who are you?" When the fellow didn't answer, Gray pressed the knife blade into the soft folds under his chin. "I want your names."

" 'E's Biggs. Me name's Wilkins."

Biggs wasn't moving. A widening swath of crimson spread across his chest and pooled in the dirt of the alleyway. "Looks like your friend Biggs is dead. You don't answer my questions, you'll be joining him."

The man wet his lips, but was careful not to move his head.

"Did you and Biggs kill Laurel Whitmore?"

"Not us, mate. Biggs works for the man what did."

"Who is he?"

"Don't know nothin' about 'im. Biggs paid me to help 'im get rid o' ye. That's all I know."

"You had orders to kill both of us?" When the man didn't answer, Gray pushed the knife blade into his flesh, and Wilkins hissed as blood trickled from the wound onto the dirty collar of his shirt.

"Said to get rid o' the pair o' ye. That's what 'e said."

"How did you know where to find us?"

"Biggs knew where ye lived. We been watching ye all week."

Gray swore softly, his hand tightening around the handle of the silver-headed cane. For an instant, Corrie feared he would thrust the blade into the man's skinny neck.

"Don't do it, mate," Wilkins pleaded.

Corrie leaned against the wall, her cheek throbbing, her heart still hammering away.

"I'll make ye a trade," the henchman said, sweat beading on his forehead. "I've got information for ye . . . valuable information.

I'll tell ye, if ye promise to let me go."

The knife blade didn't falter. "Information worth your useless life?"

Wilkins barely nodded.

"Tell me. If it's worth it, I'll let you go."

He swallowed. "The child . . . the one what was with the girl that night at the river. 'E's still alive. Least 'e is, far as I know."

Corrie surged away from the wall. "You're lying! You're just saying that to save your own skin!"

" 'Tis the truth, lass, I swear it! Biggs said the man what killed the girl didn't 'ave it in 'im to murder an innocent babe. Paid Biggs to take the child to one of them baby farms 'ere in the city."

Gray cast Corrie a glance. "You never considered it?"

Her insides were shaking, quaking like a leaf in the wind. "I — I wondered if it might be possible. I was afraid to get my hopes up, afraid to think what might be happening to him if he lived. Oh, Gray, you don't think it might be true?"

Gray moved the knife an inch or so away, and the man exhaled in relief. "If the boy is alive, where is he?"

"Don't know. 'Twas Biggs who left 'im."

Just then the second-story door they had come out burst open, and one of the guards

— Franklin, a man with a stocky build and side-whiskers — came rushing down the wooden stairs. "My lord — thank God we found you! Deavers and me, we got worried when you and her ladyship didn't come out with the others and took off looking for you."

Deavers, a beefy man with a hard face and bad complexion, came racing down the alley behind them, pistol drawn. "Lord Tremaine — thank God!"

"Ye gonna let me go?" Wilkins asked, looking hopeful.

Gray's jaw hardened. "Sorry, my friend. You tried to kill us. I don't keep promises I make to murderers."

"We'll take him, my lord," said Deavers. "The police will be glad to get their hands on him."

Deavers kept his pistol pointed at Wilkins while Franklin went for the police and Gray went to Corrie. As he drew her into his arms, he caught sight of the bruise beginning to form on her cheek.

"The bastard hit you. I should have killed him for that if nothing else."

She shuddered at the fierce look on his face. "I'm all right." She gripped his arm. "Oh, Gray, do you really think Laurel's baby might still be alive?"

452

"If he is, we'll find him, I promise you."

"His body was never recovered."

"No. I thought it was possible that some-one might have taken the child, but I didn't want you to worry about that, too."

She went back into his arms. Now that it was over, she was shaking, fighting not to cry.

Gray pressed his cheek against her hair. "I knew I could count on you," he whispered.

"You did? Why?"

He smiled down at her, so softly her heart squeezed. "Because you're Coralee and not Letty." Very gently, he kissed her.

"The police have been summoned." The guard named Franklin returned down the alley. "The carriage is coming round to pick you up."

Gray turned to Corrie. "With this man, Wilkins, we have proof that your sister was murdered. We can use help from the police to find the man who did it, and also to help find Charles's baby."

She looked up at him. "I've always thought of Joshua Michael as belonging to Laurel. But the baby is Charles's, too. We have to find him, Gray."

He squeezed her hand. "If he's alive, we'll find him. But it's been five months, love.

453

Those places are death traps. They put bastard children there to get rid of them. Most of them die. You have to face that possibility."

She swallowed against the lump that rose in her throat. "Laurel was strong and so is Charles. Perhaps the baby got his parents' strength."

"For now, that's what we'll believe." As the carriage rolled up in the alley, Gray turned to the men guarding Wilkins. "We're going home. Tell the police they can speak to us there in the morning."

Deavers nodded. "We'll take care of it, my lord. Soon as we finish here, we'll come to the house to keep watch."

"They've been watching the house. Someone knew where to find us. Keep a sharp eye out."

"Aye, milord."

Corrie felt Gray's hand at her waist as he led her over to the carriage. She was going home with her husband. Not exactly as she had planned, but it was the place she wanted to be.

The butler opened the door and Gray led his wife into the entryway of his Mayfair town house. He could feel her trembling. Gray's jaw knotted as he thought of the bastards who had attacked them. Any other woman would have crumbled beneath the onslaught of violence and death. Not his brave little Coralee.

Gray looked down at her and worry tightened his chest. He had to find the source of the attacks and he had to do it soon.

The butler took his hat and coat, along with the silver-headed cane he had carried for exactly the purpose it had served, and Gray drew in a calming breath.

"Coralee, this is Stewart," he said. "Stewart, this is your countess."

The white-haired butler bowed extravagantly. "My lady."

"We had some problems tonight." He stared down at the blood on his black broadcloth coat, then over at the bruise on Coralee's pretty cheek. "We'll need hot water sent up."

"I believe Samir has bathwater for you upstairs."

He merely nodded. The little man was always one step ahead of him. Gray urged Coralee toward the stairs, felt her stumble, and swept her up in his arms.

"It's all right, love, I've got you." And he was not about to let her go again. In the days they had spent apart, he had come to realize the precious gift he had been given.

He didn't deserve her, he knew, had never treated her as he should have, but she belonged to him and he meant to keep her.

He hurried up the stairs, her arms around his neck, her small frame nestled against him, and thought again how glad he was to have her returned. After the attack tonight, his desire for her was stronger than ever, the need to claim her, prove to himself she was his. He had dreamed of making love to her tonight, but now he only wanted to take care of her, make sure that she was all right.

Closing the door with his foot, he set her gently in front of the dresser and began to strip off her clothes. Her aqua silk gown was dirty and torn in several places, her shoulder scraped raw by the rough bricks the bastard had shoved her against. Gray bent his head and pressed a soft kiss on her tender flesh, fighting a surge of anger, wishing he had been able to spare her.

"There's a small room adjoining the bedroom," he said. "It's where I bathe and dress. Samir has a bath there waiting."

Gray tipped her chin up, forcing her to look at him. "I was so proud of you tonight. You were brave and you were smart. I've never known a woman like you."

She gazed up at him and tears filled her brilliant green eyes. "Gray . . ."

He drew her into his arms and just held her, prayed she would know how much she had come to mean to him. Then he stepped away.

Tossing off his jacket and waistcoat, he rolled up the sleeves of his shirt. "All right, let's get you cleaned up and into bed." Desire burned through him. He wanted her. He always seemed to want her. But he was determined to keep the beast inside him locked away.

Removing the rest of her clothes, leaving her in only her chemise, he pulled the pins from her fiery hair, letting it cascade round her shoulders, then carried her into the dressing room. As promised, Samir had the copper bathing tub filled with steaming water. Gray drew the chemise over Coralee's head, lifted her up and lowered her into the bath.

Even with the bruise on her cheek, she was beautiful. His loins clenched. *She is injured,* he told himself, knowing if he wasn't extremely careful, he might very well lose control.

Instead, he knelt beside the tub and gently bathed her, soaped a cloth and drew it over her tantalizing breasts. For an instant, the beast broke free and he moved the cloth between her legs, felt the brush of the russet curls at the juncture of her thighs. His shaft filled and desire heated his blood. Cursing, he pulled the cloth away.

"I'm sorry. You're hurt and the last thing you need is —"

"You're exactly what I need, Gray." Coralee rose from the tub, water cascading over the sweet curves of her body. She went into his arms, a wet, naked nymph, and his arousal strengthened to the point of pain.

"I just . . . I want you so badly. I missed you so damned much." And then he kissed her, a gentle kiss that heated and changed, seared through his determination and burned like a flame.

Coralee whimpered. Her fingers slid into his hair, freeing it of its tie, and the heavy strands tumbled forward around her face. She kissed him with all the passion he had dreamed of, kissed him as if she couldn't get enough, and desire thundered through his veins.

Carrying her into the bedroom, he set her on the edge of the bed and eased her back on the mattress, then stepped between her thighs. He wanted her now. He didn't bother removing his trousers, just unbuttoned the fly and freed himself, positioned his erection and drove himself home.

She was wet and slick and welcoming. He

groaned at the tight, hot feel of her, clenched his jaw to hold on to his control.

It wasn't easy. He wasn't the same man he had been before, one who could ignore his emotions and enjoy the pleasure from a distance. He didn't want to be that man again.

"Sweet God, Gray . . ." she whispered as he thrust into her again and again. She cried his name as she found release. Reaching for him, she wrapped her arms around his neck and dragged his lips to hers for a burning kiss. At the feel of her small tongue inside his mouth, the last of his control shattered and he followed her over the edge.

For long moments, he remained joined with her. It felt so good to be inside her, to know that she was his.

Then he began to remember the rough treatment she had suffered earlier that night, and eased himself from her seductive warmth.

"Damn, I shouldn't have done that. After what you've been through, I should have been more patient, taken more care with you."

She draped her arms around his neck. "You were perfect."

Gray bent down and kissed her. "So were you." Perfect for him as he had never really realized before. Helping her snuggle beneath the covers, he pulled them up to her chin. She was asleep by the time he finished.

Gray didn't join her.

Instead, he drew his pistol from a drawer of the dresser, sat down in the chair beside the bed and settled the gun in his lap.

TWENTY-EIGHT

Gray spoke to the police the next morning, giving them as much information as he could about the attack and how it related to the death of Laurel Whitmore some months back. Corrie added her version of events.

Afterward, Gray insisted on accompanying her to the offices of *Heart to Heart.* They needed information on baby farming, and Krista, who was active in social reform, could point them in the right direction.

They didn't travel there alone. Both Franklin and Deavers, the bodyguards Gray had hired, went with them. Corrie knew Gray would take every precaution until the man behind the attacks was apprehended.

They stepped through the door of the gazette and she caught the familiar scents of ink and oil and newsprint. The big Stanhope press took up a good deal of the main floor of the building, and immediately captured Gray's interest.

"I'd like to see it work sometime."

"We go to press on Thursdays."

He spared it a moment's more attention, then continued with Corrie through the open door into Krista's office.

"Well, good morning." Blond and pretty, Krista rose from the chair behind her desk. She wasn't as tall as Gray, but far taller than Corrie. "I'm a little surprised to see you two today." She must have thought they would be enjoying a leisurely morning in bed, which they should have been. "How was your evening at the theater?"

"I'm afraid it didn't go quite the way we planned," Gray said.

For the next half hour, he and Corrie filled Krista in on what had happened last night, nearly being killed at the theater, and the news that Laurel's child might still be alive.

"One of the men who attacked us knew about Laurel's murder," Corrie said. "He didn't know the man who had committed the crime, but he said that little Joshua Michael had been taken to a baby farm."

"Oh, dear God."

"Exactly so," Gray said darkly.

"Those places are a travesty." Krista got up from her desk and walked over to the window looking out onto street. "I've been asked to join a movement to try to make them illegal. Now I know I shall do exactly that."

"What can you tell us about them?" Corrie asked, her stomach churning at the thought of her sister's child suffering in any way.

"Baby farming started as a result of the Poor Law reform about ten years ago. It was done as an attempt to restore female morality by absolving the fathers of illegitimate children of any responsibility. It fell to the mother to feed and care for the child completely on her own. I suppose they thought that a woman facing that sort of consequence wouldn't be so easily seduced."

"I had no idea," Corrie said.

"Most people don't. Since many of the mothers work and earn barely enough to support themselves, the only solution is to get rid of the child."

Gray's jaw clenched.

"How could a mother do that?" Corrie asked softly. "How could she give up her baby?"

"That's just it," Krista said. "Baby farms are operated mostly by women. The ads in the papers say that for a small sum of money — which can often be extricated from the father — a child will be taken into a loving home. But the only way a baby farmer can make a profit is for the child to die before the money she receives runs out."

Corrie's heart squeezed so hard it hurt. "Dear God in heaven."

"Most of the babies are starved, or drugged with laudanum. Sometimes they're fed watered-down milk tainted with lime. The infants slowly die of hunger or some illness brought on by mistreatment. I'm sorry, Coralee, but most of them don't live more than a couple of months."

Corrie said nothing. Her throat was too tight to speak.

Krista sighed. "I know this isn't easy to hear."

She stiffened her spine. "I need to know, Krista."

Her friend returned to her seat behind the desk. "Sometimes one of the parents pays a monthly fee toward the infant's care. Those children have a better chance of surviving, since the fees, small as they are, continue as long as the child is alive. Still, they're kept at the barest level of subsistence and most are dead before they reach their first year."

Corrie thought of little Joshua Michael and despair settled over her. "I can't imagine a murderer paying to keep a child alive." She looked at Gray, tears welling in her eyes.

"There is still hope, Coralee."

"If he's alive, we have to find him before it's too late."

Gray reached out and caught her hand. "We'll search, love, until we find out what happened to him." He slid his chair a little closer to the desk, a little closer to Corrie. "Where do we start looking?" he asked Krista.

"As I said, the women run ads in newspapers. We refuse to carry them in *Heart to Heart,* but there are at least a dozen each day in the *Daily Telegraph* and the *Domestic Times.*"

"We'll buy copies of the papers," Gray said. "We'll track down every person involved in the trade and offer enough of a reward to encourage them to help us find the child. We know the baby was taken on January 30, the night your sister was killed. You said he was a month old at the time."

"That's right," Corrie said.

"So we're looking for a six-month-old baby."

"How will you know you've found the right child?" Krista asked.

"Allison said he was an adorable baby," Corrie said. "He was born with dark hair and eyes, but a newborn's hair and eyes can change. By now he could have blond hair and blue eyes."

"More like his mother and father," Gray said.

"Or he could be darker complexioned, like you," Corrie added, staring him straight in the face. She had read his mother's letter and believed the countess had been faithful, that Gray had indeed inherited his looks from his mother's side of the family, which meant Charles's son might also inherit dark features.

Gray stared back at her, understanding her message — that he had nothing to be ashamed of and never had.

He cleared his throat. "So we know his age but not what he looks like. In order to claim the reward, we'll require some sort of proof from whoever is caring for him. Perhaps they kept a record of who brought him or paid for his care, that sort of thing."

"There's a chance he'll have a mark on his left shoulder," Corrie said. "Allison never mentioned seeing it, but my father has it. I don't, but my sister did."

Gray reached over and caught her hand. "We'll start today. Thanks to Krista, at least we know where to begin."

"I want you to stay here, where you will be safe." They were standing in the study of

Gray's town house. For the past three days, they had been going over ads in the newspapers, locating the women who had placed them, which turned out to be no easy task.

Baby farmers had to be careful. Though some handled a single child at a time, Corrie had learned that over a period of years some were responsible for the deaths of as many as fifty or sixty infants. It was all kept very quiet, since there was really no system in place to handle the unwanted offspring of unwed mothers.

"I am going," Corrie said. "This child is my nephew. If . . . if he *is* alive, when we find him he is going to need a woman's care. Aside from that, I feel safer being with you than I do here without you, no matter whom you hire to protect me."

Gray shoved a hand through his hair, knocking loose the velvet ribbon. He swore softly, picked up the ribbon and tied back the heavy strands again.

"You are upset because you think I am right — that I would be safer if I were with you."

He stalked over to the window. One of the guards stood watch in the garden, another kept the street covered out in front. Gray turned back to her. "All right, dammit. You're right. I'd rather have you with me than here with someone else."

She smiled up at him. "You are a very smart man."

"And you are a handful of trouble, lady. But then, you always were."

Before he had come to London in search of her, she would have been hurt by the words. Now she saw that he said them with a hint of affection. She wondered if in time that affection might grow into something more.

"Are you certain we shouldn't tell Charles? If he knew, he would surely wish to help."

"We've been over this, Coralee. Charles has suffered enough. If chances of finding the boy were better . . ."

She felt a tightness in her throat. "I know."

Gray walked over to where she stood. "Are you certain you can handle this? God only knows what we'll find in some of these places."

She swallowed, afraid to imagine the horrors they might see. "I have to do it, Gray."

He simply nodded. "All right, then let's get started. We've a long day ahead of us."

With Deavers and Franklin riding at the back of the carriage, they began their search, which took them through the dregs of the city, from Southwark to the Turnbull and Cow Cross districts, to a woman in Holburn and one in St. Giles.

Most of the time, they had to knock on several doors in the area to locate the person they were looking for. Once they found the right house, they rarely went inside. The age of the child alone had the women shaking their heads.

"Sorry, but I can't help ye," a widow named Cummins told them from the porch of her home in Bedford Street. "We've nary a child o' that age."

Which meant no babies in her care had survived to the age of six months old.

"Is it possible you took a boy child in around the first of February?" Gray asked, as he did at each stop they made. "He would have come from the area round Castle-on-Avon, brought to you by a man named Biggs? If you did and you have proof, it's worth a hundred pounds."

Her gray hair dirty and unkempt, the woman looked up with widened eyes. "A hundred pounds? Even if the babe is dead?"

Corrie's stomach knotted for the tenth time that day.

"Yes," Gray said. "If you can prove it was the child we're looking for."

The widow's gaze turned shrewd.

"Weren't me what took 'im in, but I'll ask 'round a bit, see what I can find out."

Gray gave her one of his calling cards. "Should you come up with any information, you can find us here. If you do, you'll be well rewarded."

The conversation went much the same at each house they visited. They went inside only a few, and in those, the babies were kept in rooms upstairs. Corrie didn't have to see the poor sickly infants, but she could hear their pitiful, hungry wails, imagine their terrible suffering.

She was crying by the time they left the last house. "I can't stand this, Gray. All these poor, innocent children. We have to do something to help them."

Gray looked nearly as upset as she. "We'll talk to Krista about how we might do the most good."

Corrie nodded, turned away so that he wouldn't see the tears streaming down her cheeks.

They started back to the carriage. With a weary sigh, he helped her climb inside, then stepped in behind her. "We've done enough for today. Let's go home."

Corrie looked back at the run-down house they'd just left. "There's one more name on our list. It's on the way back. Baby Joshua might be there."

Gray cupped her cheek in his hand. "Are you sure, love? I can see what this is doing to you."

"Please, Gray."

He set his jaw and nodded. She knew this was affecting him nearly as much as it was her.

The house in Golden Lane was old and shabby, the paint peeling off, the shutters hanging loose at the windows. As they walked up on the porch, the boards creaked and Gray took a careful step back, afraid his foot would go through.

He had to deliver several sharp raps before someone came to the door. It opened with a groan and a woman in a mobcap, her front teeth missing, appeared in the doorway.

"Are you Mrs. Burney?" Gray asked

"Who wants to know?"

"We're looking for a child, about six months old."

A baby started crying then, a pitiful keening sound, and Corrie's chest squeezed painfully.

"Only one here and he ain't that old."

It was the same story again. Infants in these places simply didn't live that long. Corrie fought to hold back tears.

"There's a reward for the one we're

searching for." Gray gave the woman the details of the baby they were trying to find, and handed her his card.

As he finished, the child cried out again, his soft little sobs so heartbreaking, Corrie simply shoved the door wide open and walked past the woman into the house.

"Here now! Wait a minute!"

Corrie just kept walking. In the parlor, she spotted the rough wooden boards that served as the baby's cradle, went over and looked down at the small scrap of flesh lying naked in the bottom without even the comfort of a blanket. Though the infant was probably two months old, his shrunken body made him look even younger.

"What ya think yer doin'?" The woman, Mrs. Burney, marched toward her.

Corrie ignored her, reached down and lifted the child against her breast. She wrapped her arms around him, trying to share some of her warmth. "Is this your baby?"

"I'm carin' for 'im."

Corrie held him tighter. "No, you are not. You are killing him, and I am not going to let you."

"Coralee . . . sweetheart . . ." Gray walked up beside her.

"I'm taking him, Gray. I'm not letting this

poor little baby suffer a moment more."

"He isn't yours, love." His voice was so soft, his expression so tender it made the ache in her heart expand until she could barely breathe.

"He isn't *hers,* either." She looked up at him and tears rolled down her cheeks. "I can't leave him, Gray. He probably hasn't eaten in days. He's starving to death and I can't leave another child behind to die. Please don't ask it of me." She clutched the small, thin body against her, felt his faint breathing, the soft brush of fine hair against her cheek. She wouldn't let him die, she vowed. Somehow she would save him.

Gray straightened, turned his fierce gaze on the woman. "How much do you want for the child?"

"He ain't for sale."

"How much!"

"Give me twenty pounds, he's yers."

Gray drew a pouch of coins from the inside pocket of his coat, pulled it open and counted out twenty gold coins. "What's his name?"

"Jonathan. That's all, just Jonathan."

Gray took off his coat and Corrie wrapped the baby in the soft folds that still held Gray's warmth.

"You've got my card," he said. "You get

the information we need, you'll be paid for that, too."

Corrie felt his hand at her waist, urging her toward the door, and she headed there gratefully. They climbed into the carriage and it lurched into motion, making the sad little creature in her arms begin to cry again.

"He needs milk," Corrie said.

"I made arrangements for a wet nurse, a woman named Mrs. Lawsen, in case we found Charles's son. I'll send one of the servants to fetch her as soon as we get home. And I'll send for the physician."

Corrie looked up at Gray and her heart squeezed. She wondered if he could see the love she felt for him shining in her eyes. "Thank you, Gray. I'll never forget what you did today."

He reached out and touched her cheek. "He's terribly ill, love. You mustn't get your hopes too high."

She nodded, swallowed past the tight knot in her throat. The child was so small and frail, and he had been so mistreated. As the babe lay in her arms, too weak to even cry out, she said a prayer that the precious little boy might be saved.

"And please, Lord, help us find little Joshua Michael," she whispered. "Don't let us be too late."

■ ■ ■ ■

The baby was dead by morning. So terribly weak and malnourished, he passed away quietly in his sleep. At least he had been warm and dry, his stomach full, and when he slipped away, he was not in pain.

Corrie cried for the lost babe and all the others who suffered in the terrible places she had seen. In memory of the child, Gray promised to set up a fund to help unwed mothers care for their infant children.

Still, it didn't make the tiny baby's passing any easier.

And it didn't make Corrie's worry for her sister's son go away.

"You won't give up, will you?" Returning from the brief service that had been held in the churchyard at St. Andrews, she looked up at Gray. Her eyes were puffy and swollen, her cheeks wet with tears. She dabbed at them with the handkerchief he had handed her. "You won't stop until we know for sure what happened to him?"

"We won't stop, love. Not until we've done everything we can to find him."

And so they decided to run an ad in *Heart to Heart.* They gave the infant's age, the date he'd been brought to London, the name of the man who had brought him, and offered a reward for information — and a hundred pounds for the return of the child.

"It's worth a try," Krista said, studying the ad to make sure it read correctly.

"For a hundred pounds," Leif said, "if the boy still lives, someone will come forward."

But another week passed, and though a number of women appeared on their doorstep, none had credible information and none arrived with the child.

It seemed hopeless, and despair settled over Corrie with the weight of a shroud. Only Gray's tender affections kept the grief and worry at bay. He seemed to understand her pain, even share it.

Other visitors came and went. Colonel Timothy Rayburn stopped by, in London for a few days before his return trip to India. Gray filled him in on what had been happening since he had visited Castle Tremaine, the attempts on Corrie's life and the attack at the theater.

"I knew Dolph had been working on a case that involved the countess's sister," the colonel said as they sat in the drawing room after supper. "Damned sorry to hear he hasn't been able to catch the bast— er, villain who killed her."

Gray leaned forward in his chair. "We've

got to catch him, Timothy. Neither of us is safe until we do."

"Wish I were going to be here awhile longer. Might be able to help."

"We could certainly use your assistance, but you're needed far more in India."

The colonel cast Gray a speculative glance. "Still have a yen to go back? You always did seem more at home there than you did here."

Gray swirled the brandy in his glass but didn't take a drink. "There was a time I wanted to return. I joined the army to get away from my father, then wound up enthralled with the country. I hated having to come back to England." He looked over at Corrie. "Now I'm glad to be here."

Corrie's heart swelled at the soft look in his eyes.

Rayburn chuckled. "Don't blame you. Not one little bit."

Corrie watched the exchange, not quite sure what the colonel meant. Exhausted, still grief stricken over the loss of the infant, she said farewell to the officer and went upstairs to the bedroom she shared with Gray.

Tomorrow, news will come, she told herself. But each day ended the same, with no word from Dolph or Gray's family, and no news of Laurel's baby boy.

Twenty-Nine

Gray stood at the window of the study in his town house. The garden behind the house was in full bloom this time of year, the flowers along the pathways brilliantly colored. Gray barely noticed. His mind was on his wife and the danger she still faced, perhaps both of them faced, and now, to top things off, was the matter of a lost little boy.

He hadn't told Coralee, but he had hired another investigator, a man named Robert Andrews, who had an excellent reputation and a staff of half a dozen men. Gray had hired the firm to search for information on the missing child. So far they had found nothing.

He turned away from the window. Every time he thought of Coralee, his chest ached. He was so afraid for her, and he couldn't bear to see the pain in her face that losing the infant had caused. Perhaps he shouldn't have let her bring the baby home. Its death had only caused her more grief. And yet he couldn't have denied her, couldn't have forced her to leave the suffering infant, no matter the outcome.

As he did more and more, Gray thought how much he had come to care for the woman he had married. Was it love? He had tried to convince himself he wasn't the sort of man who could fall in love, but the flare of emotion he felt whenever she walked into a room, the powerful urge to protect her from any sort of pain or danger, made him wonder. . . .

Was it love he felt for Coralee?

And if it was, what did she feel for him?

She had been forced to marry him. What if he loved her and she didn't love him in return?

A painful tightness constricted his chest. He had loved his father, but received only hatred in return.

He wasn't even sure he was capable of love, and yet when he looked at Coralee and saw her lovely green eyes well with tears, he felt he would do anything — anything! — to erase her pain and make her smile again.

Gray thought of the way he had found her asleep last night, curled up in the middle of their bed, tracks of tears dried on her cheeks. He hadn't made love to her in days, not since the night of the attack at the theater. Though he ached to touch her, to lose himself inside her, he wasn't sure how she would receive his advances, and he refused to press her for something she wasn't ready to give.

He was lost in his musing, uncertain what step to take next, when a rap came at the door.

Gray crossed the room and opened it. "Samir . . . what is it?"

"Come quickly, *sahib.* There is a woman downstairs. She has news of the child you seek."

His heart quickened to a faster pace. Was it possible? Or was it just another charlatan, out for what money she might procure, as most of the others had been?

Gray hurried along the hall and down the staircase. When he reached the front parlor he was surprised to find the widow he had spoken to in Bedford Street, her gray hair as dirty and unkempt as before.

"Mrs. Cummins, if I recall. What news have you brought me?"

"The child ye seek . . . 'e's alive. I can show ye where to find 'im."

His pulse kicked up again. "What proof do you have that the baby is the one we're looking for?"

She handed him a folded piece of paper, one edge ragged, as if it had been torn out of a book. Inside was written the date the child, a boy, had arrived in London — February 2 — and his first name, Joshua. The name of the man who'd brought him was written on the next line down: Sylvester Biggs.

"You were told these things. How is this proof?"

She handed him a second piece of paper. "This here's a bank draft what come just yesterday. It's fer fifteen shillings." It wasn't much, just enough to salve a conscience.

"Name o' the man what's payin' is writ right there. Ye can see where he signed." She pointed a grimy finger at the name scrawled in blue ink, and Gray's whole body tightened.

Thomas Morton.

A wave of fury swept over him, so strong that for an instant his vision blurred. "Where is the child right now?"

She cast him a cunning glance. "What's in it fer me?"

"Fifty pounds."

Her eyes gleamed and she nodded. "I'll take ye there meself."

Gray turned to Samir, who watched from

the hallway. "We'll need the carriage. Have it readied and brought round front."

"It awaits you there now, *sahib.* You will find blankets for the child."

The man never failed to amaze him. "Thank you." He turned to the widow. "Shall we go?"

Coralee's voice, floating down from the top of the stairs, reached him before he took two steps. "That is the woman we spoke to in Bedford Street." She hurried down to the entry. "Where is she taking you?"

He clamped down on an urge to lie. If the babe was as sickly as the last . . . If it was all some sort of hoax . . .

"Tell me, Gray."

"Mrs. Cummins believes she has found Joshua Michael. She has proof of a sort." He handed Corrie the page torn from a book. "If she is right, this may be the name of your sister's murderer."

Her hand trembled as she reached for the second piece of paper, read it and looked up at him. "Thomas Morton? Squire Morton's son? Dear God, why would he wish to kill Laurel?"

"That is what we're going to discover. First we need to find her baby."

Corrie whirled toward the door, but Gray caught her arm. "This may be even worse

483

than before. Are you certain you're ready to go through that again?"

Her chin firmed. "I don't have any choice."

And so Coralee led the way out to the carriage, and Gray helped her and the widow climb aboard. He went back inside to get his pistol, stuffed it into a pocket of his coat, then ordered both Deavers and Franklin to join them.

If Morton was the man who'd sent the child, there was a good chance he was the man who had murdered Laurel. And there was also a chance he had seen the ads in the newspapers or somehow gotten wind of their efforts to find the babe. If so, this could be a way of luring them into a trap.

Gray wished he could leave his wife behind, just in case, but he knew she would fight him. And in truth, she deserved to be there.

Seated across from her, he reached inside his coat to check the pistol in his pocket.

She could smell the stench of rotting vegetation and human waste blocks before they got to the house. It was the sort of place where typhus bred and people suffered from endless poverty and despair, where children went without food in their bellies.

She closed her eyes, trying not to think what the babies here endured, what Laurel's child might be enduring even now. Instead, she concentrated on finding the baby alive, and how, once she did, she would nurse him back to health.

It wouldn't be like the last time. God wouldn't let them find him, only to have him die once they got him home. This time, they wouldn't be too late.

The widow began to stir on the seat beside her, her odor nearly as foul as the streets.

"Pull up 'ere." It was a wood-framed, two-story house in a neighborhood populated with pickpockets and women of the night. The carriage rolled to a stop, and Corrie took a calming breath, bracing herself for what they might find, knowing she could never be truly prepared.

"We stay inside the coach until Franklin and Deavers make sure this isn't a trap," Gray said, as Corrie leaned toward the door, anxious to get to the baby, praying it was truly Laurel's son.

"Ain't no trap," the widow grumbled, but Gray ignored her.

The hired guards circled the house. They went up to the door and knocked, then pushed their way inside. They reappeared a few minutes later, made their way over and opened the carriage door.

"Looks safe enough, my lord," Deavers said. "Still . . . place like this, we'd best be careful."

Gray nodded, turned to Coralee. "You're certain you don't want to stay in the carriage?" She opened her mouth. "Never mind. Let's go." He took her hand and helped her down, then helped the widow.

"She's expectin' ye," Mrs. Cummins said. "Wants the reward. Won't give ye no trouble."

Corrie hoped not. She just wanted to take the baby and go home.

Gray held open the front door, which tilted at an angle and scraped against the wooden floor as they walked inside the house. It was as dirty as the rest of the neighborhood, with unwashed plates on the tables, a filthy iron skillet on what passed for a stove, a dead rat in the corner on top of a pile of rags.

A baby wailed, a low keening sound that reminded Corrie of little Jonathan. Her heart snagged as the infant snuffled and began to cry, and her mouth flooded with bile.

"Where is he?" she asked. Gray must have heard the tremor in her voice, for his hand reached out to steady her.

"She'll be bringin' 'im."

Just then a woman appeared, slovenly and overweight, an apron tied round her considerable girth and a baby, wrapped in a dirty woolen blanket, held in her pudgy arms.

"This is him — Joshua." She held the infant against her enormous bosom.

"We need to get a look at him," Gray said.

The woman peeled away the blanket to reveal a child with blond hair and dark brown eyes. He was smaller than Corrie had imagined, thin to the point of gaunt. It was clear he had never had proper nourishment, never had the least loving care. His cheeks were sunken and his skin slightly sallow. His eyes had a hollow look, and his head lolled weakly against the woman's hand.

Corrie's heart twisted hard inside her. Reaching out, she pulled the edge of the blanket a little farther down and there it was, Laurel's tiny birthmark on his shoulder. Corrie's eyes filled with tears and her resolve turned fierce.

"Give him to me," she demanded.

"Not till I gets me money."

"You'll get your blood money," she said, looking up at Gray with pain-filled eyes. He handed the woman a pouch of gold coins and a bank draft for the balance of the reward, and she passed the baby to Coralee.

487

"It's all right, sweetheart." She pressed a kiss to the infant's cheek, her hands shaking as she settled him gently against her shoulder. "You're going home. No one's ever going to hurt you again."

As quickly as possible, Gray finished the transaction and they left the house. Inside the carriage, Corrie tossed the dirty blanket out the window, and Gray helped her wrap the infant in a soft clean woolen one Samir had left on the seat.

The baby seemed to snuggle against the softness, and Corrie's heart ached at the sight. How little comfort he had known, how hard he must have fought to survive. "He has my father's mark," she said softly as the conveyance rolled along the dirty street toward Mayfair. "It has to be Joshua Michael."

Gray's eyes found hers. "Even if he weren't, I wouldn't have left him there. Not after I saw the way you looked at him."

She glanced away, thinking how deeply she loved this man she had married. She only wished she had the courage to tell him.

Instead she nuzzled the baby's soft cheek. "You're going to be all right, sweetheart. You're going to get well and grow strong for your papa." She turned, saw Gray looking at the child with a tenderness she had never

488

seen in his face before.

"He has to be all right, Gray. I can't watch another child die."

He pulled the blanket carefully up around the baby's head. "Joshua's not going to die. He's survived this long with almost no care. Now he has you and his family to love him. We're going to make sure he grows strong and healthy."

Her heart trembled inside her. She loved this man so much. And already she loved the little boy in her arms. She brushed another kiss on top of the baby's head and settled herself against the velvet seat, whispering the same sort of soft, loving words her sister must have said.

I've found him, she silently told Laurel. *I've found your son, dearest. Soon you'll be able to rest in peace.*

Gray prowled the room impatiently. He wanted to leave London for the country. He had business with Thomas Morton — very personal business. So personal, in fact, he hadn't yet written to Dolph or any of the men in his family. He wanted to be there to confront Morton himself, wanted to hear what had happened the night Laurel Whitmore was murdered. He wanted to watch as the bastard was hauled away in chains.

489

At the very least, Morton was guilty of abducting an innocent baby and keeping him from his family. Gray was certain he was also the man behind the attacks on Coralee's life.

For those crimes alone, Gray wanted to see him hang.

But he couldn't leave the city yet. He had Coralee to consider, as well as his brother's son. He wouldn't leave without them. He wouldn't take a chance that Morton might have some other scheme in motion to rid himself of the threat they posed.

He knew Coralee was as eager to leave as he. She wanted justice for her sister and she wanted to unite Charles with his son. Yesterday and all of last night, she and Mrs. Lawsen had sat up with the baby. The wet nurse had fed him as much as he could possibly consume, and Coralee had held him, crooned to him and comforted him.

His wife was sleeping now, but he knew she wouldn't rest long. She was determined to give the child what he needed most and had never had. *Love.*

Gray felt an odd pressure in his chest. She would make a wonderful mother. He was grateful she wanted his child, and wondered if even now she might not be carrying his babe. Standing in the nursery, he looked down at the little boy asleep in the cradle Samir had found in the attic, and ached at the thought of what it might be like to have a son or daughter of his own.

He looked up as Coralee walked into the room, and a swell of emotion rose inside him. Even tired and worried, she looked beautiful.

"He's sleeping," Gray said softly. "I told Mrs. Lawsen not to wake you. I said I'd watch him until you got up."

She came toward him, smiled as she reached his side. He wanted to cup her face in his hands, to kiss away the worry he read in her eyes, to hold her and tell her how glad he was that she was a part of his world.

"Thank you for staying with him," she said.

He gazed down at the sleeping infant, his tiny fist pressed against his mouth, and felt something move inside him.

"We need to take him home, Gray."

His head came up. He wanted that above all things, but not at the risk of the child. "Do you think it's safe for him to travel?"

"It's warm and dry outside. As long as Mrs. Lawsen comes with us, there's no reason Joshua can't make the journey. He'll sleep most of the way and he's not as weak as . . . as poor baby Jonathan." She glanced away and he knew she was thinking of the pitiful little boy who had died that night in her arms. She looked back at Gray. "I think Joshua will recover even faster in the fresh country air."

He nodded, grateful they would soon be on their way, and more anxious to be home than he had ever been before. "All right, we'll leave first thing in the morning. That'll give him another day to recover."

And time for Gray to send a note to Dolph, telling him about Thomas Morton's apparent involvement in the murder and Gray's plans to confront him after they arrived at Castle-on-Avon.

His jaw knotted. By the day after tomorrow, Morton would be in prison and Coralee no longer in danger.

Soon after, the villain would be swinging from the end of a rope.

"What are you talking about — you want out? Are you insane?" Rebecca paced back and forth along the gravel path at the rear of the garden. It was late in the afternoon and they were far from the house, in a place safe for her and Thomas to meet. "We're both in this together. All we have to do is get rid of Tremaine —"

"Biggs is dead. His crony, Wilkins, is in

492

prison. By now Tremaine has undoubtedly hired a small army of guards. We won't be able to get to him again."

She paced along the path, turned and paced back. "Perhaps you're right. We would be better to wait a bit, let things cool down. Charles says that man, Petersen, hasn't come up with anything in his investigation. Waiting a little longer won't matter. We'll bide our time, plan for just the right moment. . . ."

"I don't know, Rebecca. It might be better if I just disappear."

She spun toward him. "God forbid you should do something so stupid! You leave and it will only arouse suspicion. We need to keep things perfectly normal, continue just as we have been."

She sidled over to him, allowing her hips to sway, though Thomas was not so easily played as some. Still, she knew she affected him and always had. Reaching out, she touched his cheek. "Think of the rewards, darling. You're not in line to inherit. That little house your father gave you is all you will ever own. We do this, and you'll earn the fortune I promised. And I shall have the title and money I deserve."

Thomas said nothing. His instincts were telling him to run, while his greed urged him to stay.

"Thomas?"

"I'll stay," he decided. *At least for a little while longer.* As the lady said, there was a fortune at stake.

The journey was long, but not unpleasant. The weather was mild, the sun shining and the roads dry. Corrie and Mrs. Lawsen rode in the first carriage, while Gray mostly rode outside on his stallion. A second carriage followed, carrying Samir, a nursemaid named Emma Beasley, whom Coralee had hired to help with the baby once they got home, and Mrs. Lawsen's children, a two-year-old and an infant of barely three months.

Mrs. Lawsen, a buxom, healthy woman in her thirties, had plenty of milk for both of the babies, and a sweet way of handling them that Corrie vowed to remember when she had a child of her own. The woman's husband, a clerk in the city, was staying behind with their other two offspring.

"You've quite a family," Corrie said with a smile, enjoying the older woman's company.

"I've been lucky. All of them were born healthy. My husband and I wanted a large family and God granted our wish."

Corrie made no reply. Gray had said he

494

would give her a baby. As she cradled her sister's son against her breast, she realized she wanted that above all things. She wanted Gray's child. And she wanted him to love her.

In the days since he'd come to London, he had seemed different, as if he truly cared.

Perhaps in time . . .

Gray rode up to the window just then. "It'll be dark soon. It won't be much longer until we get there." He nodded toward the infant. "How's he doing?"

"He's sleeping a lot. He hardly ever cries. He's such a sweet baby."

Gray smiled, almost a grin. "Don't count on a son of mine being that cooperative." Pulling the horse away from the window, he nudged the animal into a gallop and rode off ahead of the carriage.

Corrie stared after him, not quite able to believe what she had just heard.

"Your husband loves you very much."

Corrie turned in the older woman's direction. "Why do you say that?"

"I can see it in his eyes whenever he looks at you. Surely he's told you."

She shook her head. "I'm not sure how Gray feels about me."

"Have you told him how you feel about him?"

"I love him, but . . ."

"But?"

"But I am afraid to tell him."

"Why on earth is that?"

Why *was* she so afraid? "Gray doesn't believe in love. He would probably think I was a fool."

"Or perhaps he would like to know you love him, just as much as you'd like to know he loves you."

Was it possible? Rebecca had said Gray didn't know how to love, and yet as Corrie looked back on their time together, he had shown her his care of her in a hundred different ways.

Loving Gray was easy. Telling him was hard. But perhaps, as Mrs. Lawsen said, he needed her love as badly as she needed his.

Snuggling the baby a little closer against her, she leaned back against the seat, resolved to tell him how she felt. Somehow she would find the courage. Perhaps tonight, she thought. After Charles and his son had been reunited. When she and Gray were upstairs in bed . . .

A warm yearning sifted through her. Gray hadn't made love to her since the night they had gone to the theater. Tonight she would let him know how much she wanted him. And then she would tell him that she was in love with him.

Uncertainty sliced through her. Dear God, what would he say when she did?

THIRTY

Gray rode ahead of the carriages. Darkness had fallen and lanterns along the gravel drive lit the way. He urged Raja to the front of the house, swung down and handed the reins to the groom.

"Welcome home, milord."

"Thank you, Dickey." It was indeed good to be back, no matter the circumstances. He wondered when the place he had so gladly left behind had truly become home to him.

He clenched his jaw. He was back, but tonight he wouldn't be staying long. As soon as he had settled Charles with his son and seen to Coralee's safety, he was leaving. He had a grim date with Thomas Morton, and he wasn't about to wait until morning.

The front door opened and a pair of footmen raced down the steps. The butler wore a look of surprise at the unexpected appearance of his master standing at the bottom.

He should have sent word, Gray knew, prepared Charles for the arrival of his son. Perhaps he had delayed in an effort to postpone the confrontation his brother would undoubtedly face with Rebecca over the existence of the child.

Gray wasn't sure what his sister-in-law would do when she found out the boy he was bringing into the house was her husband's illegitimate son.

It didn't matter. Gray knew what Charles would want. He would demand the boy be raised in the care of his father, no matter what Rebecca said.

Gray waited as a footman helped Coralee down from the carriage. Her ugly mutt, Homer, raced up barking, and she leaned down to ruffle his scruffy fur, obviously glad to see him.

"Come, my lady," Gray said with the faintest of smiles as he escorted her up the front steps, the baby in her arms. The rest of the party trailed along behind them.

"Mrs. Lawsen, you and Nurse Beasley take Joshua upstairs to the nursery," he instructed, once the group had arrived in the entry. "Mrs. Kittrick, the housekeeper, will show you where it is."

"Gray . . . ?"

He heard the uncertainty in Coralee's

voice, read the question in her pretty green eyes.

"We need to handle this carefully, love, give Charles a little time to get over the shock, and set things in order."

She nodded. She knew Rebecca and understood what Gray was saying. She handed the baby to Mrs. Lawsen, who followed the housekeeper up the stairs, trailed by the baby's nursemaid.

"The family is currently in to supper," the butler told him. "Mrs. Forsythe is giving a small dinner party tonight."

"I see." Gray released a breath. "Tell my brother that I am here and need a word with him. Tell him it's important."

"Yes, my lord."

"We'll be waiting in the Sky Room."

"Yes, my lord." The gray-haired man moved swiftly down the hall and disappeared. The dining room was in another section of the house. It took a few moments for his brother to arrive.

"Thank God you are both home and safe," Charles said as he walked into the drawing room, where Gray stood waiting with Coralee. "We've all been extremely worried."

"It's quite a long story, Charles. I'm sorry to interrupt your supper, but this is urgent.

500

I think you had better sit down."

Worry crept into his brother's features as he seated himself in a chair, and Gray and Coralee sat down on the sofa. For the next fifteen minutes, Gray told him some of what had happened during the time they had spent in London, planning to ease into the subject of the baby a little at a time.

"You should have written, told us you were in danger," Charles said. "We would have come immediately. Surely the three of us could have done something."

"You were doing something important here. I figured sooner or later you would find out something that would lead us to Laurel's killer. Instead, we found the answer in London."

Charles sat forward in his chair. "You know who killed Laurel?"

Coralee reached over and caught Gray's hand, warning him to go gently. Charles had loved her sister. Her murder could not be an easy subject. And the shock of learning he was a father would be more difficult still.

"We don't know for certain," Corrie said, "but we know Thomas Morton was there the night Laurel was killed."

"Thomas? Good God, Thomas was there that night with Laurel? But she barely knew him. I — I don't understand."

"We know he was there," Gray continued. "We don't know his motive, but we believe he may be the man who killed her. Tonight, I plan to pay him a visit. I intend to find out what happened that night."

Charles stood up from his chair, his face as hard as Gray had ever seen it. "You won't have to go far. Thomas is here. He's among the guests at Rebecca's dinner party."

Gray cast a glance at Coralee, thought of the broken saddle cinch, the night she had been drugged, the attack at the theater. Rage rose like a beast inside him.

"Good of him to save me the trip." In a haze of fury, he leaped to his feet and strode out of the drawing room, down the hall to the dining room.

The rage inside would not let him slow. He burst through the door to find Rebecca in her usual seat, Jason next to the Countess of Devane, Derek next to Allison Hatfield, apparently his guest for the evening. Thomas Morton sat calmly on the opposite side of Charles's empty chair.

"Gray!" Rebecca smiled. "I didn't know you were coming home tonight."

"Good evening, everyone." He tried to control the fury pumping through him, the anger in his voice. "Especially you, Thomas. I had planned to pay you a visit this evening.

I am pleased you spared me the journey."

Morton set his fork down beside his plate, wariness settling over him. "You wished to see me tonight? It must have been a matter of some importance."

"You might say that. It involves Laurel Whitmore and the child you sent to London."

The man's face went pale. "What are you talking about?"

"I'm talking about murder, Thomas."

Both Derek and Jason went on alert, tensing in their seats at the table.

"That is insane," Thomas said.

"Is it? You hired a man named Biggs to deliver the child to a baby farm. I suppose you did it to salve your conscience. I'm sure you figured by now the child would be dead."

Rebecca shot to her feet, shoving her chair back so hard it tipped over onto the carpet. Her cheeks were red, her eyes wild. She stared at Thomas Morton as if he were something stuck on the bottom of her shoe. "You idiot!" Her hands balled into shaking fists. "You were supposed to get rid of it! You said you'd take care of it. You said you'd handle everything! Now look what you've done!"

"Sit down, Rebecca," Morton warned.

"You did it for her, then?" Gray asked, less surprised that Rebecca was involved than he should have been. He fixed a hard look on his sister-in-law, trying to fit the pieces together. "What happened, Becky? You found out about Charles's affair and wanted the girl and her baby dead?"

"Shut up," Morton demanded, his gaze piercing Rebecca. He turned to the others sitting in stunned silence at the table. "She's distraught. I can't imagine what she's talking about. I don't know anything about any of this."

Gray fought to control his temper. "We have proof, Morton. We know you were there. Did you kill her? Or was it Rebecca who pushed her into the river?"

Jason shoved back his chair. Gaslight glinted on his light brown hair, and in the soft rays, his face was pasty white. "*You* killed her? You would go that far to protect your interests, Becky? You would do murder?"

Rebecca whirled on him, her face contorted in fury. "I didn't kill her — he did!" She thrust a finger at Morton, so angry she shook. "If he had finished the job he was paid to do, she and her brat would both be dead and no one would be the wiser."

Shock quivered in Charles's deep voice.

"You knew about my relationship with Laurel?"

From the corner of his eye, Gray saw his brother near the door, his skin the color of ash.

"Of course I did. For God's sake, Charles, you were so transparent, so utterly smitten. Any idiot could tell you were in love. I thought it was over when she left, but then six months later, she returned. I followed you that night. I heard you telling her you were going to get a divorce. I couldn't allow that to happen."

"So instead of a divorce, you hired Thomas Morton to murder her." Charles seemed to be on the ragged edge of control.

Rebecca's lips thinned to an ugly line. "We had a partnership of sorts. I intercepted a note she sent you. She wanted you to meet her at the river. I didn't know she'd birthed your bastard, but apparently she planned to show it to you that night."

Rebecca cast a disgusted glare at Thomas. "If you'd gotten rid of it as you were supposed to, no one would have ever found out."

"I'm not taking the blame for you, lady." Morton rose to his substantial height, a large man made to appear even taller by the anger that stiffened his spine. Across from

505

him the Countess of Devane sat utterly frozen. Allison trembled. Jason and Derek sat on the edge of their chairs, ready in case Morton tried to run.

"Why did you try to kill Coralee?" Gray asked, pressing hard for the rest of the story. He felt her small hand on his arm and realized she had walked up beside him. Dammit to hell, he had meant for her to stay out of the way.

"She wouldn't let the matter rest," Morton said. "She was always digging, stirring things up. Sooner or later, she would have stumbled onto something — which is exactly what happened in London."

Gray's whole body tensed as Morton drew a pistol from inside his coat pocket. Bloody hell, he hadn't expected the man to be armed at a dinner party.

But then, Morton wasn't a man, he was a murderer.

Thomas held the pistol steady. It was obvious he wouldn't hesitate to use it. "Now that we've cleared the air, I'll be leaving."

Rebecca's blond eyebrows shot up. "What are you talking about? You can't just leave!"

"If you think I'm going to the gallows for you, my dear, you are sorely mistaken. I'm a businessman. As of now, our business is finished."

Instead of aiming at Charles or Gray, Morton pointed the pistol at Coralee. "I can't get you all with a single shot, but Lady Tremaine will be dead the minute one of you takes a step in my direction."

Allison made a strangled sound, drawing Morton's attention. Derek tensed, but the gun never wavered.

Fear flooded into Gray's stomach and he fought for control.

"Please," Charles implored, "don't anyone move."

"Very sensible, Charles," Thomas said. "But then, you always were a sensible man." He turned to the others. "Stay where you are and no one will have to die. I'll merely leave and you will never see me again."

He backed toward a door that led to a hallway outside the kitchen, the gun pointing dead center at Coralee's chest.

Gray's heart thundered. One wrong move and his wife would be dead.

Morton stepped back carefully. He had just reached the door when the panel swung open behind him, knocking him off balance. His arm jerked upward and Gray seized the moment, charging forward and knocking Morton to the floor, catching a glimpse of Samir as he did so.

The pistol roared and Coralee screamed.

Rebecca crumpled onto the carpet, landing in a heap of pink silk and blond curls.

"Becky!"

Gray heard Jason's voice the instant before his own fist collided with Morton's chin and the beast broke loose inside him. He jerked Morton up by the lapels and hit him again, driving his fist into his face. Morton fought back, landing a blow to Gray's jaw. He was a big man and he threw a hard punch, but Gray's fury made him unbeatable. He drove a fierce blow into Morton's body, rained blow after blow into the big man's face.

He might have kept on hitting him if Charles hadn't smashed a Chinese vase over Thomas's head, knocking him unconscious.

Knuckles bleeding, Gray stood up and took a couple of staggering steps backward.

"Gray!" Coralee leaped toward him, nearly knocking him over. He held on to her hard. Nothing had ever felt so good as having her arms around him.

"It's all right, love . . . it's over."

She looked up at him, her eyes full of tears. "Rebecca's dead, Gray. Morton's shot went wild. The lead ball broke her neck."

He glanced over to see Jason kneeling beside the beautiful blond woman gowned in pink silk. Charles moved toward them, along with Gray and Coralee.

"She's . . . she's gone, Charles." Jason looked pale and shaken.

"The child she carried . . ." Charles stared down at her.

Jason swallowed and glanced away. "It wasn't yours, Charles. I'm sorry . . . it was mine." He took Rebecca's hand and cradled it gently in his. "I never meant to betray you — I swear it. I just . . . I fell in love with her."

Charles met his cousin's tortured gaze. "Rebecca was always discreet in her affairs, but I knew from the start it wasn't mine. I wanted a child so badly I didn't care."

Jason's eyes filled with tears. "She said you couldn't give her the son she needed. She begged me to help her. I knew she hoped someday to be countess. I never knew she would kill to make it happen." He shook his head. "I'm sorry, Charles, so sorry. Perhaps someday you'll be able to forgive me."

Jason rose and moved woodenly out of the dining room, and everyone seemed to break free of the trance that held them immobile.

"Dreadful business," said Lady Devane with a sad shake of her head. "Then again, I'll have gossip enough to keep London entertained for years."

Gray's head snapped toward her. "You say

a word about what happened here, Bethany, and all of London will know every detail of your prurient tastes in bed."

The countess opened her mouth, then snapped it closed. "Fine," she said. "If that's the way you want it."

Derek looked shaken, yet solidly in control. He ran a hand through his thick golden hair, said something reassuring to Allison, then the two of them moved toward Gray.

"All of this was going on in the house and I didn't know," Derek said. "I feel as if somehow I failed you. I'm sorry, Gray."

"Everything that's happened was caused by a woman's greed. You are hardly to blame for that."

Allison came over and hugged Coralee. "I was so frightened for you, Corrie. To be truthful, I was never completely convinced you were right about Laurel being murdered. I won't ever doubt you again."

Gray could see how badly his wife wanted to tell her friend about the baby, but it was Charles who deserved the news first.

Derek tipped his head toward the unconscious man on the floor. "I'll send someone to fetch a constable. While I'm at it, I'd better get something to tie him up."

"I imagine this will do." Dolph Petersen strode through the doorway, a length of gold drapery cord dangling from his hand. A grim smile played on his lips. "It would appear I am a bit late for our appointment, my lord."

"If Morton hadn't been a supper guest, you would have been right on time."

"Yes . . . well, after I got your letter, a few bits and pieces I had been working on finally fell together." He handed the cord to Derek, who set to the task of tying up the unconscious man on the floor.

"Such as . . . ?"

"All of this happened because your sister-in-law wanted to become the Countess of Tremaine."

"That's what Jason said. I suppose that's why the attack at the theater was made against both of us. With me out of the way, Charles would inherit the title and Rebecca would be countess."

"That's right, and if Rebecca's plan had been successful, you would have been dead long ago. You see, Gray, lovely Rebecca arranged the boating accident that wound up killing your wife. But you were the target, not her."

A chill ran down his spine. Coralee's hand slipped into his, warming his suddenly cold insides. "That makes no sense. I wasn't even there."

"No, but you only decided not to go at the very last moment. By then, plans were already in motion and there was no way to stop them. Apparently Morton's accomplice — the man named Biggs you shot that night at the theater — was working among the crew, paid to knock you unconscious before you went into the water. Jillian was a casualty no one expected."

Gray said nothing. For years he had blamed himself for his late wife's death. All the while, Rebecca had been responsible. If she weren't already dead, he might have killed her himself.

"It's finished, Gray." Coralee squeezed his hand. "It's over and now we can get on with our lives." She turned and he followed her gaze to find Charles kneeling beside Rebecca on the floor.

"She was never happy," Charles said. "She wanted to marry a man with a title. She probably could have if our fathers hadn't been such close friends. When James died and you became earl, she must have seen an opportunity to make her dream come true." He rose to his feet. "I can pity her, but I cannot mourn her, not after all she has done. Perhaps her death was God's will, for justice has surely been served here tonight."

THIRTY-ONE

The constable had yet to arrive. Once he did, there would be statements to make, a man to be hauled off to prison. In all the confusion, no one had asked about the child Gray had mentioned, the child who now lay sleeping upstairs.

Corrie thought that Charles was simply too overwhelmed to realize the importance of his brother's words, that his son was alive and returned to him.

"We need to tell him," Corrie said to Gray as they stood near the balustrade at the edge of the terrace. The night was black and quiet, helping to soothe her ragged nerves. "We'll have to explain to the constable how we knew Thomas Morton was the killer. We'll have to explain about the baby."

Gray just nodded. In the flickering light of the torches, he looked heartbreakingly weary. She yearned to take him upstairs and put him to bed, to snuggle beside him and wrap him in her arms.

Tonight his family had nearly been destroyed. She ached for what he must be feeling.

"I had hoped for better circumstances," he said. "Charles has already been through so much."

Her throat tightened. *Poor dear Charles.* As he'd walked out of the dining room, he'd looked so lost, so utterly alone.

Gray took her hand and they set out in search of him, but as they crossed the terrace, Charles came walking toward them.

"We were just coming to find you," Gray said.

"I thought Jason might be out here."

"We haven't seen him."

"I need to talk to him, set things right between us. I am hardly blameless in this affair. I refuse to punish Jason for the same sin I committed."

Corrie managed to smile. "I'm glad you feel that way. I know the two of you will work things out. In the meantime, there is someone you need to meet."

He frowned. "Tonight?"

"We had hoped it would be a happier occasion," Gray said, "but yes, Charles, tonight."

They made their way back inside the

house and started up the stairs, Charles behind them.

"Where are we going?" he asked.

"The nursery," Gray said, and Charles froze midway up the staircase.

"The nursery? I don't . . . I don't understand."

Corrie reached down and caught his hand. "It's all right, Charles. We're taking you to meet your son."

His fingers trembled in hers. "My son . . . ?" His blond eyebrows drew together as he worked to put the pieces together. "Earlier . . . you said something about Laurel's baby. But everything got so mixed up, and then there was the shooting, and Rebecca, and I — I . . ." He faltered, then turned and started up the stairs at a breakneck pace, leaving them hurrying to catch up with him.

When they reached the door to the nursery, he stopped. "Is he . . . ? For God's sake, tell me he's all right. He hasn't been terribly mistreated or . . . or anything like that."

"He's going to be fine," Gray said firmly. "He just needs love and attention. He'll have plenty of that here."

Charles just stood there, too full of emotion to speak.

Gray swung the door of the nursery open

and led his brother into a room lit by the soft glow of a lamp. The nursemaid, Miss Beasley, eased silently out of the room as they moved forward to surround the cradle. Inside, nestled in the warm folds of a blanket, lay Charles's blond-haired baby boy.

"My God . . ." he said thickly as Corrie reached down to gently lift the child out of the cradle and place him in his father's arms. "My son . . ." Charles held him with such tender care that a painful lump swelled in Corrie's throat.

"I can scarcely believe it." He stroked the baby's soft cheek, tears glistening in his eyes. He kissed the top of the boy's blond head. "You're home at last, my son." He looked up as if he could see into the heavens. "Be at peace now, beloved. Your son is in his rightful place and you may be certain that he will be loved."

As if in agreement, the baby reached out and wrapped his small hand around his father's finger. Charles brought the tiny fingers to his lips. "I'll tell you everything about her," he promised. He looked over at Coralee. "Her sister and I, we'll tell you how beautiful she was and how kind, and how much she loved you."

Corrie wiped at the tears spilling onto her

cheeks. She went into her husband's arms and for a moment he just held her. Then the two of them slipped quietly away, leaving father and son alone.

"Your sister can rest easy now," Gray said as they stood together in the hallway. "You kept your vow to her, just as you promised."

"Without you, I couldn't have done it." Corrie looked up at him, her heart expanding inside her chest. "I love you, Gray. I love you so very much."

His arms came hard around her and he held her as if he would never let her go. "Coralee . . ." Cradling her face between his hands, he very gently kissed her. "You came into my life and filled the empty place in my heart. I never thought I could fall in love, but sweet God, Coralee, I love you, too."

EPILOGUE

One month later

The wind whipped the sails of the ship that carried them across the white-capped sea to France. It was past dawn, the sun a glowing orb riding low on the horizon. They had just finished making love. Corrie lay next to her tall, handsome husband in the wide berth in the owner's cabin aboard *Sea Dragon,* Leif's personal flagship, feeling as if her world had finally righted itself.

"We'll be docking sometime late this morning," Gray said. A strong arm draped around her shoulders, tucking her in beside him. "Are you excited to get there?"

She turned and smiled. "I've been excited since the moment you told me we were going. Oh, Gray, I've always wanted to see Paris." It wasn't India, but it was a start. Along with France, he had also promised to take her to Italy. She couldn't wait to see Rome.

Gray leaned over and kissed her forehead. "Remember you promised to write about your trip when we get home."

"Actually, I mean to start while we are away. Krista has asked me to do a series of articles about my travels."

"Then I suppose I shall have to make sure you have plenty of material for your stories."

And Corrie was certain he would see that she did. He was looking forward to the trip as much as she. A journey was exactly what they needed. So much had happened in both of their lives. So many changes had taken place since her sister had died.

Thomas Morton had been sentenced to hang, just as he deserved.

Charles was now a father, doting over his son worse than any nursemaid.

Both Jason and Derek had left the castle and returned to London. According to Allison, Derek had promised her he would come back, but Corrie wasn't certain of his intentions. She hoped her friend wouldn't be hurt too badly if things didn't work out with Gray's roguish half brother.

The most exciting news was that Gray had decided to take his place in the House of Lords.

"There are laws on the books that need changing," he'd said. "I can't ignore my duties any longer."

She knew he was speaking of the terrible business of baby farming, but there were other injustices that also needed to be dealt with, and Corrie believed Gray was exactly the man for the job. Duty had always been so much a part of him. She was only surprised he had waited this long.

She snuggled closer against him, enjoying the solid warmth of his body, the play of muscle whenever he moved. "There is one thing I keep wondering. . . ."

One dark eyebrow arched. "What is that?"

"Rebecca said Charles couldn't father a child, and yet it is clear that he did."

"Charles was in love with your sister. Perhaps that made the difference."

"Yes, I suppose it must have." She traced a finger through the crisp mat of hair on Gray's chest and felt his heartbeat quicken.

"You are playing with fire, my love." The gruff note in his voice made her smile.

"And if love was truly the cause, it's a very good thing we left England when we did, because I love you desperately — which might just mean that very soon I'll be —"

He cut off her words with a kiss. "It might just mean that very soon you'll be heavy with my babe. I love you, lady trouble. And I think that perhaps we should give this baby-making another try."

She laughed as he came up over her and began to make a very thorough attempt at becoming a father.

Corrie had the strangest feeling that this time his efforts would succeed.

And inwardly she smiled.

AUTHOR'S NOTE

Hope you enjoyed *Heart of Fire,* the second in the Heart Trilogy that started with *Heart of Honor.* The third in the series is *Heart of Courage,* Thor and Lindsey's story. Theirs is a tale of two headstrong people who fight the attraction between them — until they realize love conquers all, even rebellious spirits such as theirs.

Hope you'll watch for *Heart of Courage* and that you enjoy it.

All best wishes,
Kat

ABOUT THE AUTHOR

Kat Martin is a *New York Times* bestselling author of over thirty-five historical and contemporary romance novels. To date, she has more than ten million copies of her books in print and has been published in seventeen foreign countries, including Sweden, China, Korea, Russia, South Africa, Argentina, Japan and Greece. Kat and her husband, author Larry Jay Martin, live on their ranch in Missoula, Montana.

The employees of Thorndike Press hope you have enjoyed this Large Print book. All our Thorndike and Wheeler Large Print titles are designed for easy reading, and all our books are made to last. Other Thorndike Press Large Print books are available at your library, through selected bookstores, or directly from us.

For information about titles, please call:
(800) 223-1244

or visit our Web site at:
http://gale.cengage.com/thorndike

To share your comments, please write:
Publisher
Thorndike Press
295 Kennedy Memorial Drive
Waterville, ME 04901